1968

F

TO: $Fg^2 \sqrt{-1}$, who inspires and understands.

Number Systems:

MERVIN L. KEEDY *Purdue University*

A MODERN INTRODUCTION

 ADDISON-WESLEY READING, MASSACHUSETTS

This book is in the

ADDISON-WESLEY

SERIES IN SCIENCE AND MATHEMATICS EDUCATION

Consulting Editors

R. S. PIETERS · P. ROSENBLOOM

G. B. THOMAS, JR. · J. WAGNER

ADDISON-WESLEY PUBLISHING COMPANY, INC.

READING, MASSACHUSETTS, · PALO ALTO · LONDON

NEW YORK · DALLAS · ATLANTA · BARRINGTON, ILLINOIS

Preface

Experience in teaching undergraduates at the junior and senior levels has pointed up the need for an early introduction to abstractions, proofs, and number system structure. A student who comes to his first course in abstract algebra or modern geometry after completing the usual calculus prerequisite may find himself ill equipped. The "mathematical maturity" which is often supposed to be attained through the prerequisite calculus courses may be lacking. In particular, proofs may be difficult for the student. In fact the whole concept of mathematical rigor may be so new that it is a shock. It thus appears that there is a need for an introductory course, without a calculus prerequisite, which will give the student some experience with mathematical structure and proof. This book is intended to serve such a need, among others.

At the beginning, this text is not highly rigorous, but the rigor increases fairly gradually, so that the student may have a chance to grow and develop as he gains experience. There has been an earnest attempt to make the exposition clear and gradual, so that the student may also learn to read mathematics for himself, increasing that skill as he gains experience. No prerequisite is assumed beyond two years of high school mathematics, including algebra and geometry. After completing the book the student should have a good basic understanding of the properties of the various number systems treated here. This treatment includes a careful development of the rational numbers and a brief look at the real numbers, with particular attention to the structural features of the algorithms of ordinary arithmetic. The book should thus be useful for teachers in service, both as a reference and as a text for in-service courses. It is also suitable for a terminal course for students of liberal arts, as well as for an early course for students majoring or minoring in mathematics.

The present text is based upon the author's earlier book, *A Modern Introduction to Basic Mathematics*. This shorter version of the earlier book was felt to be more suitable in several kinds of situations, particularly where a one-semester course is to be based upon this kind of material. The present book is not only an abridgment of the earlier work, but there have also been a great many changes and improvements

v

in the development of topics, based upon the experiences of the author and others in teaching from the earlier text. There have also been added sets of Review Practice Exercises, which have been found very effective in providing a quick brush-up and incidental review of certain skills. These exercise sets are placed at strategic places throughout the text, to provide a review which is needed for a topic to be covered soon thereafter.

At Purdue this book is used in the first of two four-semester-hour courses for prospective elementary school teachers, following rather closely the recommendations of CUPM for Level I. A companion volume, *Geometry: A Modern Introduction,* is used in the second course. It has been found that the material of this book can be essentially covered in the four-hour course, when some of the material in Chapters 4 and 5 is used for outside reading, rather than a part of the regular class work. For further details about using the book in this way, the reader is referred to the *Commentary for Instructors.* A course for prospective teachers should probably emphasize the applications of laws of numbers to the algorithms of arithmetic and algebra. At Purdue this is done, while in courses for students of liberal arts less emphasis is given to algorithms and more to such topics as logic. For prospective teachers Chapter 6 is important, since it contains almost all of the theory of the elementary arithmetic of nonnegative rational numbers. For students with other career objectives this chapter might well receive less emphasis. In fact, from a strictly logical point of view there is some advantage in constructing the integers and rational numbers, bypassing the so-called numbers of ordinary arithmetic developed in Chapter 6. Such an approach is possible without undue difficulty.

The author is most grateful to those who have contributed to the improvement of this book. Among those who have read parts of the manuscript and made suggestions are Vincent Brant, Henry Walbesser, Donald Woytowitz, Charles W. Nelson, and Mrs. Judy King. There are also many students, teachers, and colleagues, who, by virtue of their influence on me in the course of our associations, have contributed substantially to the work. These persons are too numerous to mention here, but they all deserve special thanks.

Lafayette, Indiana   M.L.K.
October 1964

Contents

CHAPTER *1*

Numeration

1. NUMERALS AND NUMBERS

There are many kinds of numerals, but people today are most familiar with the Hindu-Arabic numerals, since they are in universal use. Roman numerals, of course, are also used to a great extent, and still other symbols for numbers are used occasionally. There are many different kinds of symbols that might be called *numerals*. Their essential property is that they represent *numbers*.

Number is an abstract concept, not easy to define simply. Nonetheless, a number is not a symbol; it is not a numeral. Marks made on paper, scratched on the sand, or chiseled in stone may be numerals, but they are never numbers. This distinction is often forgotten, for it is common to say such things as "write a number larger than ten." It may be argued that the loss of this distinction is not very important. For certain purposes, and from certain points of view, this is true. As will be seen, however, a good deal is to be gained with respect to understanding properties of numbers if the distinction is revived and steadfastly maintained, where practicable.

School arithmetic has in the past consisted, to a large extent, of learning to manipulate Hindu-Arabic numerals in computing. The abstract concept of *number* thus has tended to be lost, or somehow identified with symbols themselves. That numbers have properties of their own, *independent* of the symbols used for them, was a foreign idea. Therefore, learning arithmetic, and other mathematics, has been more a matter of memory than understanding, and this is unfortunate.

1

In this chapter, numerals, their structure and their meaning, are considered. The familiar Hindu-Arabic numerals, based on the number ten and hence known as *decimal* numerals, are considered in some detail. Numerals of the Hindu-Arabic type, but based on some number other than ten, have similar structure and meaning, and consideration of them shows clearly, by analogy and by contrast, the structure of ordinary decimal numeration.

2. WHAT IS A NUMERATION SYSTEM?

Most people of the world are familiar with at least two types of symbols for numbers. Those most widely used are the Hindu-Arabic numerals, such as 3, 45, and 254. The Roman numerals, such as XII and XLIV, are also well known and widely used, but generally for different purposes. The former are much more useful for calculating than the latter, for example. In writing numerals of either type, a certain set of basic symbols is used. These symbols are combined according to certain rules in such a way that a symbol can be written for any ordinary number.

The symbols XIII and 13 represent the same number. For any counting number it is possible to write both a Roman numeral and a Hindu-Arabic numeral. After some reflection, it is clear that the symbols themselves are *not* numbers. If they were, then XIII and 13 would be different numbers. Rather, the symbols represent, or stand for, or *name* numbers. This point will be considered in more detail later. For the present, suffice it to say that numerals are not the same thing as numbers. Numerals are "names" for numbers.

A *system of numeration* is therefore a system for naming numbers. It consists of a set of basic symbols, together with rules for their combination to form numerals, or names of numbers.

3. THE ROMAN SYSTEM OF NUMERATION

In the Roman system of numeration, some of the basic symbols are I, V, X, L, C, and M. Standing alone these symbols represent the numbers one, five, ten, fifty, one hundred, and one thousand, respectively. When the symbols are to be combined, they are written side by side. When a numeral consists of two basic symbols, one standing for a smaller number than the other, the entire symbol stands for the sum if the symbol on the right represents the smaller number. If the symbol on the left represents the smaller number, then the entire numeral represents the number found by subtracting the smaller number from the larger. Thus it follows that the numerals IV, XIV, and XL represent the numbers four, fourteen, and forty, respectively.

When two or more symbols which represent the same number are written together, the entire symbol represents the sum. Thus the numerals II, XXX, and CC represent the numbers two, thirty, and two hundred, respectively. There are further rules for the formation of numerals in the Roman system of numeration, which are well known and need not be elaborated here. Those mentioned above are sufficient to review and illustrate the nature of this system, so that it may be compared with other systems of numeration.

REVIEW PRACTICE EXERCISES

Add

1. $7 + (-3)$	2. $19 + (-5)$	3. $10 + (-10)$
4. $-4 + 17$	5. $-18 + 43$	6. $-16 + 32$
7. $3 + (-7)$	8. $1 + (-15)$	9. $14 + (-20)$
10. $-15 + 8$	11. $-27 + 14$	12. $-30 + 17$
13. $-3 + (-5)$	14. $-7 + (-16)$	15. $-17 + (-5)$

Subtract

16. $8 - 7$	17. $13 - 5$	18. $17 - 3$
19. $4 - 10$	20. $16 - 20$	21. $13 - 27$
22. $-6 - 7$	23. $-17 - 5$	24. $-21 - 9$
25. $8 - (-2)$	26. $14 - (-8)$	27. $17 - (-25)$
28. $-9 - (-2)$	29. $-8 - (-12)$	30. $-17 - (-3)$
31. $-9 - (-13)$	32. $-45 - (-51)$	33. $-102 - (-41)$

4. NAMES AND EQUALITY

The contrast between Hindu-Arabic numerals and Roman numerals illustrates that a single number can be denoted, or *named*, in more than one way. In fact, a number can be named in many ways. The number five, for example, can be named

$$5, \text{V}, \text{NY}, 4 + 1, \tfrac{10}{2}, 3 + \tfrac{4}{2}, \text{ or } 7.1 - 2.1$$

The list of possible names for this number is endless, as is the list of possible names for any one number.

The meaning of *equal* is often not clear. Now that a distinction has been made between numbers and symbols, a satisfactory definition or explanation can be given, as follows: A sentence with $=$ for the verb, such as $3 + 2 = 5$, asserts that the symbol on the left, '$3 + 2$' and the symbol* on the right, '5,' represent, or *name*, the same number.† This meaning of equality will be used throughout this book.

———————

* The single quotation marks here are being used, in accordance with a common practice, to indicate that a symbol, rather than its referent, is being spoken of. See also Chapter 4, p. 72, 73.

† Note that such sentences can be false. The sentence $4 \cdot 2 = 65$ asserts that '$4 \cdot 2$' and '65' represent the same number. It is clear what is being asserted and it is clear that the assertion is false.

5. THE EGYPTIAN SYSTEM OF NUMERATION

Among the many ancient systems of numeration, that of the Egyptians may profitably be considered. Its basic symbols are as follows:

> | (stroke) Names the number 1
>
> ∩ (heel bone) Names the number 10
>
> ? (coiled rope) Names the number 100
>
> ⚇ (lotus flower) Names the number 1000
>
> ⌐ (bent reed) Names the number 10,000
>
> ↶ (burbot fish) Names the number 100,000
>
> ⚹ (astonished man) Names the number 1,000,000

The rule of combination of the basic symbols for this system is simple. The symbols are simply written together, usually on a horizontal line. The number represented by a numeral is the sum of the numbers named by the basic symbols. The order in which they are written makes no difference, and any symbol may be used any number of times. Thus the numerals ?∩∩||| and |∩∩??? represent the numbers 123 and 421, respectively. One of the essential differences between Roman and Egyptian numeration is that in the latter, position is unimportant. That is, a basic symbol has the same meaning regardless of its position in the numeral. Thus the symbols ?∩∩||| , |||?∩∩ , and ∩∩|||? all name the same number.

REVIEW PRACTICE EXERCISES

Multiply

EXAMPLE: $6^5 \cdot 6^{-3} = 6^2$ (add exponents)

1. $8^4 \cdot 8^2$	2. $3^5 \cdot 3^6$	3. $4^3 \cdot 4^3$
4. $5^6 \cdot 5^{-2}$	5. $6^{-4} \cdot 6^6$	6. $8^7 \cdot 8^{-5}$
7. $9^6 \cdot 9^{-8}$	8. $5^{-10} \cdot 5^4$	9. $6^8 \cdot 6^{-4}$
10. $4^{-5} \cdot 4^{-2}$	11. $6^{-12} \cdot 6^{-2}$	12. $7^{-8} \cdot 7^{-5}$
13. $(-5)^4 \cdot (-5)^2$	14. $x^{-2} \cdot x^{-5}$	15. $y^4 \cdot y^{-10}$

Divide

EXAMPLE: $8^5 \div 8^3 = 8^2$ (subtract exponents)

16. $4^3 \div 4^2$	17. $5^6 \div 5^2$	18. $4^3 \div 4^3$
19. $6^{-5} \div 6^2$	20. $8^4 \div 8^{-3}$	21. $5^{-7} \div 5^4$
22. $3^{-1} \div 3^{-1}$	23. $5^{-6} \div 5^{-6}$	24. $4^6 \div 4^{-5}$
25. $9^{-3} \div 9^{-5}$	26. $11^{-8} \div 11^{-2}$	27. $14^{-3} \div 14^{-5}$
28. $x^2 \div x^{-4}$	29. $y^{-6} \div y^5$	30. $x^{-2} \div x^{-5}$

6. THE DECIMAL SYSTEM OF NUMERATION

The Hindu-Arabic system of numeration uses ten basic symbols. Since it is based on ten, it has come to be known as the *decimal system*, the word "decimal" being derived from the Latin word "decem," meaning ten. The basic symbols are the digit symbols 0, 1, 2, 3, 4, 5, 6, 7, 8, 9. In this system basic symbols are combined by writing them on a horizontal line, and the position of the digit symbols in a numeral is important. The numeral 423, for example, names the number obtained by adding 400, 20, and 3, whereas the numeral 324 names the number obtained by adding 300, 20, and 4.

The final digit symbol in such a numeral represents a number of units, or ones. The next-to-last digit symbol represents a number of tens, the next a number of hundreds, or (ten $\times$ ten)s. The next digit symbol represents a number of (ten $\times$ ten $\times$ ten)s, and so on. Thus the numeral 648373 represents a number which could be named in the following explanatory way:

$$6 \times (10 \times 10 \times 10 \times 10 \times 10) + 4 \times (10 \times 10 \times 10 \times 10)$$
$$+ 8 \times (10 \times 10 \times 10) + 3 \times (10 \times 10) + 7 \times 10 + 3.$$

For additional brevity we may write

$$6 \times 10^5 + 4 \times 10^4 + 8 \times 10^3 + 3 \times 10^2 + 7 \times 10^1 + 3 \times 10^0.$$

Both of the above symbols are called *expanded numerals*. It should be noted that in the latter, the symbol '10^5' replaces the longer symbol '$10 \times 10 \times 10 \times 10 \times 10$' in the former. It is by *agreement* that the two symbols mean the same thing. Similarly, the symbols '10^3' and '$10 \times 10 \times 10$' mean the same thing, and the symbols '10^1' and '10' mean the same thing. By agreement also, the symbol '10^0' represents the number one.

In this system of numeration, a *decimal point* is used to separate digit symbols which represent numbers less than one from those digit symbols which represent whole numbers. This is illustrated by writing an expanded numeral for 352.416:

$$3 \times 10^2 + 5 \times 10^1 + 2 \times 10^0 + 4 \times 10^{-1} + 1 \times 10^{-2} + 6 \times 10^{-3}.$$

The first digit symbol to the right of the decimal point represents a number of tenths, the second one a number of hundredths, and the third one a number of thousandths, and so on. Thus the symbol '10^{-1},' by agreement, represents the number $\frac{1}{10}$. The symbol '10^{-2}' represents the number $\frac{1}{100}$, or $(\frac{1}{10})^2$; the symbol '10^{-3}' represents the number $(\frac{1}{10})^3$, and so on, all by agreement.

To summarize the positional scheme of this system of numeration, it may be said that each digit symbol in a numeral represents a number which is to be multiplied by a power of ten. This power of ten may be found by counting digit symbols, starting at the decimal point. To the left, counting begins with zero and increases. To the right, counting begins with -1 and decreases. Thus the third symbol to the right of the decimal point represents a number which is to be multiplied by the negative three power of ten. The number named by the fifth digit symbol to the left of the decimal point is to be multiplied by the positive four power of ten. The number named by the numeral is then the sum of all of these products.

EXERCISES

1. Write expanded numerals for the following numbers.
   (a) 25314.178   (b) 16   (c) 0.001034   (d) 500.0005
2. Write Roman numerals for the following numbers.
   (a) 36   (b) 249   (c) 1963   (d) 38
3. Write Egyptian numerals for the following numbers.
   (a) 123   (b) 1975   (c) 10,553   (d) 689
4. What number is represented by each of the following symbols? How do these symbols get their meaning?
   (a) 10^4 (b) 10^{-2} (c) 10^{-4} (d) 10^0

REVIEW PRACTICE EXERCISES

Simplify

EXAMPLE: $(4^2)^3 = 4^6$ (multiply exponents)

1. $(3^2)^4$ 2. $(4^6)^2$ 3. $(5^4)^4$
4. $(5^4)^{-2}$ 5. $(6^3)^{-4}$ 6. $(8^5)^{-3}$
7. $(9^{-2})^3$ 8. $(4^{-3})^5$ 9. $(3^{-5})^4$
10. $(6^{-5})^{-6}$ 11. $(3^{-2})^4$ 12. $(8^{-5})^{-5}$
13. $(x^3)^{-5}$ 14. $(y^{-4})^6$ 15. $(x^{-5})^{-6}$

7. NONDECIMAL SYSTEMS OF NUMERATION

The fact that the decimal system of numeration is used so universally is probably due in part to anatomical accident. Human beings, who are the creatures who invent both numbers and numerals, have ten fingers. These were probably the earliest kinds of symbols used to represent numbers. If man were equipped with 12 fingers, or *digits*, he would most probably be using a numeration system based on twelve, rather than ten, and using twelve digit symbols, rather than ten.

A numeration system based on twelve is not difficult to construct. In fact it is not difficult to construct a numeration system of the Hindu-Arabic type for any whole number greater than one. In a *septimal* system, based on seven, for example, the numeral 352.416 has a meaning similar to that in the decimal system, except that powers of seven are used rather than powers of ten. An expanded numeral for this number is

$$3 \times 7^2 + 5 \times 7^1 + 2 \times 7^0 + 4 \times 7^{-1} + 1 \times 7^{-2} + 6 \times 7^{-3}.$$

Thus the first digit symbol represents a number of forty-nines, the second a number of sevens, and the third a number of units. The first digit symbol to the right of the septimal point represents a number of sevenths, the second one a number of forty-ninths, and so on. Again it is by *agreement* that '7^2' represents 7×7, '7^{-3}' represents $(\frac{1}{7})^3$, '7^0' represents 1, and so on.

Nondecimal numerals can be identified by means of subscripts. For example, '234_7' is a septimal (base seven) numeral, representing 2 forty-nines, 3 sevens, and 4 units. The symbol 231_8 is an octimal, or base eight, numeral representing 2 sixty-fours, 3 eights, and 1 unit.

Suppose that a base seven, or other nondecimal base, numeral for a number is given and the decimal numeral for that number is desired. The decimal numeral may be found by writing an expanded numeral and then simplifying.

EXAMPLE. Find the decimal numeral for 3123_5.

$$
\begin{aligned}
3123_5 &= 3 \times 5^3 + 1 \times 5^2 + 2 \times 5 + 3 \\
&= 3 \times 125 + 1 \times 25 + 10 + 3 \\
&= 375 + 25 + 10 + 3 \\
&= 413_{10}
\end{aligned}
$$

From the preceding example it may be noted that the expanded numeral is decimal in that it does not use base five symbolism. If it did, then the symbol '5' would not appear. The expanded numeral is therefore decimal, and it remains only to simplify it, to obtain the standard decimal numeral for the number in question.

EXERCISES

1. Find decimal numerals for the following numbers.

(a) 670_8 (b) 210_3 (c) 367_9 (d) 314_5

(e) 1112_3 (f) 313_4 (g) 125_7 (h) 415_6

2. Is there a number b for which 33_b will be even?
3. Is there a number b for which 46_b will be odd?

REVIEW PRACTICE EXERCISES

Simplify

EXAMPLE: $\frac{2}{5} + \frac{3}{4} = \frac{2}{5} \cdot \frac{4}{4} + \frac{3}{4} \cdot \frac{5}{5} = \frac{8}{20} + \frac{15}{20} = \frac{23}{20}$

1. $\frac{3}{3} + \frac{1}{4}$ 2. $\frac{4}{5} + \frac{3}{5}$ 3. $\frac{9}{8} + \frac{1}{8}$

4. $\frac{3}{4} + \frac{1}{2}$ 5. $\frac{2}{3} + \frac{5}{6}$ 6. $\frac{5}{8} + \frac{3}{4}$

7. $\frac{3}{5} + \frac{9}{10}$ 8. $\frac{2}{3} + \frac{3}{4}$ 9. $\frac{3}{5} + \frac{4}{7}$

10. $\frac{4}{9} + \frac{7}{10}$ 11. $\frac{4}{11} + \frac{5}{13}$ 12. $\frac{5}{18} + \frac{7}{24}$

Calculations using nondecimal numerals may be carried out in a manner similar to that used with decimal numerals. This will be illustrated for septimal numerals. To add a column, one may add the units digits first, then the sevens digits, and so on. However, the numbers carried to another column are sevens or powers of seven, whereas in the decimal system the numbers carried are tens or powers of ten. Addition using septimal numerals is illustrated in the following example:

$$
\begin{array}{r}
32 \\
26 \\
43 \\
\hline
134
\end{array}
$$

The sum of the units digits is eleven, or 14_7. The '4' is written and 1 seven is carried to the sevens column. The sum of that column is ten, or 13_7. Thus the sum is 134_7.

Here is the same problem done using decimal numerals:

$$
\begin{array}{l}
23 \quad \text{(three sevens and two units)} \\
20 \quad \text{(two sevens and six units)} \\
\underline{31} \quad \text{(four sevens and three units)} \\
74
\end{array}
$$

The sum is 74_{10}. The septimal addition may be checked by finding the decimal numeral for 134_7. This septimal numeral represents 1 forty-nine, 3 sevens, and 4 units, which is 74_{10}, and the answer checks.

In order to avoid confusion, nondecimal numerals should be read by pronouncing the name of each digit. For example, '134_7' is read "one-three-four, base seven," and not "one hundred thirty-four," because it actually represents the number seventy-four. It would be possible to invent different spoken names to accompany numerals of each numeration base, rather than to use the familiar ones used for the decimal system. However, this would take more time than is warranted. The decimal system is adequate for all ordinary calculations. Therefore a rapid working knowledge of other numeration systems is not necessary, and a set of special spoken names would be merely a curiosity.

Multiplication using septimal numerals is illustrated as follows:

$$
\begin{array}{r}
134 \\
25 \\
\hline
1036 \\
301 \\
\hline
4046
\end{array}
$$

The same problem using decimal numerals is:

$$
\begin{array}{r}
74 \\
19 \\
\hline
666 \\
74 \\
\hline
1406
\end{array}
$$

The calculation can be checked by showing that $4046_7 = 1406_{10}$.

If the septimal system were in standard use, school children would learn to write their addition and multiplication tables according to the scheme given in the following tables.

+	1	2	3	4	5	6
1	2	3	4	5	6	10
2	3	4	5	6	10	11
3	4	5	6	10	11	12
4	5	6	10	11	12	13
5	6	10	11	12	13	14
6	10	11	12	13	14	15

×	1	2	3	4	5	6
1	1	2	3	4	5	6
2	2	4	6	11	13	15
3	3	6	12	15	21	24
4	4	11	15	22	26	33
5	5	13	21	26	34	42
6	6	15	24	33	42	51

If one had learned these tables instead of the decimal tables, the above example of multiplication in base seven would have been much easier than a multiplication in base ten. Calculations in base ten are easier because of their familiarity. It is possible to use these tables in performing calculations with septimal numerals. Again it may be said that the time required to become even reasonably adept is more than any ordinary advantage would merit.

EXERCISES

Add

1. (base 4)   (a)   32   (b) 3123
                      3   213

2. (base 7)   (a)   543   (b) 6035
                   126   1606

3. (base 8)   (a) 3746   (b) 7007
                 7157   1736

Subtract

4. (base 5)   (a)   341   (b) 4143
                   123   3414

5. (base 6)   (a)   453   (b) 5102
                   344   3015

6. (base 9)   (a)   785   (b) 8010
                   638   7888

Multiply

7. (base 4)   (a)   312   (b)   132
                     3   23

8. (base 7)   (a)   613   (b)   564
                     4   206

9. (base 8)   (a)   376   (b) 6071
                     4   306

10. In what numeration system has the following subtraction been performed? One digit in the answer is wrong. Which one?

$$63532$$
$$4534$$
$$\overline{54665}$$

11. Solve the following puzzles:

(a)
SEND
MORE
MONEY

(b)
TEN
TEN
FORTY
SIXTY

Each letter stands for a digit symbol of a decimal numeral. Different letters stand for different digit symbols. The puzzle shows an addition problem. Find what digit symbol each letter represents.

Converting from nondecimal to decimal symbolism has been considered. The reverse problem will now be considered, i.e., the finding of septimal, or other base, numerals for numbers when decimal numerals are given. It will be helpful first to to compare place values in base ten and base seven, as shown in the following place-value charts.

Base Ten	10^4 or 10,000	10^3 or 1000	10^2 or 100	10	1

Base Seven	7^4 or 2401	7^3 or 343	7^2 or 49	7	1

The grouping of a set of objects in a certain fashion may easily be envisioned with respect to any base. A set of sixty-seven objects would be thought of as being grouped into 6 tens and 7 ones, as follows, for base ten:

X X X X X X X X X X

X X X X X X X X X X

X X X X X X X X X X

X X X X X X X X X X

X X X X X X X X X X

X X X X X X X X X X

X X X X X X X

To visualize base seven grouping one might begin by encircling sets of seven objects each, as follows:

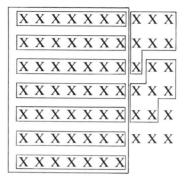

When seven of the circled sets occur, those seven sets are circled, to obtain one set of 7^2, or 49. Thus sixty-seven objects consist of one set of 7^2, plus two sets of 7, plus four. The base seven numeral for 64 is thus 124_7.

The use of circled x's to obtain a base seven numeral, as in the above example, is not necessary. There are more clever ways of finding a nondecimal numeral. One may use a place-value chart directly, as follows: To find the septimal numeral for 67_{10}, consult the chart, noting that $67 < 343$. This means there will be no 7^3's digit. On the other hand, $67 > 49$; hence there will be a 7^2's digit. The question now is, what will that digit be? In this case it is easily seen that the digit is 1, since two 49's would be greater than 67. Since 49 of the 67 objects are now accounted for, 49 is subtracted from 67, leaving 18. The next place value is then found from the chart to be 7. Since $18 > 7$, there will be a nonzero 7's digit. There are two 7's, but not three, contained in 18; hence the 7's digit is 2. Since two sevens, or 14 more objects, are accounted for, 14 is subtracted from 18, leaving 4. Thus 67 consists of one 7^2, plus two 7's, plus 4, and thus $67_{10} = 124_7$.

A third procedure can be used for finding nondecimal numerals. To find the septimal numeral for a number, one first divides the number by 7. The quotient will be the number of sevens contained, and the remainder will be the number of units left over. The information thus obtained is the same as obtained by circling x's above. The remainder is therefore the units digit. The quotient gives a number of 7's. If this is divided by 7, the new quotient will be a number of 7^2's and the remainder a number of 7's. Thus this second remainder is the 7's digit. This repetitive process can be continued until a quotient of 0 is obtained. The remainders will be the digits of the septimal numeral, in reverse order. It should be noted that the divisions by 7 may be performed using

$$
\begin{array}{r}
89 \\
7\overline{)625} \\
56 \\
\hline
65 \\
63 \\
\hline
2
\end{array}
$$
(units digit is 2)

$$
\begin{array}{r}
12 \\
7\overline{)89} \\
84 \\
\hline
5
\end{array}
$$
(sevens digit is 5)

$$
\begin{array}{r}
1 \\
7\overline{)12} \\
7 \\
\hline
5
\end{array}
$$
(forty-nines digit is 5)

$$
\begin{array}{r}
0 \\
7\overline{)1} \\
0 \\
\hline
1
\end{array}
$$
(7^3 digit is 1)

numerals of any sort, i.e., septimal, decimal, or any other. Since the decimal system is familiar, it will be the easiest to use.

Using the above principle, one may, by repeated division, find the septimal numeral for any whole number. This is illustrated above, where the septimal numeral for 625_{10} is found to be '1552_7.' A study of an expanded numeral for this number may help further in visualizing and understanding the procedure. The expanded numeral for 1552_7 is

$$1 \times 7^3 + 5 \times 7^2 + 5 \times 7^1 + 2.$$

Upon dividing by 7, one obtains a remainder of 2 and a quotient of 155_7. Dividing 155_7 by 7, yields a remainder of 5 and a quotient of 15_7. Dividing again by 7, yields a remainder of 5 and a quotient of 1. A final step, dividing 1 by 7, yields a quotient of 0 and a remainder of 1.

EXERCISES

1. Make a place-value chart for the following bases.

    (a) base five   (b) base four   (c) base two   (d) base twelve

2. By drawing x's and circling them, find the numerals in the base indicated, for the following numbers.

    (a) 89_{10} (base 5)   (b) 85_{10} (base 4)   (c) 35_{10} (base 2)   (d) 81_{10} (base 7)

3. By using a place-value chart and subtracting, find numerals in the base indicated, for the following numbers.

    (a) 384_{10} (base 7)   (b) 1294_{10} (base 5)
    (c) 85_{10} (base 4)   (d) 35_{10} (base 2)

4. By division, find numerals in the base indicated, for the following numbers.

    (a) 384_{10} (base 7)   (b) 384_{10} (base 5)   (c) 384_{10} (base 2)
    (d) 82_{10} (base 8)   (e) 2751_{10} (base 6)   (f) 2751_{10} (base 4)
    (g) 133_{10} (base 3)   (h) 8650_{10} (base 9)

8. NUMERALS FOR FRACTIONS

Finding septimal, or other base, numerals for fractions is in general slightly more complicated than for whole numbers. One of the reasons for this appears when one considers the fact that $\frac{3}{7} = 0.428571 \ldots_{10}$, whereas $\frac{3}{7} = 0.3_7$. The decimal numeral for $\frac{3}{7}$ is an unending one, while the septimal numeral consists of a single digit symbol.

A method of finding a septimal numeral for a fraction less than one is illustrated. It is based on the fact that $\frac{7}{7} = 1$, and when any number n is multiplied by 1, the result is n:

$$0.75_{10} = .75 \times \frac{7}{7} = \frac{5.25}{7}$$

$$= \frac{5}{7} + \frac{.25}{7}.$$

Since $0.75 = \frac{5}{7} + .25/7$, it is apparent that the first digit after the septimal point (the sevenths digit) is 5. The next step is as follows:

$$0.75_{10} = \frac{5}{7} + \frac{.25}{7} \times \frac{7}{7} = \frac{5}{7} + \frac{1.75}{7^2}$$

$$= \frac{5}{7} + \frac{1}{7^2} + \frac{.75}{7^2}.$$

It is now apparent that the second, or 49ths digit is 1. The following step is again accomplished by multiplying by $\frac{7}{7}$:

$$0.75_{10} = \frac{5}{7} + \frac{1}{7^2} + \frac{.75}{7^2} \times \frac{7}{7} = \frac{5}{7} + \frac{1}{7^2} + \frac{5.25}{7^3}$$

$$= \frac{5}{7} + \frac{1}{7^2} + \frac{5}{7^3} + \frac{.25}{7^3}.$$

The third digit is 5. A repeating pattern has now begun, and it is clear that the septimal numeral for 0.75 is $0.515151\ldots_7$.

The essential part of the preceding example consists of successive multiplications by 7, and could be summarized as follows. Use decimal numerals. Multiply the number in question by 7. The units digit of the result will be the sevenths digit of the septimal numeral. Then multiply the remaining fraction by 7. The units digit of this result will be the forty-ninths digit of the septimal numeral. Then multiply the remaining fraction by 7, and continue. If eventually some product is a whole number, then the numeral ends.

When a septimal numeral is given for a fraction, the decimal numeral may be found as in the following example:

$$0.515_7 = \frac{5}{7} + \frac{1}{49} + \frac{5}{343} = \frac{49 \times 5}{343} + \frac{7}{343} + \frac{5}{343} = \frac{257}{343} = 0.7492+.$$

Another method is the reverse of that described above for finding septimal numerals. To illustrate, we consider $0.5151\ldots_7$. We multiply successively by ten, but this time using septimal numerals:

0.5151	0.3323	0.6532	0.4546
13	13	13	13
10.3323	4.6532	12.4546	6.6064

Thus the decimal numeral for $0.5151\ldots_7$ is '0.7496+.' This method yields an inexact result, since only a part of '$0.5151\ldots_7$' was used.

EXERCISES

1. Find a base 7 numeral for 0.35_{10}.   2. Find a base 8 numeral for 0.57_{10}.

3. Find a base 4 numeral for 0.313_{10}.   4. Find a base 3 numeral for 0.815_{10}.

Find decimal numerals for the following.

5. 0.3_5 6. 0.312_5 7. 0.35_7 8. 0.436_8

9. Translate the following paragraph.

I left college when I was 43 years old. Two years later, when I was 100, I met a 33-year-old girl and we were married. The difference in our ages was only 12 years. A few years later we had 10 children, and my wife scarcely looked her 101 years. I had a job paying $2200 per month, and 0.1 of my salary went to help support my parents. We lived adequately on the remainder of $1430.

10. If you take a number whose base b numeral has three different digits, write another numeral having the same three digits, but in reverse order, subtract the smaller number from the larger, what can you expect the result to be? Can you prove your answer? [*Hint:* Consider expanded numerals.]

9. BINARY AND DUODECIMAL NUMERATION

Of all nondecimal systems of numeration, two may be mentioned as being of special interest: the binary (base two) and the duodecimal (base twelve). The binary system of numeration uses only two digit symbols, '0' and '1.' No positional system of numeration can have fewer. For working with this system, one would not need to learn extensive addition and multiplication tables. The only basic facts needed are that $0 + 0 = 0$, $0 + 1 = 1$, $1 + 1 = 10$, $0 \cdot 0 = 0$, $0 \cdot 1 = 0$, and $1 \cdot 1 = 1$. To the person who disliked learning addition and multiplication tables as a child, this would surely seem to be an advantage. However, numerals for large numbers in this system have many digit symbols, and the time required to write them would be excessive. The binary numeral for 45_{10}, for example, is '101101' ($1 \times 2^5 + 0 \times 2^4 + 1 \times 2^3 + 1 \times 2^2 + 0 \times 2^1 + 1 \times 2^0$). This disadvantage far outweighs, for ordinary use, any advantage that would be gained by having fewer basic facts and symbols to learn.

A real advantage of the binary system is found in connection with electronic calculating machines. Electronic switches in the machines may be in one of two states, namely off or on. A switch "on" corresponds to the digit 1, and a switch "off" corresponds to the digit 0. Therefore it is natural and convenient to design these computers so that they use the binary system. The large number of digits in binary numerals does not prove a great handicap to these machines, since they work at amazing speeds. Answers are usually converted to the decimal system before they are written down.

The duodecimal system is of interest as being a system whose base is greater than ten. It is also of interest because of the fragments of it which are still found in daily use in merchandising, where objects are sold by the dozen and the gross. Vestiges of the duodecimal system also appear in time measure, where a day is divided into two twelve-hour periods, and the year into twelve months.

If the base of a numeration system is a number larger than ten, it must include some digit symbols which are not used in the decimal system. For the duodecimal system two such symbols must be used for ten and eleven. The symbols δ and ϵ may be used for ten and eleven, respectively, and they may be read "dec," and "el," respectively. The duodecimal numeral for the number twelve is of course '10'; for one gross it is '100.' For twenty-two the numeral is '1δ,' and for thirty-five the numeral is '2ϵ.' The first digit symbol to the right of a duodecimal point represents a number of 12ths, the second a number of 144ths, and so on.

EXERCISES

1. Make addition and multiplication tables for base two and base twelve.

Add

2. (base two)   (a) 101   (b) 111101   (c) 101110110
                        110   10110   11101101

3. (base twelve) (a) 14   (b) 2δ (c) 9δ8
                        27   ϵ4 ϵ4δ

Multiply

4. (base two)   (a) 101   (b) 1011   (c) 1101101
                         11   101   1011

5. (base twelve) (a) 37   (b) 6ϵ (c) 4δ6ϵ
                        12   δ1 ϵ0δ

6. Write binary numerals for the following.

   (a) 17_{10} (b) 35_{10} (c) 63_{10} (d) 0.75_{10}

7. Write duodecimal numerals for the following.

   (a) 0.5_{10} (b) 23.75_{10} (c) 0.35_{10} (d) 0.95_{10}

8. How can one recognize an even number by inspecting its binary numeral?   Its
duodecimal numeral?

1 3 5	2 3	4 5 6	8 9 10
7 9 11	6 7	7 12 13	11 12 13
13 15	10 11	14 15	14 15
	14 15		

FIGURE 1–1

9. Here is a "mind reading" trick. You have four cards, as in Fig. 1–1. You ask a
victim to choose a number from 1 to 15 and tell you on which cards it appears. You quickly
add the first numbers of those cards, and the sum is the victim's number. Why does this
work?

10. SOME CLOSING REMARKS

The development of a numeration system as a satisfactory aid to calculation was
extremely important for the progress of mathematics, and also for the progress of
civilization itself. It has been suggested that an early Roman who could perform
long division, now commonly done by children, would have commanded the highest
respect as a skilled mathematician. This is probably true, but in any case it points
up the fact that calculation can be extremely difficult without an adequate system of
numeration.

The purpose of studying nondecimal systems of numeration is not to acquire
facility in calculating with them. The decimal system is wholly adequate for ordinary

calculations. It is so familiar, however, that its structure and the concepts involved in the calculating processes are easily overlooked. As a study of a foreign language aids one in understanding better his mother tongue, so a study of less familiar numeration can aid in understanding the familiar. The study of nondecimal systems should also point up the fact that the decimal system is not necessarily the best system. Any whole number greater than one can be used as a base, and all kinds of calculations can be performed in each system. There are those who insist that the duodecimal system is the best, and their organization, called *The Duodecimal Society*, is striving for the widespread adoption of that system. It is difficult to see that the advantages claimed for the duodecimal system are sufficient to warrant such a change.

Upon studying nondecimal numeration systems, one should clearly see that there is a distinction to be made between *numbers* and *numerals*. The symbols which are used to represent numbers are not numbers themselves, but are *names* of numbers, and the properties of numbers in no way depend on the names used for them. This point is often obscured for school children by confining their arithmetic activity to the use of the decimal system. They are prone, therefore, to think of arithmetic as consisting of manipulation of decimal symbols, rather than as a study of numbers and their properties. For example, although to "add two numbers" means to find (by any means whatever) a third number which is their sum, they may feel that until they have performed a certain manipulation of symbols in which they have been drilled, they have not really added. Or they may retain the idea that "a number is even if its last digit is even," although the property of being even is a property of the number itself, while the digits depend on the system of numeration used. For example, the number eight is even, whether it is named '8,' '13$_5$,' or 'VIII.' It may be commented that school arithmetic, as conventionally taught in the past, was a subject dealing mainly with manipulation of decimal numerals, rather than the more proper subject of the properties of numbers.

REVIEW PRACTICE EXERCISES

Simplify

1. $3 - (-5)$	2. $-4 + 6$	3. $-5 - 5$
4. $-5 + 2$	5. $8 + 12$	6. $7 - (-20)$
7. $-14 + (-6)$	8. $15 - (-15)$	9. $-13 - (-7)$
10. $8^4 \div 8^2$	11. $3^5 \div 3^6$	12. $4^3 \div 4^3$
13. $5^6 \div 5^{-2}$	14. $6^{-4} \div 6^6$	15. $8^7 \div 8^{-5}$
16. $9^{-6} \div 9^{-8}$	17. $5^{-10} \div 5^{-4}$	18. $x^{-2} \div x^{-5}$
19. $3 \cdot (-4)$	20. $-6 \cdot 5$	21. $5 \cdot 5$
22. $-5 \cdot (-6)$	23. $4 \cdot (-\frac{1}{2})$	24. $3 \cdot (-5)$
25. $-6 \cdot (-4)$	26. $7 \cdot (-8)$	27. $-8 \cdot (-9)$

CHAPTER **2**

Natural Numbers
and Whole Numbers

1. WHAT ARE NATURAL NUMBERS?

The natural numbers are those numbers used for counting, beginning with the number one. They are familiar from early life, when the recitation of a sequence is learned for use in the process of counting. Yet when one is asked to give a definition of a number, the task may appear to be impossible once it is established that numbers are not numerals. The difficulty is that numbers are abstract concepts, and are therefore not easy to point out or illustrate. It is not difficult to find a set of three objects, for example, but to point out such a set is not to point out *the number three*. An analogy with another abstract concept is illustrative. The color *red* is an abstract concept. One may see a red car, a red house, or a red shirt, but none of these things *is* the color red. The color red is an abstraction, an idea, a concept, and cannot be seen, but only contemplated. As a child, one learns abstract concepts such as these from a large number of experiences. He is taught to recognize three pencils, three books, three pennies, and so on, until eventually he understands the abstract notion of three. He is taught to recognize a red car, a red hat, a red truck, and so on, until he understands the abstract notion of red. There are many other abstract concepts, such as *bravery*, *kindness*, and *sympathy*.

For the purpose at hand it will suffice that one realize the abstract nature of numbers. No attempt will be made here to define natural numbers precisely.

17

Numbers, as well as numerals, are inventions of man. At least this is the prevalent modern view. It was once thought that numbers existed apart from the existence of human beings, and were *discovered* by them, but few if any twentieth-century mathematicians hold such a view. Today's view is that the mathematician creates, rather than discovers, new mathematics.

The natural numbers were no doubt the first numbers invented by man, and for a long time they must have constituted his entire mathematical repertoire. There are of course other kinds of numbers, such as fractions and negative numbers. It will become clear later that these other kinds of numbers are invented in such a way that the natural numbers remain basic, and such that these other numbers have many of the same properties as the natural numbers. The German mathematician Kronecker once remarked that God gave us the natural numbers and man did the rest. It is not clear how serious this statement was intended to be, but it points out that once the properties of natural numbers are known, one can pass along to the invention and study of other kinds of numbers. Therefore, a study of the natural numbers is basic and important.

The properties of principal interest are those properties which are independent of numeration. At first it may seem difficult to find number properties which are independent of numeration, but there are several important ones which are not difficult to grasp once they have been pointed out. Perhaps the primary reason that they can be overlooked so easily is that they are so obvious.

REVIEW PRACTICE EXERCISES

Subtract and check by adding.

1.	416	2.	6520	3.	6824
	212		1347		5692

4.	712_8	5.	6142_7	6.	110110_2
	456_8		4356_7		11011_2

Divide and check by multiplying (and adding the remainder, if any).

7.	$65 \overline{)13780}$	8.	$32 \overline{)13312}$	9.	$53 \overline{)36252}$
10.	$26 \overline{)10870}$	11.	$65 \overline{)20290}$	12.	$83 \overline{)34200}$

2. OPERATIONS FOR NATURAL NUMBERS

Given any two natural numbers, one may add them, finding a result known as the sum. The usual intuitive interpretation given to addition of natural numbers is based on counting, and can be illustrated by examples such as the following. The sum $2 + 3$ is found by counting out a set of 2 objects and a set of 3 objects (without common members), after which all the objects are put together and the members of the resulting set counted, as in Fig. 2–1.

This example illustrates one method of *adding* natural numbers. There are of course other and better methods of finding a sum. Any process by which a sum may be found is called *adding*. The operation of addition is a fundamental operation for natural numbers.

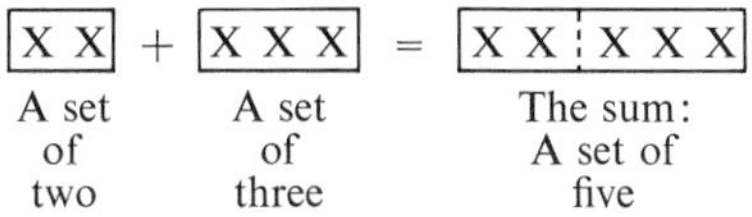

$$\boxed{\text{X X}} + \boxed{\text{X X X}} = \boxed{\text{X X} \mid \text{X X X}}$$

| A set of two | A set of three | The sum: A set of five |

FIGURE 2–1

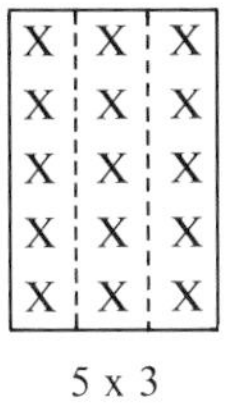

X	X	X
X	X	X
X	X	X
X	X	X
X	X	X

5 x 3

FIGURE 2–2

A second fundamental operation for natural numbers is multiplication. The intuitive interpretation of this operation, based on counting, may be illustrated as follows. The product 5 × 3 is found by counting out 3 sets, each of which has 5 objects (no two of which have common members). Then all the objects are put together and the members of the resulting set counted, as in Fig. 2–2. This process, or any process, for finding a product is called *multiplying*.

The essential property of an operation is uniqueness. Addition is an *operation*, meaning that for a given pair of natural numbers a and b, the sum, $a + b$, if it exists, is unique, i.e., there is *only* one sum. Similarly, multiplication is an operation, because the product of two natural numbers is *unique*. For addition, the sum of *any* two natural numbers exists. Similarly, the product of any two natural numbers exists. This is a desirable property for an operation to have, but not a necessary one. Subtraction, for example, is an operation, because given any natural numbers a and b, the difference, $a - b$, is unique *if it exists*. Not all differences exist in natural numbers. For example, $3 - 5$ does not exist in natural numbers. If a difference does exist in natural numbers, however, such as $8 - 2$, it is unique.

Since uniqueness is what characterizes an operation, there are many relations among numbers that may be called operations. The following example shows a situation in which a unique natural number is associated with an ordered pair of numbers (the pairs are called *ordered* because it may make a difference which member of the pair is first):

$$(3, 2) \rightarrow 7,$$
$$(4, 3) \rightarrow 10,$$
$$(5, 8) \rightarrow 21,$$
$$(5, 10) \rightarrow 25,$$
$$(6, 2) \rightarrow 10.$$

After studying this list, the reader may discover a pattern and be able to formulate a rule for associating a unique natural number with each ordered pair of natural numbers. The rule might be verbalized by saying "double the second number and then add the first number to that result." At any rate, there is some way of associating a unique natural number with each ordered pair of numbers. Any such relation is called an *operation*. A definition of operation can thus be given. It is as follows.

Any relation which associates a unique (at most one) number with each ordered pair of numbers is called an *operation*.

The operation illustrated in the above example is not a common one and has no common name. An operation symbol can easily be devised and assigned to it, however. The symbol '*' would serve, for example, in the same way that '+' serves for denoting addition. Then the associations in the above example could be shown as follows:

$$3 * 2 \;\; = \;\; 7,$$
$$4 * 3 \;\; = \;\; 10,$$
$$5 * 8 \;\; = \;\; 21,$$
$$5 * 10 = 25,$$
$$6 * 2 \;\; = \;\; 10.$$

The operation * could be defined by saying that for any natural numbers a and b,

$$a * b = a + 2b.$$

The operation of subtraction is not ordinarily considered fundamental because it is easily defined in terms of addition, as follows.

The difference $a - b$ is that number c (if it exists) such that $a = b + c$.

In other words, $(a - b) + b = a$. One might also state this definition by saying that $a - b$ is the number one adds to b to get a.

The operation of division likewise need not be considered fundamental, since it may be defined in terms of multiplication.

The quotient $a \div b$ is that number c (if it exists) such that $c \cdot b = a$.

In other words, $(a \div b) \cdot b = a$, or, the number $a \div b$ is the number one multiplies by b to get a. Not every ordered pair of natural numbers has a quotient in natural numbers, but if a quotient does exist, it is unique. Therefore division is an operation.

It is largely a matter of choice which operations are taken to be fundamental. In school arithmetic all four of the operations addition, subtraction, multiplication, and division are usually so considered, but this is contrary to current mathematical practice, where only addition and multiplication are taken as fundamental. One may reasonably inquire why multiplication of natural numbers is considered a fundamental operation, since it can be considered to be a kind of rapid addition. A good pedagogical reason for considering both addition and multiplication as fundamental is that for numbers other than natural numbers, multiplication is not necessarily rapid addition, and it is psychologically advantageous to be consistent in studying various number systems, considering the analogous two fundamental operations in each.

REVIEW PRACTICE EXERCISES

Add these natural numbers. In each case determine whether or not the sum is a natural number.

1. $36 + 42$
2. $915 + 12$
3. $615 + 418$
4. $16 + 814$
5. $961 + 48$
6. $8142 + 916$

Subtract these natural numbers. In each case determine whether or not the difference is a natural number.

7. $14 - 5$
8. $16 - 12$
9. $17 - 25$
10. $64 - 100$
11. $815 - 402$
12. $615 - 715$

Multiply these natural numbers. In each case determine whether or not the product is a natural number.

13. $6 \cdot 14$
14. $8 \cdot 102$
15. $65 \cdot 14$
16. $75 \cdot 40$
17. $812 \cdot 2$
18. $15 \cdot 15$

Divide these natural numbers. In each case determine whether or not the quotient is a natural number.

19. $28 \div 2$
20. $100 \div 10$
21. $81 \div 3$
22. $40 \div 10$
23. $12 \div 20$
24. $14 \div 28$

3. CLOSURE

The set of natural numbers is infinite. That is, the natural numbers cannot all be counted or enumerated in any conceivable length of time. No matter how far counting may proceed, it may be continued further. Even though this is the case, it is not difficult to visualize the entire set of natural numbers.

Given any two natural numbers, their sum is a number in the set of natural numbers. Thus we say that *the set of natural numbers is closed under addition.* This closure property is one of the important and fundamental ones for natural numbers. Likewise *the set of natural numbers is closed under multiplication,* since for any two numbers in the set, their product is also in the set. The closure property for multiplication is the second fundamental property of natural numbers.

A set is said to be *closed* under an operation if *for every* ordered pair of elements in the set, the result of performing that operation with them *exists* and *is a member of the set.*

A further reason for considering only addition and multiplication as fundamental operations is that the set of natural numbers is not closed under subtraction or division. It is not true that for all natural numbers a and b, the difference $a - b$ is in the set. The difference may be considered to exist outside the set of natural numbers, or it may be considered not to exist. In either case, closure fails to hold.*

---

* Some mathematicians prefer not to speak of an operation unless for any two elements of the set the result of performing the operation on them is also in the set. In this event closure would be superfluous and subtraction and division would not be operations.

Similarly, the set of natural numbers is obviously not closed under division, since it is easy to find a pair of natural numbers a and b for which $a \div b$ either does not exist, or exists outside the set of natural numbers.

EXERCISES

1. Is division an operation in natural numbers? Why? Is the set of natural numbers closed under division? Why?

2. If '$a * b$' represents a, does '$*$' represent an operation in natural numbers? Why? If so, is the set of natural numbers closed under the operation?

3. If $a \circ b = 2a + b$, is $\circ$ an operation in natural numbers? If so, is the set of natural numbers closed under it?

For each of the following, answer the same questions as in exercise 3.

4. $a * b = 2a - b$ 5. '$a \square b$' represents either a or b
6. '$a \bigtriangledown b$' represents a^b 7. $a * b = 2(a + b)$
8. $a * b = ab - (a + b)$

4. THE COMMUTATIVE LAWS

Any two natural numbers have a *sum*, which is also a natural number. Furthermore, the order in which two natural numbers are considered does not affect the result. In other words, if a and b are natural numbers, their sum is $a + b$; it is also $b + a$. Since this holds for any two natural numbers, it is usually spoken of as a *law*, to emphasize its generality. This law, which has just been stated informally, is known as the *commutative law of addition* for natural numbers. It can be stated more formally as follows.

For any natural numbers a and b, $a + b = b + a$.

For the second fundamental operation in natural numbers, the order is likewise immaterial. That is,

For any natural numbers a and b, $a \cdot b = b \cdot a$.

This is the *commutative law of multiplication* for natural numbers.

Both of the commutative laws for natural numbers are easy to grasp intuitively. To demonstrate, for example, that $5 + 3 = 3 + 5$, one may use diagrams as in Fig. 2–3. It is clear that, conceptually at least, a similar diagram can be drawn to

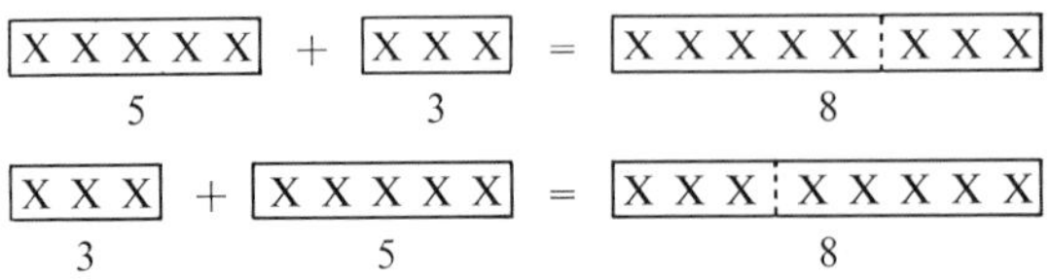

FIGURE 2–3

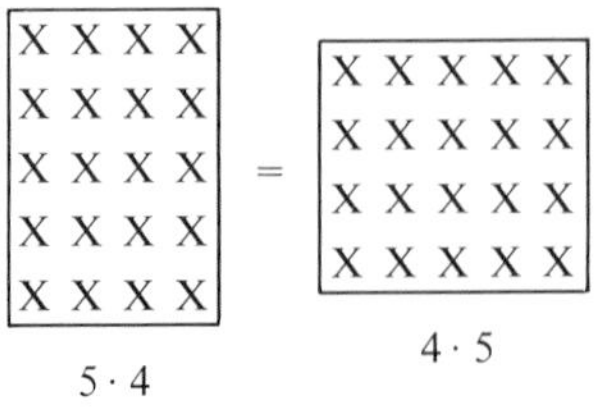

FIGURE 2–4

illustrate addition of any two natural numbers. Thus it is easy to accept, intuitively, the commutative law of addition for natural numbers. To demonstrate that $5 \cdot 4 = 4 \cdot 5$, one may use diagrams as in Fig. 2–4. Note that by rotating the figure on the left 90°, the figure on the right is obtained. Since rotation does not affect the number of objects in the rectangle, there is the same number in both figures. A similar diagram can, at least conceptually, be drawn to illustrate multiplication of any two natural numbers. Hence, it is easy to accept intuitively the commutative law of multiplication for natural numbers.

REVIEW PRACTICE EXERCISES

Simplify

1. $2 \cdot (-3)$	2. $-\frac{5}{3} \cdot \frac{3}{4}$	3. $-3 \cdot (-\frac{5}{4})$
4. $-3 + (-5)$	5. $4 + (-6)$	6. $-8 + (-10)$
7. $-(-5)$	8. $-(-6)$	9. $-1 \cdot 5$
10. $-1 \cdot 6$	11. $-1 \cdot (-5)$	12. $-1 \cdot (-10)$
13. $13 \cdot (5 - 5)$	14. $6 + (7 - 7)$	15. $0 \cdot 4 \cdot (4 + 2)$
16. $6 + (-6)$	17. $4 + (8 - 4)$	18. $4 + (4 - 8)$
19. $(-2) \cdot (-3) \cdot (-5)$	20. $(-4)(-3)(-2)(-1)$	21. $x \cdot (-y)$
22. $3x \cdot (-4x^2)$	23. $-x \cdot (-y)$	24. $-3x^2 \cdot (-5x)$
25. $-3x + (-5x)$	26. $-(-2x^2)$	27. $-x \cdot (-y) \cdot (-z)$
28. $(-x)(-y)(-z)(-w)$	29. $-1 \cdot 3x$	30. $-1 \cdot (-x)$
31. $-1 \cdot x + 1 \cdot x$	32. $-1 \cdot (4x) + (-4x)$	33. $-1 \cdot (-3x^2)$

5. THE ASSOCIATIVE LAWS

Since addition is an operation which involves two numbers at a time, it would seem that if more than two numbers are to be added, they must be grouped successively into pairs. For example, to add 2, 3, and 6, one may find the sum $2 + 3$, or 5, after which the sum $5 + 6$ would be found. In this manner the sum of *two* numbers is found at each stage. On the other hand, one may wish to find first the sum $3 + 6$, or 9, and then the sum $2 + 9$. In either case the final result is 11. Had different numbers been chosen for this example, the same point would have been illustrated. The manner of associating the numbers into pairs for adding would not affect the final result. Since this is true for all natural numbers, it is another fundamental law, *the associative law of addition* for natural numbers, which may be stated as follows.

For any natural numbers a, b, and c, $a + (b + c) = (a + b) + c$.

For multiplication of natural numbers, the manner of associating into pairs is likewise immaterial. That is,

For any natural numbers a, b, and c, $a \cdot (b \cdot c) = (a \cdot b) \cdot c$.

This is the *associative law of multiplication* for natural numbers.

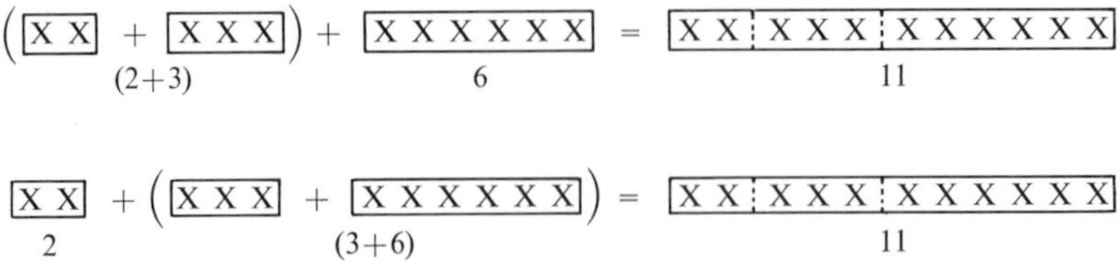

$$\left(\boxed{\text{X X}} + \boxed{\text{X X X}}\right) + \boxed{\text{X X X X X X}} = \boxed{\text{X X} \vdots \text{X X X} \vdots \text{X X X X X X}}$$

$$\underset{(2+3)}{} \qquad \underset{6}{} \qquad \underset{11}{}$$

$$\boxed{\text{X X}} + \left(\boxed{\text{X X X}} + \boxed{\text{X X X X X X}}\right) = \boxed{\text{X X} \vdots \text{X X X} \vdots \text{X X X X X X}}$$

$$\underset{2}{} \qquad \underset{(3+6)}{} \qquad \underset{11}{}$$

FIGURE 2–5

The associative law of addition for natural numbers may be illustrated diagrammatically as in Fig. 2–5. In the first case, the sets of objects containing 2 and 3 members, respectively, are combined, after which the set containing 6 members is included. In the second case, the sets containing 3 and 6 members, respectively, are combined, and then the set containing 2 members is included. It is easily seen that the final results will be the same, no matter how many members the three sets contain.

A three-dimensional picture as in Fig. 2–6 is useful in illustrating the associative law of multiplication. To show $(3 \cdot 4) \cdot 5$ one first constructs a diagram to illustrate $3 \cdot 4$. This will be a rectangular array containing 12 objects. Then to show the product $12 \cdot 5$, five of the arrays are placed together, making a three-dimensional array.

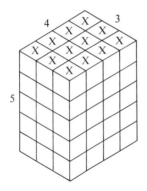

FIGURE 2–6

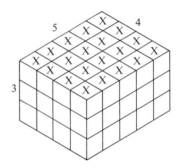

FIGURE 2–7

To show $(4 \cdot 5) \cdot 3$, one first constructs a 4 by 5 array and then places three of them together, again making a three-dimensional rectangular array as in Fig. 2–7. By the commutative law of multiplication, this array also contains $3 \cdot (4 \cdot 5)$ objects. It can be seen that Figs. 2–6 and 2–7 are the same except that they are oriented differently. Conceptually at least, figures like these can be drawn to illustrate that multiplication is associative for any three natural numbers.

When more than three numbers are to be added, the associating into pairs may be done in several ways. For example, in finding the sum of a, b, c, and d, one may write

$$(a + b) + (c + d), \qquad \text{or} \qquad [a + (b + c)] + d,$$

or

$$[(a + b) + c] + d, \qquad \text{or} \qquad a + [b + (c + d)].$$

Since the associative law guarantees that the results are identical, parentheses and brackets may be omitted, in order to shorten the writing. Thus one may write simply

$$a + b + c + d.$$

It is important to note that an *agreement* is involved here, that is, an agreement to simplify symbolism. Knowledge of the associative law makes it natural to arrive at the agreement to omit grouping symbols. It should also be noted that if an operation is not associative, then an agreement about omitting grouping symbols is not as natural or as easy to make. For example, '8 − 3 − 2' is an ambiguous symbol because subtraction is not an associative operation. If the association is made as (8 − 3) − 2, then the result is 3. On the other hand, if the association is made as 8 − (3 − 2), the result is 7. For some purposes, such as the writing of mental arithmetic problems for use by a teacher, the agreement is made to associate to the left. That is, the problem is considered as if all grouping symbols begin at the extreme left, as follows:

$$\{[(a + b) - c] + d\} - e.$$

In other words, the operations are taken in order as they occur, from left to right. For many purposes, however, such an agreement is not useful, and it is not often used.

The above discussion is concerned with addition. A similar situation exists with respect to multiplication. That is, by agreement where multiplication of natural numbers is involved, grouping symbols may be omitted, since the operation is associative.

Together, the associative and commutative laws provide a great deal of freedom in grouping and ordering numbers in addition. The commutative law permits one to change the order of numbers in addition, and the associative law permits grouping them at will. Thus for the sum $(a + b) + c$, there are eleven other arrangements, all of which are different and all of which, by the commutative and associative laws, are equivalent to this one. Some of them are

$$a + (b + c), \qquad b + (a + c), \qquad (b + c) + a, \qquad \text{and} \qquad (c + a) + b.$$

The reader may wish to complete the list. Similarly, the associative and commutative laws of multiplication allow the same freedom in grouping and ordering numbers for that operation.

In arithmetic and algebra, the associative and commutative laws are used together freely, if not consciously, to perform any combination of changes in order and grouping. For this reason it is sometimes difficult at first to regard these laws as being separate and independent, as they indeed are. The fact that one can change order and grouping at will often helps to simplify calculations in arithmetic. For example, the addition

$$7 + 5 + 3 + 25$$

can be done directly from left to right. It is easier, however, if one adds 7 and 3, to obtain 10, then adds 5 and 25 to obtain 30, and finally adds the 10 and the 30.

EXERCISES

1. Do the following calculations, choosing your grouping and ordering so as to simplify the calculation.

(a) $8 + 4 + 5 + 2 + 6 + 15 + 1$ (e) $2 \cdot 7 \cdot 3 \cdot 5$

(b) $1 + 13 + 9 + 6 + 7$ (f) $2 \cdot 12 \cdot 2 \cdot 2$

(c) $14 + 3 + 5 + 7 + 35$ (g) $4 \cdot 65 \cdot 5 \cdot 5$

(d) $11 + 45 + 9 + 6 + 5$ (h) $25 \cdot 13 \cdot 3 \cdot 4$

2. Grouping and ordering can be changed in $a + (b + c)$ to obtain $b + (a + c)$. This may be done in steps, using only one law in each step, as follows:

$a + (b + c)$

$(a + b) + c$ (using the associative law of addition)

$(b + a) + c$ (using the commutative law of addition)

$b + (a + c)$ (using the associative law of addition).

By a similar procedure, establish the following:

(a) $a + (b + c) = c + (a + b)$

(b) $a + (b + c) = b + (c + a)$

(c) $(a + b) + (c + d) = (b + d) + (a + c)$

(d) $(a + b) + (c + d) = [(b + c) + a] + d$

REVIEW PRACTICE EXERCISES

Multiply

EXAMPLE: $x(x + 2) = x^2 + 2x$

1. $x(2x + 3)$ 2. $x^2(x - 1)$ 3. $2x(x + 4)$

4. $3y(y - 3)$ 5. $x(y + z)$ 6. $2x(x - y)$

7. $5y(6x - 2y)$ 8. $3x^2(x - 2y)$ 9. $4y^3(y^{-3} + 2)$

Factor

EXAMPLE: $2x^2 + 2x = 2x \cdot x + 2x \cdot 1 = 2x(x + 1)$

10. $3x^2 + 3x$ 11. $4x^3 + 2x$ 12. $3y^2 - 3y$

13. $5x^2 + 5$ 14. $2xy + 2x$ 15. $5x^2y - y$

16. $2x^2y - 2xy^2$ 17. $3x + 3y$ 18. $6x^2 - 6y^2$

6. THE DISTRIBUTIVE LAW

To this point the operations of addition and multiplication have been considered separately. There is, however, an important law which considers the two operations together. To illustrate, consider '$2 \cdot (3 + 5)$,' in which both operations are involved. The symbol indicates that the sum $3 + 5$, or 8, is to be found and then the product $2 \cdot 8$. However, if one first multiplies $2 \cdot 3$ and then $2 \cdot 5$ and then adds, he obtains the same final result. In the first case, the addition is performed first and then the multiplication. In the second case, the multiplication is performed first and then the addition. The multiplication in the second case has been *distributed*, so to speak, over the addition. This example illustrates the general principle for natural numbers known as the *distributive law of multiplication over addition.*

For any natural numbers a, b, and c, $a \cdot (b + c) = (a \cdot b) + (a \cdot c)$.

This law can also be illustrated by diagrams as in Fig. 2–8.

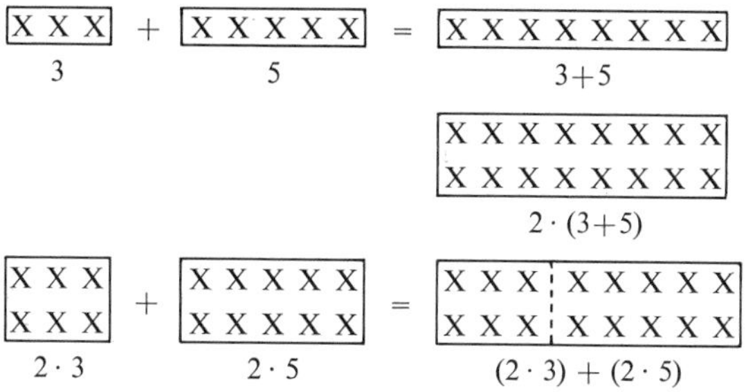

FIGURE 2–8

Where the two operations of addition and multiplication occur together, a further agreement about omitting grouping symbols is convenient. The standard convention in algebraic writings is that symbols which set off multiplications may be omitted. For example, instead of '$(a \cdot b) + (a \cdot c)$,' one would write '$a \cdot b + a \cdot c$.' Instead of '$[3 \cdot (x + y)] + (5 \cdot z)$,' one would write '$3 \cdot (x + y) + 5 \cdot z$.' Note that the parentheses around '$x + y$' cannot be omitted without changing the meaning.

The distributive law could also be stated as follows: "For any natural numbers a, b, and c, $(b + c) \cdot a = (b \cdot a) + (c \cdot a)$." In this case '$a$' appears on the right instead of the left, as it does in the statement above. Since multiplication of natural numbers is a commutative operation, these statements amount to the same thing. To see this, note that $a \cdot (b + c) = (b + c) \cdot a$, and thus the left sides of the two equations represent the same thing. Also note that $(a \cdot b) + (a \cdot c) = (b \cdot a) + (c \cdot a)$, and therefore the right sides of the equations represent the same thing. If the operation of multiplication were not commutative, the two statements of the law would not necessarily be equivalent. The first statement,

For any a, b, and c, $a \cdot (b + c) = (a \cdot c) + (a \cdot c)$,

would describe a *left-hand* distributive law, and the second statement,

For any a, b, and c, $(b + c) \cdot a = (b \cdot a) + (c \cdot a)$,

would describe a *right-hand* distributive law. It might happen that one law would hold and the other would not.

The preceding arguments about the various laws of natural numbers make those laws *plausible*, and easy to accept intuitively. They should not, however, be regarded as proofs. Therefore in what follows, these laws should be regarded as axioms, or assumptions. It is possible, by using some more primitive notions for axioms, to prove all of these laws, but neither space nor the spirit of this book permits a discussion of that development here. The interested reader is referred to the work of Peano, as developed in several of the references.

EXERCISES

1. Refer to exercises 2 through 8 on page 22. For each of the relations that are operations, answer the following questions.

(a) Is the operation commutative?

(b) Is the operation associative?

2. Make diagrams to illustrate $a + (b \cdot c)$ and $(a + b) \cdot (a + c)$. Formulate a statement (which may or may not be true) which asserts that addition is distributive over multiplication for natural numbers. Is your statement a law of natural numbers?

3. Make diagrams to illustrate $a \cdot (b - c)$ and $a \cdot b - a \cdot c$. Formulate a statement (it may be true or it may not) which asserts that multiplication is distributive over subtraction for natural numbers. Is your statement a law of natural numbers?

4. Formulate a statement which asserts that division is left-hand distributive over addition. Is your statement a law of natural numbers?

5. Formulate a statement which asserts that division is right-hand distributive over addition. Is your statement a law of natural numbers?

6. What law(s) of natural numbers are illustrated by each of the following sentences?

(a) $3 + 2 = 2 + 3$

(b) $7 \cdot 1 = 1 \cdot 7$

(c) $5 + (3 + 2) = (5 + 3) + 2$

(d) $(3 + 2) + 5 = 5 + (3 + 2)$

(e) $3 \cdot (5 + 2) = 3 \cdot 5 + 3 \cdot 2$

(f) $4 \cdot (8 + 6) = (8 + 6) \cdot 4$

(g) $3 \cdot 2 + 3 \cdot 5 = 3 \cdot (2 + 5)$

(h) $4 \cdot 6 + 4 \cdot 7 = (7 + 6) \cdot 4$

(i) $4 + (2 + 3) = (2 + 4) + 3$

(j) $3 \cdot (5 + 2) = (2 + 5) \cdot 3$

(k) $(8 + 2) \cdot (9 + 4) = (9 + 4) \cdot (8 + 2)$

(l) $(8 + 2) \cdot (9 + 4) = (2 + 8) \cdot (9 + 4)$

7. Consider the following sentence, where '$\square$' is a symbol for an operation in natural numbers:

$$a \,\square\, b = b \,\square\, a$$

Replace '$\square$' by (a) '$+$,' (b) '$-$,' (c) '$\times$,' (d) '$\div$.' For which of these replacements is the resulting sentence true for all natural numbers a and b? For each of the others, give a counterexample (an example in which the sentence becomes false for some numbers a and b).

8. Consider the following sentence, where '$\square$' is a symbol for an operation in natural numbers:

$$a \,\square\, (b \,\square\, c) = (a \,\square\, b) \,\square\, c.$$

Replace '$\square$' by (a) '$+$,' (b) '$-$,' (c) '$\times$,' (d) '$\div$.' For which of these replacements is the resulting sentence true for all natural numbers a, b, and c? For each of the others, give a counterexample.

9. Consider the following sentence, where '$\square$' and '$\triangle$' are symbols for an operation in natural numbers:

$$a \,\square\, (b \,\triangle\, c) = (a \,\square\, b) \,\triangle\, (a \,\square\, c).$$

Replace '$\square$' and '$\triangle$,' respectively, by (a) '$\times$,' '$+$,' (b) '$+$,' '$\times$,' (c) '$-$,' '$\times$,' (d) '$+$,' '$-$,' (e) '$\div$,' '$+$,' (f) '$\times$,' '$\div$.' For which of these replacements is the resulting sentence true for all natural numbers a, b, and c? For each of the others give a counterexample.

7. THE LAWS OF NATURAL NUMBERS IN ARITHMETIC

The procedures, or *algorithms*, by which addition, multiplication, subtraction, and division are carried out are familiar to all those who have profited by attending school.   In order to explain or understand these procedures, one must lean heavily on the commutative, associative, and distributive laws for natural numbers. To illustrate, the algorithms for addition, multiplication, and division will be discussed.

Addition. An example of a commonplace addition problem will illustrate the importance of the commutative and associative laws:

$$
\begin{array}{r}
215 \\
367 \\
\underline{123} \\
705
\end{array}
$$

Using expanded numerals, one would write the problem to be solved as follows:

(i) $\qquad (200 + 10 + 5) + (300 + 60 + 7) + (100 + 20 + 3).$

In adding using a column arrangement, one may begin by adding the units digits, then the tens, followed by the hundreds, and so on. In other words, the calculation performed may be represented as

(ii) $\qquad (5 + 7 + 3) + (10 + 60 + 20) + (200 + 300 + 100),$

assuming that one adds from top to bottom in each column. If one adds from bottom to top, then the numerals should be reversed in each of the preceding parentheses. It is by the commutative and associative laws of addition that one may change the order and the grouping of the summands in order to arrive at (ii). After performing the addition indicated in each of the parentheses of (ii), one obtains the result

(iii) $\qquad 15 + 90 + 600.$

However, in the usual procedure, powers of ten are carried into succeeding columns. This can be illustrated as follows:

(iv) $\qquad (5 + 10) + 90 + 600,$
(v) $\qquad 5 + (10 + 90) + 600,$
(vi) $\qquad 5 + (100 + 600).$

Note that the steps shown in (iv), (v), and (vi) depend upon the associative law of addition. The final result is $5 + 700$, for which one writes the decimal numeral '705.'

It is well worth noting that the ordinary addition algorithm is not the only possible procedure to use in columnar addition. It would be about as easy to begin by adding the hundreds or thousands digits, for example, instead of adding the units digits first. Such a procedure can be justified by considering the commutative and associative laws, and in fact it would have the advantage that the digits of the more important places would be found first. Thus adder's fatigue would be less likely to cause a large error than a small one.

Multiplication. Consider the following multiplication problem:

$$\begin{array}{r} 316 \\ \times 7 \\ \hline 2212 \end{array}$$

Using expanded numerals, one would write the problem to be solved as

(i) $$7 \cdot (6 + 10 + 300).$$

Since one actually multiplies 6, 10, and 300 successively by 7, it is clear that the distributive law of multiplication over addition is being employed. In other words, the calculation actually performed is

(ii) $$(7 \cdot 6) + (7 \cdot 10) + (7 \cdot 300),$$

and it results in

(iii) $$(40 + 2) + 70 + 2100.$$

In order to carry powers of ten into succeeding columns, the associative and commutative laws of addition are used:

(iv) $$2 + [10 + (30 + 70)] + 2100,$$

(v) $$2 + (10 + 100) + 2100,$$

(vi) $$2 + 10 + 2200.$$

The final result is written '2212.'

The following example illustrates the repeated use of the distributive law of multiplication over addition in cases where the numeral for the multiplier has several digits:

$$\begin{array}{r} 427 \\ 36 \\ \hline 2562 \\ 1281 \\ \hline 15372 \end{array}$$

In this case, the numeral for the multiplier has two digits, and therefore the distributive law must be used twice. The problem to be solved is the calculation

(i) $$(6 + 30) \cdot (7 + 20 + 400).$$

By the distributive law, this is equivalent to

(ii) $$6 \cdot (7 + 20 + 400) + 30 \cdot (7 + 20 + 400).$$

Note that two multiplications are to be performed: a multiplication by 6 and a multiplication by 30, after which the products are to be added. This is precisely what one does when using the ordinary multiplication algorithm. It is well to look at the first multiplication in detail:

(iii) $6 \cdot (7 + 20 + 400) = (6 \cdot 7) + (6 \cdot 20) + (6 \cdot 400),$

by the distributive law. By using the commutative and associative laws of addition, one arrives at

(iv) $2 + 60 + 2500,$ or $2562,$

which is the result found by the ordinary algorithm upon multiplying by 6. The second multiplication may be considered in similar detail:

(v) $30 \cdot (7 + 20 + 400) = (30 \cdot 7) + (30 \cdot 20) + (30 \cdot 400),$

again by the distributive law. By using the commutative and associative laws of addition, one finds the result of the multiplication by 30 to be 12810. The two products are then to be added, as indicated in (ii), producing the final answer, 15372. It is left to the reader to explain why, in using the ordinary algorithm, one writes the numeral '1281' in a position under, but to the left of, the numeral '2562.'

The ordinary multiplication algorithm is not the only possible one, nor does it seem to be the best one for all purposes. It has the advantage of being very definite and straightforward, and no tentative results need be written. However, the units digits are multiplied first, so that errors due to fatigue are more apt to be found among the digits of higher places. An algorithm in which one works from left to right would therefore have the advantage of producing the most important digits first, and in cases where an approximate answer is sufficient, only part of the calculation need be done. Its disadvantage lies in the need to write some tentative results, which may later be crossed out and other results substituted for them.

REVIEW PRACTICE EXERCISES

Simplify

1. $4 \cdot 0$ 2. $6 + 0$ 3. $2x + (x - x)$
4. $xy \cdot 0$ 5. $4x^2 + 0$ 6. $7x^2 + (y^2 - y^2)$
7. $4x(2y - 2y)$ 8. $(8 - 8) \cdot 7264$ 9. $4x + 2y - 4x$
10. $6y^2 + 2x - 6y^2$ 11. $(47x + 2)(3x - 3x)$ 12. $4x^2 + (8y - 8y)$

8. THE NUMBER ZERO AND WHOLE NUMBERS

In the above examples, which illustrate algorithms for calculating with natural numbers, zero occurs repeatedly. Yet zero is not a natural number. The invention of the number zero, by the Hindus and Arabs, provided one of the most important advances in mathematical history. Before the number zero was devised, algorithms were long and involved; whereas now every school child learns them without great difficulty, save that which may accompany a distasteful attitude toward the subject.

The number zero might have been devised earlier but for the conception that numbers must represent *something*, whereas zero means "nothing." Unfortunately, a view something like this is still working its havoc today. Many a student learns that "zero means nothing," and concludes that zero is therefore not a number. This is of course entirely misleading, since the number zero is a most interesting and important number.

Zero is sometimes referred to as a *placeholder*, meaning that in decimal numeration the symbol '0' holds a place for a missing digit. This is also misleading, since zero may itself be a digit, and therefore plays the same kind of role as any of the other numbers which are used as digits. The only sense in which it may seem strange is that in numeration for natural numbers, zero is the only number used as a digit which is not itself a natural number.

Whole numbers. If the number zero is put with the natural numbers, the new set is often referred to as the set of *whole numbers*. Thus a whole number is either zero or a natural number. For some purposes it is convenient to consider the set of whole numbers rather than the set of natural numbers. In this case, it is important that the behavior of the number zero be known, with respect to the two fundamental operations. This is easily specified as follows:

(i) $0 + n = n + 0 = n$, for any whole number n,

(ii) $0 \cdot n = n \cdot 0 = 0$, for any whole number n. (Note that no product $a \cdot b$ of whole numbers can be zero unless $a = 0$ or $b = 0$, for products of natural numbers are natural numbers.)

(iii) The commutative and associative laws of multiplication and addition and the distributive law of multiplication over addition hold for all whole numbers, including cases in which the number zero occurs.

Thus this new set of numbers follows the same laws as the set of natural numbers, and calculations in whole numbers are performed in a similar fashion. Nothing need be unlearned; the new set of numbers is simply an enrichment of the old.

One may ask about the behavior of zero in subtraction and division, and wonder why statements about these operations were not included above. The reason is that, since subtraction is defined in terms of addition and division is defined in terms of multiplication, the behavior of zero in subtraction and division has already been specified. If one subtracts zero from any whole number, the result is the original number. This can be seen as follows:

$x - 0$ is some number, which may be called 'p,' such that $p + 0 = x$. Thus the number called 'p' must be the same number which was called 'x,' because $p + 0 = p$, for any whole number p.

If zero is divided by any nonzero whole number, the result is zero, as may be seen as follows:

$0/n$ is some number, which may be called 'q,' such that $q \cdot n = 0$. Since n is not zero, q must be zero, in order that $q \cdot n$ be zero.

Division of a whole number by zero is not possible if division is to be an *operation*. This may be seen as follows:

n/0 would be some number, which may be called 'r,' such that $r \cdot 0 = n$. But $r \cdot 0 = 0$, and therefore cannot be n unless n is zero. Thus no nonzero number can be divided by zero. 0/0 would be some number, which may be called 't,' such that $t \cdot 0 = 0$. In this case, *any* number will work for t, and therefore division of zero by zero must be excluded. Otherwise results of dividing would not be unique and division would not be an operation.

EXERCISES

1. Perform the addition
$$
\begin{array}{r}
3276 \\
148 \\
8795 \\
\hline
\end{array}
$$

Use expanded numerals to illustrate how the algorithm works. Would the same algorithm work if one used base six numerals?

2. Perform the multiplication
$$
\begin{array}{r}
754 \\
316 \\
\hline
\end{array}
$$

Use expanded numerals to show how the algorithm works. Would the same algorithm work if one used binary numerals?

3. Devise an addition algorithm for whole numbers in which one begins with the column on the left and works from left to right.

4. Devise a multiplication algorithm for whole numbers in which one begins on the left in both the multiplication and the addition.

5. An interesting multiplication algorithm for natural numbers is based on the binary numeration system, and is sometimes known as the "Russian peasant" method. It seems that the Russian peasant can do all kinds of additions, but can multiply only by two and can divide only by two. He knows nothing about fractions or remainders, so when dividing by two he disregards remainders. To multiply two numbers, he begins by doubling one and halving the other. If there is a remainder when he divides by 2, he discards it. Then he takes the results and repeats, doubling the first number and halving the second. He continues this process until the series of numbers being halved reaches 1. Looking over the results of his work, and not caring for even numbers, the peasant crosses out all even numbers in the series of numbers being halved, as well as the corresponding numbers in the other series. Then he adds the remaining numbers in the series of numbers that were doubled. The result is the product of the original two numbers. To illustrate, the product of 217 and 35 is found as follows:

$$
\begin{array}{cc}
217 & 35 \\
434 & 17 \\
\cancel{868} & \cancel{8} \\
\cancel{1736} & \cancel{4} \\
\cancel{3472} & \cancel{2} \\
6944 & 1 \\
\hline
7595 &
\end{array}
$$

Explain why the "Russian peasant" method is a valid algorithm for multiplication of natural numbers. Will this algorithm also work if one uses base seven numerals?

6. Multiply 119 by 357 using the "Russian peasant" method.

7. Does the commutative law of multiplication hold for the "Russian peasant" method?

8. Illustrate and explain the usual subtraction algorithm for natural numbers.

9. Property (iii) of the number 0 is actually a consequence of properties (i) and (ii). Prove this.

9. THE DIVISION ALGORITHM

It may be recalled that division is defined in terms of multiplication. If a and b are whole numbers, the quotient, $a \div b$ is some number c (if it exists), for which $b \cdot c = a$. Division is not possible for every ordered pair of whole numbers. For example, the division $13 \div 5$ is not possible in natural numbers. It is possible, however, to find a "quotient" and a "remainder," by a process familiar to school children. In the example $13 \div 5$, the quotient is 2 and the remainder 3, as may be verified by noting that $5 \cdot 2 + 3 = 13$.

It is in fact possible to find such a quotient and remainder for $D \div d$, when D and d are any whole numbers except that $d \neq 0$. The process (or *algorithm*) for finding the quotient and remainder is known as *long* (or *short*) *division*. The two processes are not essentially different, and may be considered to be the same except for the manner of writing. Here, both will be referred to as the *division algorithm*. Division, like multiplication and addition, is based on the properties of the whole numbers. Unfortunately, the division algorithm is usually learned in such a manner that myriad details stand out as important, and the essential character of the process is thereby obscured.

The division algorithm consists basically of repeated guessing, multiplying, and subtracting. Any other details of the process merely contribute to its refinement. An example will illustrate that partial quotients may be guessed *at random* without invalidating the process. Consider the problem of dividing 1506 by 32. Suppose that a partial quotient of 5 is guessed. Then multiply and subtract as follows:

$$
\begin{array}{r}
5 \\
32\overline{)1506} \\
160 \\
\hline
1346
\end{array}
$$

It may be checked that the product of the quotient and divisor, plus the remainder, is the dividend: $1506 = 32 \cdot 5 + 1346$. For the next step, a partial quotient of 20 is guessed. It is multiplied by the divisor, 32, and the product subtracted from the first remainder:

$$
\begin{array}{r}
20 \\
32\overline{)1346} \\
640 \\
\hline
706
\end{array}
$$

As before, the product of the quotient and divisor, plus the remainder, is the dividend for this step (which is the remainder of the first step): $1346 = 32 \cdot 20 + 706$. For the next step, a partial quotient of 2 is guessed:

$$
\begin{array}{r}
2 \\
32\,\overline{)706} \\
64 \\
\hline
642
\end{array}
$$

As expected, $706 = 32 \cdot 2 + 642$. For the next step a partial quotient of 20 is guessed:

$$
\begin{array}{r}
20 \\
32\,\overline{)642} \\
640 \\
\hline
2
\end{array}
$$

As expected, $642 = 32 \cdot 20 + 2$. The process cannot be continued further, because subtraction would not be possible another time, no matter what natural number should be guessed for a partial quotient.

Now the partial quotients are added to produce the final quotient. The remainder of the last step is the final remainder. In other words, the quotient is 47 and the remainder is 2. This checks, since

$$1506 = 32 \cdot 47 + 2.$$

The partial quotients in this example could have been guessed in any manner whatsoever, as long as the accompanying subtractions are possible. This will become clear later. It may be instructive here to write the above steps together:

$$
\begin{array}{r}
5 + 20 + 2 + 20 \\
32\,\overline{)1506} \\
160 \\
\hline
1346 \\
640 \\
\hline
706 \\
64 \\
\hline
642 \\
640 \\
\hline
2
\end{array}
$$

When the steps are written together in this fashion, the algorithm bears a bit more resemblance to the process learned in school.

The division algorithm as learned in school may seem much more complicated than the above example. As remarked earlier, the complication arises because the refinements are considered, rather than the basic process. Before considering refinements here, it will be established that the process is a valid one.

Consider as dividend and divisor, respectively, any whole numbers D and d for which $d \neq 0$. The first step in the alogrithm is to guess a partial quotient, i.e., some whole number Q_1. The product dQ_1 is found and subtracted (if possible) from D, to obtain the first remainder, R_1, as follows:

$$
\begin{array}{r}
Q_1 \\
d\,\overline{)\,D} \\
dQ_1 \\
\hline
D - dQ_1, \quad \text{or } R_1
\end{array}
$$

If the subtraction $D - dQ_1$ is not possible, then a smaller guess must be made. If the subtraction $D - dQ_1$ is possible, the product dQ_1 plus the remainder R_1 is the dividend, D. That is,

$$D = dQ_1 + R_1$$

or

$$D = dQ_1 + (D - dQ_1).$$

This is true because the number $D - dQ_1$ is, by definition of subtraction, the number which when added to dQ_1 produces D. Here it is added to dQ_1, and hence the result is D.

The second step is entirely analogous to the first. The dividend for the second step, however, is the first remainder R_1:

$$
\begin{array}{r}
Q_2 \\
d\,\overline{)\,R_1} \\
dQ_2 \\
\hline
R_1 - dQ_2, \quad \text{or } R_2
\end{array}
$$

Of course $R_1 = dQ_2 + R_2$ for reasons exactly similar to those given above for the first step.

It must now be established that the sum of the partial quotients, $Q_1 + Q_2$, is also a partial quotient. That is,

$$D = d(Q_1 + Q_2) + R_2.$$

This can be proved as follows. It has been established that

$$D = dQ_1 + R_1, \tag{1}$$

and also that

$$R_1 = dQ_2 + R_2. \tag{2}$$

The 'R_1' in equation (1) can be replaced by '$dQ_2 + R_2$,' since the two symbols represent the same number, according to equation (2). The result is then

$$D = dQ_1 + (dQ_2 + R_2).$$

By the associative law of addition, it follows that

$$D = (dQ_1 + dQ_2) + R_2.$$

Now, by the distributive law of multiplication over addition,

$$D = d(Q_1 + Q_2) + R_2.$$

Thus $Q_1 + Q_2$ is a partial quotient, as was to be shown. Evidently a similar argument will show that the sum of three or more such partial quotients will also be a partial quotient.

Since each remainder is smaller than the preceding one, this process will eventually produce a remainder smaller than d, the divisor. (If the remainder is zero the division is said to come out "exact.") At this stage, the process is at an end, because with another step no subtraction would be possible.

By the division algorithm, then, given any whole numbers d and D, where $d \neq 0$, it is always possible to find whole numbers Q and R for which $D = dQ + R$, and where $R < d$.

Examination of the preceding proof shows that the division algorithm depends on (1) the associative law of addition and (2) the distributive law of multiplication over addition. The only other requirement is that the partial quotients be chosen so that the subtractions are possible.

One rather important (even if not essential) refinement of this process is to guess partial quotients in such a way that the digits of a quotient are obtained directly. In the example $1506 \div 32$, the first partial quotient would thus be 40 and the second one 7. For 40 one would write '4.' Then when the '7' is written next to it, the result is a numeral for the sum of the partial quotients 40 and 7:

$$
\begin{array}{r}
47 \\
32\overline{)1506} \\
1280 \\
\overline{226} \\
224 \\
\overline{2}
\end{array}
$$

In this example, it may be noted, the '0' in '1280' might often be omitted, after which the '6' would be "brought down." The '4' of the quotient has been very carefully positioned over the '0' in the symbol below, the way the author learned to do it in elementary school.

It is left to the reader to ponder the fact that too much attention to such minor details inevitably blocks the pathway to an understanding of the basic process.

The character of the division algorithm may be further illustrated by considering examples with nondecimal numerals. The algorithm may be performed, using numerals of any base, by anyone who knows how to guess, multiply, and subtract with that kind of symbolism.

EXAMPLE:

$$
\begin{array}{r}
\overline{20 + 3 + 10 + 4 + 1} \\
14_5) \overline{1324_5} \\
330 \\
\hline
444 \\
102 \\
\hline
342 \\
140 \\
\hline
202 \\
121 \\
\hline
31 \\
14 \\
\hline
12
\end{array}
$$

The quotient is 43_5 and the remainder is 12_5.

The process in the preceding example could be refined in such a way that the digits of the base five numeral will be obtained directly, by guessing numbers of ones, fives, or twenty-fives, and so on, as follows:

$$
\begin{array}{r}
\overline{40 + 3} \\
14_5) \overline{1324_5} \\
1210 \\
\hline
114 \\
102 \\
\hline
12
\end{array}
\qquad \text{or} \qquad
\begin{array}{r}
\overline{43} \\
14_5) \overline{1324_5} \\
1210 \\
\hline
114 \\
102 \\
\hline
12
\end{array}
$$

EXERCISES

1. Perform the following divisions of whole numbers by guessing partial quotients at random. Check the answers.

(a) $23) \overline{975}$ (b) $41) \overline{0}$ (c) $417) \overline{36403}$ (d) $606) \overline{120511}$

2. Perform the following divisions of whole numbers as in exercise 1, without converting to decimal symbolism.

(a) $12_7) \overline{46267}$ (b) $23_5) \overline{12314_5}$ (c) $101_2) \overline{11101101_2}$ (d) $261_8) \overline{35714_8}$

3. Prove that the sum of the first three partial quotients, Q_1, Q_2, and Q_3, obtained in the division algorithm, is also a partial quotient, i.e., that $D = d(Q_1 + Q_2 + Q_3) + R_3$.

4. In the example

$$
\begin{array}{r}
4 \\
32) \overline{1506} \\
1280 \\
\hline
226
\end{array}
$$

(a) discuss the significance of omitting the '0' in '1280.' (b) Discuss a rationale, based on properties of natural numbers, for the phrase "bring down the '6'." (c) Discuss possible reasons for positioning the '4' of the quotient directly over the '0' of the dividend.

5.   What are some other refinements in the division algorithm for whole numbers? Discuss how they are (or are not) based on the properties of whole numbers.

REVIEW PRACTICE EXERCISES

Solve these equations.
EXAMPLE:

$$4x + 5 = 31$$
$$4x + 5 - 5 = 31 - 5$$
$$4x = 34$$
$$\tfrac{1}{4} \cdot 4x = \tfrac{1}{4} \cdot 34$$
$$x = \tfrac{34}{4}, \quad \text{or} \quad \tfrac{17}{2}.$$

1. $3x + 2 = 41$ 2. $-5x + 4 = x + 5$
3. $6x + \tfrac{2}{3}x = x - \tfrac{2}{3}$ 4. $\tfrac{4}{3}x - 5 = \tfrac{3}{4}x + 5$
5. $3x + 2 = 3x + 3$ 6. $-6x + 4 - 3x = 4x - 5$
7. $1.3x + 4.6 = 6.7x - 5.1$ 8. $13.6x + 7 - 4.1x = 0$
9. $16.7x + 13.2 = 14.2x - 6.1$ 10. $6x - 4.2 = 3x - 2.1$

10. ORDER OF THE WHOLE NUMBERS

The set of whole numbers can be arranged in order (ordered) in a very natural way. In this arrangement the number zero, being the smallest number, would come first. The next larger number, the number 1, would come next, then the number 2, and so on. For any pair of numbers a and b, if a is larger than b, then in this ordering, a comes after b. This is not the only way of ordering the set of whole numbers, but it is the most natural. This arrangement, or ordering, is often shown with a line graph, as in Fig. 2–9. This ordering is made according to a knowledge of whether one number is larger than another. Intuitively this poses no difficulty, but if one were asked how to tell when one number is larger than another, intuition would not be adequate. Some criterion based on the properties of whole numbers would be needed. The establishing of such a criterion amounts to making a definition of "greater than" for whole numbers, and is not difficult to do. The following is such a definition. It should be noted that it is in accord with intuition, but that it involves only the notion of subtraction, which in turn is defined in terms of the fundamental operation of addition.

For any whole numbers a and b, $a > b$ is defined to mean that $a - b$ is a natural number.

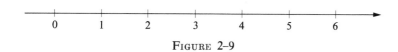

FIGURE 2–9

This definition could have been stated equivalently in terms of addition, since subtraction is defined in terms of addition. The difference $a - b$ is defined to be a number c such that $b + c = a$. Thus the above definition is equivalent to saying "$a > b$ means that there is some natural number c for which $b + c = a$."

The sentence $a > b$, of course, says that a is greater than b. The sentence $c < d$, read "c is less than d," by agreement means that $d > c$. For any pair of whole numbers a and b, it follows that one of the following must hold: $a > b$ or $b > a$. This assumes, of course, that a and b are actually different numbers. If it is to be allowed that 'a' and 'b' might possibly represent the same number, then one and only one of the following must hold:

$$a > b \qquad \text{or} \qquad b > a \qquad \text{or} \qquad a = b.$$

Sentences such as $a < b$ or $a > b$ are called *inequalities*. In the subsequent study of number systems they become increasingly important, and the ability to handle and manipulate such symbolism is vital in many kinds of mathematics. One question that arises is whether one may add the same number to both members of an inequality, as can be done with an equation. In other words, if $a > b$ is true and c is any number whatever, is it then true that $a + c > b + c$? The answer is affirmative; hence the following statement is true.

For any whole numbers a, b, and c, if $a > b$, then also $a + c > b + c$.

To prove this statement, one must appeal to the definition of $>$, as follows: If $a > b$, this means that $a - b$ is a natural number, n; or equivalently that there is a natural number n for which $b + n = a$. Now $b + n = a$ asserts that '$b + n$' and 'a' represent the same number. If a number c is added to this number, the sum exists and is a natural number (by closure of the set of natural numbers under addition). Furthermore there is *just one* sum (since addition is an operation). The sum can be named '$c + (b + n)$' or it may be named '$c + a$.' Since '$c + (b + n)$' and '$c + a$' represent the same number, the sentence $c + (b + n) = c + a$ is true. Using the associative law of addition, one sees at once that $(c + b) + n = c + a$ is also true. Now it is clear that there is some natural number (n) which when added to $c + b$ gives $c + a$, or $(c + a) - (c + b)$ is a natural number. The definition of $>$ can now be applied to arrive at the fact that $c + a > c + b$ (or, using the commutative law of addition, $a + c > b + c$). Thus it has now been shown that if $a > b$, then $a + c > b + c$.

The statement, or *theorem*, which has just been proved guarantees that one may indeed add the same number to both members of an inequality. If in some situation a *pair* of inequalities should arise, one might wonder whether corresponding members could be added. For example, if $a > b$ and $c > d$ are known to be true, must it then follow that $a + c > b + d$? The answer is again affirmative, as stated in the following theorem.

For any whole numbers a, b, c, and d, if $a > b$ and $c > d$, then $a + c > b + d$.

This theorem can also be proved by applying the definition of $>$. An outline of a proof is given here, but a complete proof will be left as an exercise.

Outline of proof. We assume that $a > b$ and $c > d$ are true. Then it follows that $a - b = n$ for some natural number n. Also $c - d = m$ for some natural number m. Why? These equations are equivalent to $n + b = a$ and $m + d = c$. Why? Now the sum $a + c$ must be the same as the sum $(n + b) + (m + d)$, or $(b + d) + (m + n)$. Why? Of course $(m + n)$ is a natural number. Why? Thus $(a + c) - (b + d)$ is a natural number. Why? Hence $a + c > b + d$. Why? Finally, it has been proved that if $a > b$ and $c > d$, then $a + c > b + d$.

EXERCISES

1. Show, by applying the definition of $>$, that the following inequalities are true.

(a) $5 > 3$ (b) $17 > 2$ (c) $5 > 0$ (d) $112 > 5$

2. Suppose that $x > y$ and $t > u$. Then which of the following must be true?

(a) $x + 2 > y + 2$ (b) $4 + x > x + 4$
(c) $x + t > y + u$ (d) $u + t > x + y$
(e) $x + t + 5 > y + u + 5$ (f) $x + 10 > y + 3$
(g) $x + u > y + t$ (h) $u + y < x + t$

3. Prove that every natural number is greater than 0.

4. Prove that for any whole numbers a, b, c, and d, if $a > b$ and $c > d$, then $a + c > b + d$.

11. INTRODUCTION TO NUMBER THEORY

The study of the properties of natural numbers is often known as *number theory*. It is unfortunate that it has ever been separated from arithmetic, since a study of the properties of numbers is a most important one for anyone who needs to use numbers and perform calculations with them. Number theory originated long ago. A tablet dating from 1500–2000 B.C. shows that the Babylonians had some knowledge of it, and the ancient Greek mathematicians developed, geometrically, many number-theory concepts. In earlier times, philosophers of all kinds habitually attributed mystical significance to certain numbers. Modern-day mathematicians no longer spend their professional efforts in discovering the magical properties of numbers. However, those concerned with the theory of numbers have not been interested primarily in producing results which are of immediate practical use, but have rather been interested in the properties of numbers because of their extreme fascination. Although it may at first seem that there are no problems left to which answers are not known, this is by no means the case. In fact, there are many questions which appear simple, but to which many fine mathematicians have failed to find any answer at all.

In the study of mathematics, a study of number theory cannot be recommended too highly, for in this subject are to be found hundreds of questions which can provide fascination, motivation, and stimulation for the student. For the amateur mathematician, who wishes to make mathematical discoveries of his own, the area of number theory today offers more promise than most others. It is one of few branches of mathematics remaining in which interesting discoveries of results not already known can still be made by those without extensive training in the subject.

REVIEW PRACTICE EXERCISES

Add

EXAMPLE:

$$6x^2 + 2x + 1$$
$$5x^2 - 3x - 4$$
$$\overline{11x^2 + x + 5}$$

1. $(3x^2 + 5x + 1) + (-7x^2 + 2x - 5)$
2. $(4x^5 + 7x^3 + 5x^2 - 5) + (-2x^5 + x^4 - 6x^2 - 7)$
3. $(8x^2 - 7x + 3) + (-7x^2 + 2x - 5)$
4. $(-6x^4 + 3x^2 + x - 5) + (4x^4 - 4x^3 + 10x + 7)$
5. $(17x^7 + 6x^4 - 5x^2 + x) + (13x^6 + 5x^3 + 10x - 2)$

Subtract

EXAMPLE:

$$8x^3 + 6x^2 + 4$$
$$3x^3 + 9x^2 + 6$$
$$\overline{5x^3 - 3x^2 - 2}$$

6. $(6x^2 + 5x + 7) - (4x^2 + 2x + 3)$
7. $(8x^3 + 6x^2 - 4) - (6x^3 + 9x^2 + 6)$
8. $(7x^5 + 4x^2 + 6x - 1) - (4x^5 + 7x^3 - 4x^2 - 1)$
9. $(-8x^4 - 6x^3 + 4x + 7) - (6x^4 - 7x^3 + x^2 - 7)$
10. $(13x^5 + 7x^2 - 16x) - (5x^4 + 2x^3 - 10x^2 + 5)$

12. FACTORS AND PRIME NUMBERS

It is possible to find a natural number such that, when it is multiplied by 3, the result is 12. Therefore, 3 is a factor of 12. The number 12 also has other factors. The number 2 is a factor of 12, since there is some natural number which when multiplied by 2 yields 12. The numbers 1, 4, 6, and 12 are also factors of 12, by the same criterion. In general, a natural number n has a number m as a factor if there is some natural number q such that $m \cdot q = n$. Since for any natural number n, it is true that $n \cdot 1 = n$, every natural number has factors. Every natural number has at least itself and the number 1 as factors. Given a natural number n, one may seek several numbers whose product is n. For example, for 24, the product of 2, 3, and 4 is a possibility. One may write the symbol $2 \cdot 3 \cdot 4$ for the number 24, to show that it is the product of 2, 3, and 4. To find several numbers whose product is 24 is to *factor* the number, or to *find a factorization* of the number. Some other factorizations of 24 are: '$2 \cdot 12$,' '$6 \cdot 4$,' '$1 \cdot 24$,' '$6 \cdot 2 \cdot 2$,' '$8 \cdot 3 \cdot 1$,' and '$2 \cdot 2 \cdot 2 \cdot 3$.' The factorizations '$6 \cdot 2 \cdot 2$' and '$2 \cdot 6 \cdot 2$' are not considered to be different, in view of the commutative law of multiplication.

If a natural number n is a factor of the natural number m, then the number m is said to be a *multiple* of the number n. For example, 3 is a factor of 18, and therefore 18 is a multiple of 3. Some other multiples of 3 are 3, 6, 9, 12, 15, 30, and 300.

Certain natural numbers have two, and only two, different factors, namely themselves and the number 1. Such numbers are called *prime numbers*. The number 1 is not a prime number, since it has only one factor, and not two *different* factors. The number 2 is prime, since it has the numbers 1 and 2 as its only two factors. Likewise 17 is prime, since it has just two different factors, 17 and 1. If a natural number is not prime, but has more than two different factors, then it is called a *composite* number. Thus the natural numbers may be classified as being either prime, composite, or 1, the number 1 falling into a class by itself, since it is neither prime nor composite.

A natural number is *prime* if it has exactly two *different* factors. A natural number different from 1 which is not prime is called *composite*.

Finding prime numbers is not, in general, an easy task, nor is it easy to tell whether or not a large number is prime. Nobody has ever succeeded in finding a formula which will produce all of the prime numbers. For this reason, mathematicians have constructed tables of prime numbers. At least one of these tables lists all primes less than 100 million. A simple, although not rapid, method of finding primes was devised about 200 B.C. by Eratosthenes. His method is known as the *sieve of Eratosthenes*, and with it one may find all primes smaller than any given natural number. Figure 2–10 illustrates the method, used to find all primes less than 50. First, numerals for all natural numbers up to 50 are written. The number 1 is not prime, so its numeral is marked out. The number 2 is a prime, so its numeral is not marked out. However, all higher multiples of 2, such as 4, 6, 8, and so on, are composites, so these numerals are marked out. The first unmarked numeral after 2 must represent the next prime, namely 3. Now, counting by 3, every third numeral is marked out, beginning with '9' ('6' having already been marked out). These represent composite numbers, all of which are multiples of three. The number 4 and all of its multiples have already been eliminated, since any multiple of 4 is also a multiple of 2. The next unmarked numeral, '5,' represents the next prime. It will not be marked out, but numerals for all of its higher multiples will be. It will be noted that 6 has already been eliminated, being both a multiple of 2 and of 3. Therefore, all multiples of 6 have already been eliminated, and 7 is considered next. The number 8 has already been deleted. It is not necessary to continue, since the numbers which are now left are the primes. Note that 8^2 is greater than 50, and the crossing-out process is completed when the numerals for multiples of 8 have been marked out. It is left to the reader to determine the significance of this remark, and to generalize it if appropriate. (See exercise 2, Article 13.)

$$\begin{array}{cccccccccc}
\not 1 & 2 & 3 & \not 4 & 5 & \not 6 & 7 & \not 8 & \not 9 & \not{10} \\
11 & \not{12} & 13 & \not{14} & \not{15} & \not{16} & 17 & \not{18} & 19 & \not{20} \\
\not{21} & \not{22} & 23 & \not{24} & \not{25} & \not{26} & \not{27} & \not{28} & 29 & \not{30} \\
31 & \not{32} & \not{33} & \not{34} & \not{35} & 36 & 37 & \not{38} & \not{39} & \not{40} \\
41 & \not{42} & 43 & \not{44} & \not{45} & 46 & 47 & \not{48} & \not{49} & \not{50}
\end{array}$$

FIGURE 2–10

The problem of finding prime factorizations of natural numbers is an important one in many situations arising in arithmetic. By a *prime factorization* is meant a factorization in which all the factors are prime. To find a prime factorization for a composite number, one may start by finding a factorization which is easy to find, but not necessarily a prime factorization, and then find further factorizations of the composite factors. For example, to find a prime factorization of the number 48, one may think first of the factorization '6 · 8.' Neither 6 nor 8 is prime, since '2 · 3' is a factorization of 6 and '2 · 4' is a factorization of 8. Thus a further factorization is '2 · 3 · 2 · 4.' The only factor here which is composite is 4, having the factorization '2 · 2.' Therefore, a prime factorization of 48 is '2 · 3 · 2 · 2 · 2.' It is preferable to write '2 · 2 · 2 · 2 · 3,' however, making a grouping of the like factors.

REVIEW PRACTICE EXERCISES

Multiply

1. $3x(x + 2)$
2. $2x^2(x + 2)$
3. $(x + 4) \cdot 5x^3$
4. $3(x + y + 4)$
5. $4(x^2 + 3x + 1)$
6. $x^2(5x + y + 2)$
7. $3x^2(3x^2 + 5x + 1)$
8. $6x^4(y^2 + x^3 + z)$
9. $3x^2(x^5 + 4)$
10. $x^{-2}(x^4 + x^2 + 1)$
11. $x^{-4}(x^{-2} + x^2)$
12. $x^2(x^{-4} + x^2)$
13. $5(x - 2)$
14. $3x(x^2 - 5 + y)$
15. $x^2(x^2 - x)$
16. $3x^{-1}(x^2 - x^{-5})$
17. $4x^{-2}(x^{-5} - y^{-1})$
18. $-5x(x^{-2} - 1)$

13. THE FUNDAMENTAL THEOREM OF ARITHMETIC

If, in finding a prime factorization of 48, one had thought first of the factorization '2 · 24,' or '12 · 4,' the question arises whether or not the final result would be '2 · 2 · 2 · 2 · 3.' In other words, does one arrive at the same prime factorization no matter how the factorization is started? It is fairly obvious, at least for small numbers, that this is the case. However, the fact that it may be obvious in no way diminishes its importance. This fact is so important in number theory, or arithmetic, that it is usually known as the *fundamental theorem of arithmetic*, and may be stated as follows.

Every composite number has one and only one prime factorization. (The prime factorization of any composite number is unique.)

Of course it is understood that two factorizations are considered to be the same if they differ only in the order of writing numerals for the factors. No proof of this theorem will be given here,* but some simple applications of it will be considered.

Least common multiple. The problem of finding least common multiples is important in some applications of the natural numbers to the arithmetic of fractions, to be considered later. By the least common multiple (L.C.M.) of several numbers

---

* For a proof of this theorem, see Courant & Robbins, *What is Mathematics?* Chapter 1, supplement, or Le Veque, *Elementary Theory of Numbers*, p. 27.

is meant the smallest natural number which is a multiple of all of them. Each of the given numbers, therefore, is a factor of the L.C.M. Thus to find the L.C.M. of several numbers, one may use their prime factorizations. If a number occurs in any prime factorization, then it is a factor of one of the given numbers, and is hence also a factor of the L.C.M. The procedure consists of picking out the right factors from the prime factorizations and finding their product. For example, to find the L.C.M. of 60 and 90, one first finds their prime factorizations

$$2 \cdot 2 \cdot 3 \cdot 5 \quad \text{and} \quad 2 \cdot 3 \cdot 3 \cdot 5.$$

The number 2 occurs twice in the first one and once in the second one. Therefore, the number $2 \cdot 2$ must be a factor of the L.C.M., since it is a factor of 60. Similarly, the number $3 \cdot 3$ is a factor of the L.C.M., since it is a factor of 90. The number 5, named in both factorizations, is also a factor of the L.C.M. Therefore, the L.C.M. is

$$2 \cdot 2 \cdot 3 \cdot 3 \cdot 5 \quad \text{or} \quad 180.$$

Note that the prime factorization of the L.C.M. does not contain 2 more than twice, although 2 occurs twice in one factorization and once in the other. Since $2 \cdot 2$ is a factor of 60 and 2 is a factor of 90, the L.C.M. must have factors of 2 and 4. But, if a number has the factor 4, then it already has the factor 2, and it is not necessary to use '$2 \cdot 2 \cdot 2$' in the factorization of the L.C.M. In fact, if this were done, the result would not be the *least* common multiple, for it would have the factor 8, which is not a factor of either 60 or 90.

REVIEW PRACTICE EXERCISES

Multiply

EXAMPLE:

$$
\begin{array}{r}
3x^2 - 5x + 2 \\
3x - 4 \\
\hline
-12x^2 + 20x - 8 \\
9x^3 - 15x^2 + 6x \\
\hline
9x^3 - 27x^2 + 26x - 8
\end{array}
$$

1. $(6x^2 - 2x + 3)(5x - 3)$
2. $(3x - 4)(3x + 4)$
3. $(7x^3 + 5x^2 - 7x + 6)(-3x^3 + x + 2)$
4. $(14x^5 - 3x^2 + 5)(x^2 - 2x + 6)$
5. $(-13x^4 - 6x^2 - 5x - 1)(-7x^2 - 6x - 3)$
6. $(5x^3 - 3x^2 - 12x + 6)(4x^2 - 2x - 3)$
7. $(3x^5 - 7x + 5)(-6x^4 + x^3)$
8. $(x^5 - 5x)(x^5 + 5x)$

Greatest common factor. The greatest common factor (G.C.F.), sometimes called the greatest common divisor (G.C.D.), of several numbers may also be found by inspecting their prime factorizations. To illustrate, the greatest number which is a factor of both 60 and 90 must have the factor 2, since both 60 and 90 have the factor 2. However, the G.C.F. does not have the factor 4, since although 60 has that factor, 90 does not. Similarly, the G.C.F. has the factor 3 but not the factor 9. It also has the factor 5. Therefore, the G.C.F. of 60 and 90 is

$$2 \cdot 3 \cdot 5 \quad \text{or} \quad 30.$$

Thus one can pick out from the prime factorizations those factors which are common to all the numbers involved. Their product is the G.C.F. of the numbers.

No largest prime. It seems natural to ask how many prime numbers there are. Is there a largest one? If so, there must be a definite and finite number of primes. If there is not a largest one, then there must be an infinite number of them. This question was answered long ago. In fact Euclid gave a geometric proof that there is no largest prime. It will be of interest to see a proof, which is essentially like that of Euclid. First, assume that the theorem is false, i.e., that there is some largest prime number. From this assumption, it will be shown that something absurd follows. Therefore, the assumption itself must be false, and the original theorem is true.

Suppose there is a largest prime number p. Then find the product of all the prime numbers, from 2 to p. To this number add 1. The result is

$$(2 \cdot 3 \cdot 5 \cdot 7 \cdot 11 \cdots p) + 1.$$

Now according to the assumption, this number cannot be prime, since it is larger than p, which is the largest prime. But divide it by any prime number, as one might do in trying to factor the number, and a remainder of 1 is obtained. Therefore, this number has no prime factors, and is itself a prime number. Now it is clear that a contradiction has occurred. The assumption that p is the largest prime number has led to the conclusion that p is not the largest prime number. The final conclusion is that there is no largest prime number, which was to be proved.

EXERCISES

1. Use the sieve method to find all primes smaller than 400. The process is finished when multiples of what number are eliminated?

2. Show that in the sieve method of finding primes up to n, the marking-out process is finished when multiples of all numbers whose *squares* are less than n have been eliminated.

3. Find the prime factorizations of the following numbers.
   (a) 180   (b) 825   (c) 1700   (d) 8778   (e) 4551   (f) 3542

4. Find the L.C.M. of the following.
   (a) 60, 126   (b) 74, 102   (c) 18, 42, 154   (d) 30, 105, 40
   (e) 10, 105, 14, 15   (f) 8778, 3542

5. Find the G.C.F. of the following.
   (a) 105, 180   (b) 210, 385   (c) 266, 151   (d) 91, 95
   (e) 126, 30, 105   (f) 1540, 210, 1820

6. Prove that if a natural number n greater than 1 has no prime factors less than n, then that number is prime.

7. If two odd numbers are consecutive, i.e., differ by 2, and if they are both prime, the numbers are known as *prime twins*. Find three pairs of prime twins.

8. Can you find three odd numbers which are consecutive, all of which are prime? How many such triples can you find? Explain.

14. SOME SPECIAL KINDS OF NUMBERS

A number which has the factor 2 is called an *even* number. A number which is not even is called an *odd* number. Thus the whole numbers fall into two classes: odd numbers and even numbers. Since an even number, by definition, has the factor 2, any even number may be represented by a symbol such as '$2 \cdot r$,' where 'r' represents some whole number. The even numbers are thus 0, 2, 4, ... If a natural number does not have the factor 2, then there must be a nonzero remainder when the number is divided by 2. This remainder must be smaller than 2, the divisor, and hence can only be 1. Therefore, any odd number may be represented by a symbol such as '$2 \cdot t + 1$,' where 't' represents some whole number. It is clear that the result of dividing $2 \cdot t + 1$ by 2 is a quotient of t with a remainder of 1.

Consider the set of all even numbers. A question of interest is whether or not this set is closed under the operation of addition. One can try several examples, adding pairs of even numbers, to see if their sums are also even. If a case is found in which the sum of two even numbers is not even, then it will have been proved that the set of even numbers is not closed under addition. However, if no such case is found, it is not proved that closure holds. In order to make a proof, some kind of reasoning must be found which is known to apply to *all* pairs of even numbers. Since symbols such as '$2 \cdot r$,' '$2 \cdot t$,' and '$2 \cdot q$' represent any even number, it may be helpful to write, to represent the sum of *any two* even numbers, the symbol

$$2 \cdot r + 2 \cdot q.$$

By closure, since the set of whole numbers is closed under addition and multiplication, this symbol represents a whole number. By the distributive law of multiplication over addition,

$$2 \cdot r + 2 \cdot q = 2 \cdot (r + q).$$

Since $2 \cdot (r + q)$ clearly has the factor 2, it is an even number. Thus the foregoing is a *proof* that the sum of any two even numbers is an even number. Therefore, the set of even numbers is closed under addition.

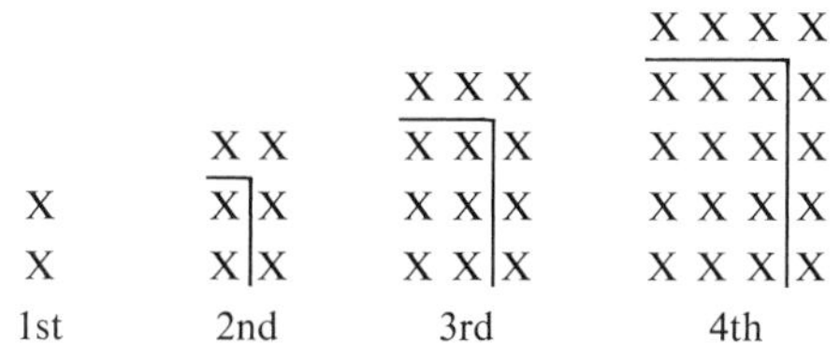

FIGURE 2–11

Another class of special numbers, called *figurate* numbers, consists of numbers obtained by considering certain geometric configurations of objects. For example, there are the *rectangular*, or *oblong*, numbers, so called because of the rectangular arrangement shown in Fig. 2–11. The first rectangular number is 2. The second one is 6, the third is 12, and so on. It is easily noted that the first rectangular number is $1 \cdot (1 + 1)$, the second is $2 \cdot (2 + 1)$, the third is $3 \cdot (3 + 1)$, and so on. In general it may be said that the kth rectangular number is $k \cdot (k + 1)$. Interesting relationships may be discovered by looking at figures such as these. For example, one may obtain the kth rectangular number from the preceding one by adding $2 \cdot k$. Also it can be seen that rectangular numbers may be represented as follows:

$$1 + 1,$$
$$1 + 1 + 2 + 2,$$
$$1 + 1 + 2 + 2 + 3 + 3,$$
$$1 + 1 + 2 + 2 + 3 + 3 + 4 + 4,$$
$$1 + 1 + 2 + 2 + 3 + 3 + 4 + 4 + 5 + 5,$$

and so on. Thus it is apparent that the sum

$$1 + 1 + 2 + 2 + 3 + 3 + 4 + 4 + \cdots + k + k$$

is the same as $k \cdot (k + 1)$.

The *triangular* numbers are 1, 3, 6, 10, 15, and so on, and can be illustrated geometrically as in Fig. 2–12. From the figures it appears that the triangular numbers may also be represented as

$$1, \quad 1 + 2, \quad 1 + 2 + 3, \quad 1 + 2 + 3 + 4, \quad 1 + 2 + 3 + 4 + 5,$$

and so on. In other words, the kth triangular number is the sum of all the natural numbers up to and including k. From Fig. 2–13 it is apparent that every triangular number is just half the corresponding rectangular number. Therefore it seems reasonable that the kth triangular number is

$$\frac{k \cdot (k + 1)}{2}.$$

It is also apparent from this demonstration that the sum of the first k natural numbers is $k \cdot (k + 1)/2$.

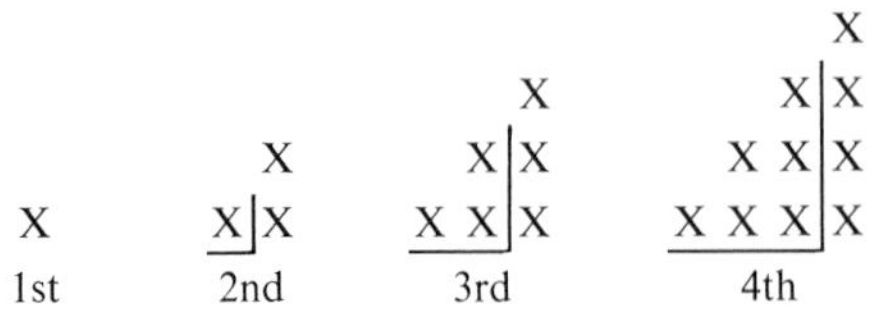

FIGURE 2–12 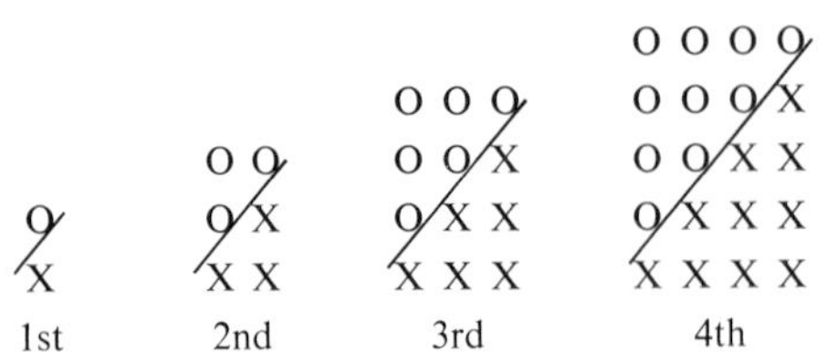   FIGURE 2–13

The *square* numbers, 1, 4, 9, 16, 25, 36, 49, and so on, have the configurations shown in Fig. 2–14. From this figure it appears that the kth square number can be obtained from the preceding one by adding $2 \cdot k - 1$. The square numbers are also the sums of the odd numbers, as follows:

$$1, \quad 1 + 3, \quad 1 + 3 + 5, \quad 1 + 3 + 5 + 7,$$
$$1 + 3 + 5 + 7 + 9, \quad 1 + 3 + 5 + 7 + 9 + 11,$$

and so on. Thus the sum of the first k odd numbers is the kth square number. For example, the sum of the first 12 odd numbers, 1, 3, 5, 7, 9, 11, 13, 15, 17, 19, 21, and 23, is 12^2, or 144.

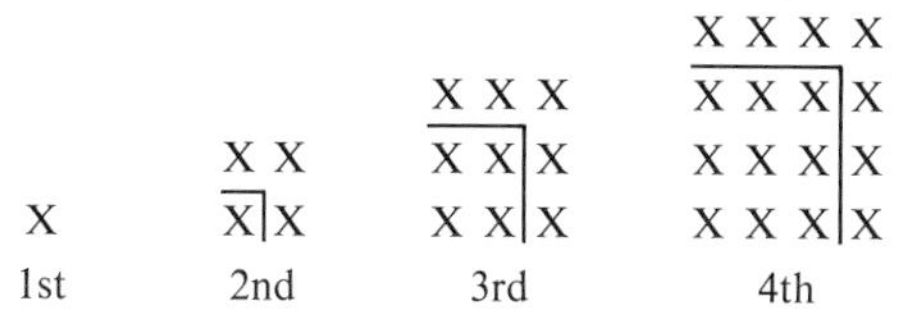

```
                                    X X X X
                          X X X     X X X|X
                  X X     X X|X     X X X|X
          X       X|X     X X|X     X X X|X
         1st       2nd      3rd        4th
```

FIGURE 2–14

Also of special interest are the cubes, which can be represented by three-dimensional pictures. Other kinds of figurate numbers can also be studied from a viewpoint similar to that demonstrated above.

EXERCISES

1. Show that the set of even numbers is closed under multiplication.

2. Find whether or not the set of odd numbers is closed under addition. Prove your result.

3. Find whether or not the set of odd numbers is closed under multiplication. Prove your result.

4. Using the results of exercises 1 through 3, and any other information necessary, construct tables as follows for sums and products of odd and even numbers:

+	even	odd
even		
odd		

×	even	odd
even		
odd		

5. What is the 12th rectangular number? The 25th? The 37th? The 197th?

6. Find the sum $2 + 2 + 2 + 3 + 3 + 4 + 4 + \cdots + 112 + 112$.

7. What is the 8th triangular number? The 17th? The 35th? The 112th?

8. What is the sum of the first 17 natural numbers? The first 35? The first 527?

9. (a) What is the sum of the first 32 natural numbers? (b) What is the sum of the first 16 odd numbers? (c) From the results of (a) and (b), find the sum of the first 16 even numbers.

10. Draw figures for the first few hexagonal numbers, and see what you can discover about them.

11. Draw figures for the first few pentagonal numbers and see what you can discover about them.

REVIEW PRACTICE EXERCISES

Divide

EXAMPLE:

$$
\begin{array}{r}
x^2 - 2x + 4 \\
x - 3 \overline{\smash{\big)}\, x^3 - 5x^2 + 10x - 12} \\
\underline{x^3 - 3x^2} \\
-2x^2 \\
\underline{-2x^2 + 6x} \\
4x \\
\underline{4x - 12}
\end{array}
$$

1. $(x^3 - 2x^2 - 2x + 12) \div (x + 2)$
2. $(6x^3 + 11x^2 + 8x + 5) \div (2x + 1)$
3. $(x^3 + 2x^2 + 3x + 1) \div (x^2 + 1)$
4. $(2x^4 + 6x^3 - x^2 - 3x) \div (2x^2 - 1)$
5. $(12x^2 + 46x + 40) \div (2x + 5)$
6. $(4x^5 + 2x^3 + 4x + 2) \div (2x^2 + x)$
7. $(x^3 + 1) \div (x + 1)$
8. $(y^5 + 32) \div (y + 2)$

15. DIVISIBILITY

There is an easy and well-known rule for determining whether or not a whole number is exactly divisible by 2. It involves inspection of the final digit of the decimal numeral, to determine whether or not that digit is even. It is well to inquire how one could arrive at such a rule. In the absence of any information, one would probably wish to write decimal numerals for many multiples of 2, to see what pattern may exist. In this way, one could make a good guess at a rule, and then try to prove that it is correct. It may be proved that the rule for divisibility by 2 is correct by considering expanded numerals, such as

$$a \cdot 10^5 + b \cdot 10^4 + c \cdot 10^3 + d \cdot 10^2 + e \cdot 10 + f.$$

Since the base, ten, is an even number, any power of it greater than the zero power is even, because the set of even numbers is closed under multiplication. Also, the product of any number and an even number is even, so it is clear that each of the summands above, except possibly the last, is an even number. Furthermore, the sum of all but the last must be even, by closure of the set of even numbers under addition. Therefore, the number itself is even if the last digit is even, but if the last digit is odd, the number is the sum of an even number and an odd number, and is therefore odd.

Rules are also well known for determining whether or not a natural number is exactly divisible by 5 or by 10. These likewise involve inspection of the last digit of the decimal numeral. There is also a rather simple rule for deciding whether or not a number is exactly divisible by 9. If one writes decimal numerals for some multiples of 9, such as 18, 63, 81, 90, 99, 162, and 189, it becomes apparent that the sum of the digits is always 9 or a multiple of 9. In other words, the sum of the digits is exactly divisible by 9. That this is in fact true can be seen by considering an expanded numeral, such as

$$a \cdot 10^4 + b \cdot 10^3 + c \cdot 10^2 + d \cdot 10 + e.$$

If one divides 10 by 9, the remainder is 1. If one divides each of the d tens in $d \cdot 10$ by 9, the remainder is 1 each time, leaving d remainders of 1 (a total of d). That the remainder is d can also be seen as follows:

$$d \cdot 10 = d \cdot (9 + 1) = d \cdot 9 + d.$$

The remainder after dividing 10^2 by 9 is also 1, so the remainder after dividing each of the c hundreds in $c \cdot 10^2$ by 9 is c. This can be shown as follows:

$$[c \cdot 10^2 = c \cdot (99 + 1) = c \cdot 99 + c].$$

Likewise the remainder after dividing any power of ten, greater than the zero power, by 9 is 1, so the remainder after dividing each of the b thousands in $b \cdot 10^3$ by 9 is b, and the remainder after dividing each of the a ten-thousands in $a \cdot 10^4$ by 9 is a. From this argument, it can be seen that the remainder after dividing the number by 9 is the same as after dividing the sum of the digits by 9. If the sum of the digits is a multiple of 9, so that there is zero remainder after dividing by 9, then the number itself is also a multiple of 9.

In order to tell whether or not a large number is exactly divisible by 4, one may inspect the last two digits of its decimal numeral. For example, the number 35716412 is divisible by 4, because the last two digits when taken together represent twelve, which is divisible by 4. It does not matter what digits precede the last two, because whatever they are, they represent a whole number of hundreds, and hundreds are exactly divisible by 4. Thus the rule is: if the number represented by the last two digits of the decimal numeral for a whole number is divisible by 4, then the number itself is divisible by 4.

It should be noted that all the rules of divisibility discussed above depend on *decimal* numerals. If nondecimal numerals are used, the rules of divisibility may be quite different. For example, in base seven numeration, the rule for telling divisibility by two cannot be the same as for base ten numeration. The number twenty-four, which is divisible by 2, has the septimal numeral '33_7,' whose last digit is not even. By considering expanded septimal numerals, one can arrive at a rule. For example, in

$$a \cdot 7^5 + b \cdot 7^4 + c \cdot 7^3 + d \cdot 7^2 + e \cdot 7 + f,$$

the powers of seven are all odd numbers, because 7 is odd, and the set of odd numbers is closed under multiplication. Therefore, any summand is odd if the digit is odd, and even if the digit is even. One may consider all the even summands. Their sum is even. The sum of all the odd summands is odd or even, depending on how many of them there are. If there is an even number of them, the sum will be even. If there is an odd number of them, the sum will be odd. Therefore, one may simply count the number of odd digits in the septimal numeral. If this is odd, then the number named is odd. Otherwise the number is even.

EXERCISES

1. Find and prove a rule for divisibility by 3, in decimal numeration.

2. Find and prove a rule for divisibility by 6 in decimal numeration. [*Hint:* Use the result of exercise 1.]

3. Show that the well-known rule for divisibility by 5 in decimal numeration is valid.

4. Show that the well-known rule for divisibility by 10 in decimal numeration is valid.

5. Devise and prove a rule for divisibility of a large number by 8 using decimal numeration.

6. Find a rule for divisibility by 2 using any numeration system with an odd number for the base.

7. Find a rule for divisibility by 2 using any numeration system with any even number for the base.

8. Find a rule for divisibility by 6 using base seven numeration. [*Hint:* This is similar to divisibility by 9 using decimal numeration.]

9. Find a rule for divisibility by 6 using base twelve numeration. [*Hint:* This is similar to divisibility by 5 using decimal numeration.]

10. Find a rule for divisibility by 11 using decimal numeration.

16. CASTING OUT NINES

In the preceding article, it was established that when a natural number is divided by 9, the remainder is the same as if the sum of the digits is divided by 9. This fact is the basis of a check for computation, once widely used, and known as the check of "casting out nines." The method is illustrated below for checking addition:

$$
\begin{array}{rcccc}
4312 & \to & 10 & \to & 1 \\
7614 & \to & 18 & \to & 0 \\
\underline{4359} & \to & \underline{21} & \to & \underline{3} \\
16285 & \to & 22 & \to & 4
\end{array}
$$

The sum of the three numbers is found to be 16285. To check the calculation, the sum of the digits is found for each of the summands to be 10, 18, and 21, respectively. Since these sums are all 9 or greater, they are reduced further by adding the digits and casting out nines, obtaining 1, 0, and 3, respectively. (Note that the sum of the digits of '18' is 9, but that '0' has been written instead. The reason for this will become clear.) The sum of these is 4. The sum of the digits of the answer is also found and reduced, giving also a result of 4. Thus the computation checks.

To see how this works, note first that the numbers 1, 0, and 3 are the remainders which would be obtained upon dividing the summands respectively by 9. Thus we know that the number 4312 is a product of some number and 9, plus 1. Or, $4312 = 9 \cdot q_1 + 1$. Similarly, $7614 = 9 \cdot q_2 + 0$, where 'q_2' represents some natural number. It is the quotient of 7614 by 9. This number could be found, but it is not

needed here. Likewise, $4359 = 9 \cdot q_3 + 3$, for some natural number q_3. Now the
addition problem can be represented as

$$(9 \cdot q_1 + 1) + (9 \cdot q_2 + 0) + (9 \cdot q_3 + 3),$$

or, by the commutative and associative laws of addition,

$$(9 \cdot q_1 + 9 \cdot q_2 + 9 \cdot q_3) + (1 + 0 + 3).$$

By the distributive law, we may write equivalently

$$9 \cdot (q_1 + q_2 + q_3) + (1 + 0 + 3).$$

Remember that this symbol represents the *sum* of the three summands, and note that
whatever this number is, if it is divided by 9, the remainder will be $(1 + 0 + 3)$.
Therefore, addition of the remainders for the summands must give the remainder
for the sum. If it does not, a mistake in calculation must have been made.

In the example just given, the sum of the remainders for the summands, $1 + 0 + 3$,
was less than 9. It often happens that this sum is greater than 9, in which case it must
be further reduced by adding the digits before comparing with the remainder for
the sum.

It should be noted that this method of checking is not a final and certain one.
However, it will show up a great many errors. It should also be noted that the above
example does not provide a proof that the method works in all cases. To give a
complete proof, one must avoid using specific numbers, but rather use symbols such
as letters, which can represent *any* whole numbers. The appearance of such a proof
would be very similar to the explanation given for the example above, and the reasoning would be the same at all stages.

Casting out nines may also be used to check subtraction, multiplication, and
division. The checks for subtraction and multiplication are direct. That is, to check
a subtraction, one subtracts the remainders, and to check multiplication, one multiplies the remainders. To check division, however, one does not divide the remainders.
The ordinary check for division is to multiply divisor and quotient, then add the
remainder, to see if the dividend is obtained. To check by casting out nines, one
simply uses this method to check this multiplication and addition. In other words,
quotient, dividend, divisor, and remainder are all reduced. Then the remainders for
the divisor and quotient are multiplied and the remainder for the remainder added,
with reductions where necessary, to see if the remainder for the dividend is obtained.

It may be wondered whether casting out nines may be used to check calculations
with numbers other than whole numbers. The answer is affirmative, as long as
decimal numerals are used in the calculations. An illustration or two should be
convincing. Consider the addition

$$\begin{array}{r} 43.12 \\ 7.614 \\ \hline \end{array}$$

and compare it with the addition

$$\begin{array}{r} 43120 \\ 7614 \\ \hline \end{array}$$

Clearly the digits for the two results will be the same, the only difference being that a decimal point is missing in the second case. Therefore, to check the first problem, one may simply ignore the decimal points, so that in effect the second problem is being checked. Thus casting out nines provides a check on the correct digits, but not on the position of the decimal point.

Consider the multiplication

$$43.12$$
$$7.614$$

and compare it with

$$4312$$
$$7614$$

The situation is similar to the above addition. The answers to these two problems will have the same digits. Therefore, casting out nines may be used, but not as a check on the position of the decimal point. It should be noted that the above are not proofs, but only illustrative examples.

EXERCISES

1. Perform the following calculations and check by casting out nines.

    (a) Add

    1523
    7986
    8805
    4098

    (b) Multiply

    80763
    487

    (c) Subtract

    810956
    782411

    (d) Divide

    $$824\overline{)16308}$$

2. Show that casting out nines works for multiplication. [*Hint:* Consider a product $A \cdot B$, and represent A by '$9 \cdot q_1 + r_1$' and represent B by '$9 \cdot q_2 + r_2$.']

3. In the demonstration asked for in exercise 2, is there anything special or particularly important about the number 9? Could a similar demonstration be given for 5 or 6 or 8?

4. Casting out nines works in decimal numeration. Is there a similar procedure which could be used with base seven numeration? If so, describe it and justify your position.

5. Show that an error caused by a transposition of digits (such as writing '73' instead of '37') would not be detected by the method of casting out nines. Explain.

6. In checking his bank balance as given by the checkbook against the bank statement, Mr. Jones discovered the difference between the two was exactly divisible by 9. He therefore suspected that he might have made an error of transposition such as described in exercise 5. Explain why such a conjecture is reasonable.

CHAPTER 3

Mathematical Systems

1. INTRODUCTION

The natural numbers constitute a good example of what is known as a *mathematical system*. It may be recalled that the natural numbers were devised for use primarily as an aid in describing situations in which counting is involved. The numbers to be used were first defined, or devised, after which operations of addition and multiplication were defined, and certain basic properties ascribed to them. From these basic properties and definitions, other properties of natural numbers were deduced, and rules for calculating with them were devised. Thus the natural numbers, together with definitions of basic operations and their properties, constitute a *system*—a mathematical system.

The whole numbers also constitute a mathematical system. The set of whole numbers contains the natural numbers and the number zero, while the system of natural numbers does not contain zero. Therefore, the system of whole numbers is different from the system of natural numbers. The former has properties other than those enjoyed by the latter, and can thus be used in more diverse situations.

In general, a mathematical system is described by specifying some set of numbers or other entities, defining one or more operations or relations for members of that set, together with basic properties of those operations, and, on occasion, stating important properties of one or more special members of the set. Mathematical systems are usually constructed as an aid in performing a certain kind of task. There are many different kinds of mathematical systems, some containing numbers, some containing no numbers, some containing many members, and others only a few members. Some of them find wide application, while the uses for others are more limited.

2. CLOCK ARITHMETIC

The construction of a mathematical system may be illustrated with a simple example. For a four-minute clock (Fig. 3–1), a mathematical system can be devised which contains just four numbers: 0, 1, 2, and 3. Addition may be defined in a natural way, $1 + 3$ being interpreted to mean that the hand of the clock moves from 0 to 1, and then moves 3 more places. Thus $1 + 3 = 0$.

FIGURE 3–1

A complete definition of addition in this mathematical system, or *arithmetic*, can be given by listing all possible sums in a table, as in Table 3–1. To find the sum $2 + 3$ from the table, one locates '2' in the left-hand column and '3' in the top row. The symbol for the sum is then found in the row headed '2' and the column headed '3'; it is at the intersection of that row and column. The symbol for the sum $3 + 2$ is found in a different location, i.e., the intersection of the row headed '3' and the column headed '2.'

TABLE 3–1

+	0	1	2	3
0	0	1	2	3
1	1	2	3	0
2	2	3	0	1
3	3	0	1	2

TABLE 3–2

×	0	1	2	3
0	0	0	0	0
1	0	1	2	3
2	0	2	0	2
3	0	3	2	1

Multiplication in this mathematical system may also be defined in a natural way. For example, '$2 \cdot 3$' may be interpreted to mean a 6-place movement of the hand, which would amount to one complete revolution, and 2 places more. Thus $2 \cdot 3$ would be defined to be 2. The complete definition of multiplication, made in this manner is given in Table 3–2.

EXERCISES

1. Make an addition table for a three-minute clock.

2. Make a multiplication table for a three-minute clock.

3. Use Tables 3–1 and 3–2 to find the following sums and products.

(a) $3 \cdot 2$ (b) $2 \cdot 3$ (c) $1 \cdot 2$ (d) $2 \cdot 1$

(e) $2 + 3$ (f) $3 + 2$ (g) $3 \cdot (1 + 2)$ (h) $(3 \cdot 1) + (3 \cdot 2)$

REVIEW PRACTICE EXERCISES

Simplify

1. $\frac{2}{3} \cdot \frac{1}{5}$

2. $\frac{1}{2} \cdot \frac{3}{7}$

3. $\frac{4}{5} \cdot \frac{1}{7}$

4. $\frac{1}{7} \cdot \frac{1}{5}$

5. $\frac{1}{5} \cdot \frac{1}{25}$

6. $\frac{3}{9} \cdot \frac{4}{11}$

7. $\frac{1}{3} \cdot \frac{1}{31}$

8. $\frac{2}{7} \cdot \frac{7}{2}$

9. $\frac{5}{9} \cdot \frac{9}{5}$

10. $\frac{2}{3} \cdot \frac{8}{11} \cdot \frac{1}{2}$

11. $\frac{3}{9} \cdot \frac{4}{7} \cdot \frac{6}{11}$

12. $\frac{1}{4} \cdot \frac{8}{9} \cdot \frac{3}{4}$

13. $\frac{2}{3} + \frac{1}{5}$

14. $\frac{1}{2} + \frac{3}{7}$

15. $\frac{4}{5} + \frac{1}{7}$

16. $\frac{1}{7} + \frac{1}{5}$

17. $\frac{1}{5} + \frac{1}{25}$

18. $\frac{3}{9} + \frac{4}{11}$

19. $\frac{2}{7} + \frac{7}{2}$

20. $\frac{5}{9} + \frac{9}{5}$

21. $\frac{2}{3} + \frac{8}{11} + \frac{1}{2}$

22. $\frac{3}{9} + \frac{4}{7} + \frac{6}{11}$

23. $\frac{2}{3} \cdot (\frac{8}{11} + \frac{1}{2})$

24. $(\frac{3}{9} + \frac{4}{7}) \cdot \frac{6}{11}$

Tables 3–1 and 3–2 completely determine all of the properties of this arithmetic of a four-minute clock. A mathematical system has been described completely. However, the structure of even so simple a system is not obvious from cursory inspection of tables. In order to understand it more fully, one needs to find which properties the operations enjoy. It might be asked, for example, whether or not the set is closed under the operations of addition and multiplication. It would also be interesting, as well as important in calculating, to know whether or not those operations have the commutative and associative properties, and whether or not the distributive law of multiplication over addition holds.

Addition and multiplication are clearly *operations* because results are unique. If this were not the case, there would be multiple entries in the table. Since only single entries are to be found in either table, each of them defines an operation.

For this small system, in which the operations are defined by means of a table, it is not difficult to tell if the set is closed under each of the operations, and if the operations are commutative. If the body of a table contains no entries which are not also found in the left and top headings, and there is an entry in each position in the table, then the set is closed under that operation. This arithmetic is closed under both of its operations. To check commutativity it suffices to look for symmetry within the body of the table. If one compares the position of any sum $a + b$ with the position of $b + a$, it becomes apparent that they are reflections across the main diagonal of the table, from upper left to lower right. Therefore, if the table would not be altered by a reflection across that diagonal, the operation defined by the table is commutative. Examination of the above tables shows that both operations are commutative.

It is easily noted from Table 3–1 that the number 0 plays a role in this small mathematical system similar to that in the system of whole numbers. That is, for any number n in the system, $n + 0 = n$. The number 0, for this reason, is referred to as an *identity element* for the operation of addition. It may also be called a *neutral element* for addition, or it may be called an *additive identity*.

An additive identity in a number system is an element (usually called '0') with the property that $x + 0 = x$ and $0 + x = x$ *for any* x in the system.

A multiplicative identity in a number system is an element (usually called '1') with the property that $x \cdot x = x$ and $1 \cdot x = x$ *for any* x in the system.

Inspection of Table 3–2 shows that the number 1 is a *multiplicative identity*, or neutral element, for multiplication, in this system. In general the existence of an identity element is easily discerned whenever an operation is defined by means of a table. One merely looks for a row identical with the top heading and a column identical with the left heading. In certain mathematical systems which have noncommutative operations, there may occur an element which is an identity when used on the left but not when used on the right. That is, there may be an element i in a mathematical system such that $i \cdot x = x$ for all x in the system, but for which $x \cdot i$ is not always x. Such an element would be called a *left-identity*, and would be identified by finding a row in the table identical with the top heading. Similarly, a right-identity would be identified by finding a column in the table identical with the left heading. The number zero in the system of whole numbers is an example of a right-identity for subtraction, since $n - 0 = n$ for all whole numbers n. Zero is not a left-identity, however. In all mathematical systems considered here, *identity element* will refer to an element which is both a right- and a left-identity.

There is no easy way to tell by inspecting a table which defines an operation whether or not that operation is associative. The task involves checking all possible cases for which three elements are involved in the operation, unless some easier kind of proof can be found. In other words, it must be checked that $(a + b) + c = a + (b + c)$ for all a, b, and c in the system. For example, to check associativity for addition in this system, one of the cases involves comparison of $(2 + 1) + 3$ and $2 + (1 + 3)$. The first sum is $3 + 3$, or 2, and the second is $2 + 0$, or 2. Thus this case checks. Actually every case checks, and addition is an associative operation. Multiplication is also an associative operation, although it is not apparent from simple inspection of the table.

It is possible, for the arithmetic of a four-minute clock, to deduce the associative laws by considering the system of whole numbers, from which this system was partly derived, and in which the corresponding two operations are known to be associative. The entries in Tables 3–1 and 3–2 were made by performing operations in the system of whole numbers and then subtracting multiples of 4. For example, $2 \cdot 3 = 6$ in the system of whole numbers. Subtracting the largest multiple of 4 contained in 6 yields 2, the product of 2 and 3 in the arithmetic of the clock. Since addition and multiplication of whole numbers are associative operations and it is clear that subtracting multiples of 4 would not affect the associativity, it may be readily concluded that the corresponding operations in the arithmetic of the clock are associative. Similarly, it is not difficult to see that the distributive law of multiplication over addition holds in this system, even though it is not apparent from simple inspection of the tables.

EXERCISES

Answer the following questions about arithmetic of a three-minute clock, using the tables constructed for exercises 1 and 2 of Article 1.

1. Is the set of elements closed under addition? Multiplication?
2. Is addition commutative? Why?

3. Is multiplication commutative? Why?

4. Is there an additive identity in the set? If so, what is it? How can you tell from the tables?

5. Is there a multiplicative identity in the set? If so, what is it? How can you tell from the tables?

6. Check for associativity of addition by computing $(1 + 2) + 2$ and comparing with $1 + (2 + 2)$. Check at least three other instances.

3. ADDITIVE INVERSES AND SUBTRACTION

The arithmetic of a four-minute clock has most of the properties of the system of whole numbers, and others besides. For example, every element of this system has what is known as an *additive inverse*.

An additive inverse of an element x is a member of the system which when added to x yields 0, the additive identity.

The additive inverse of x will be represented by the symbol '^-x' (read "the additive inverse of x"). To say that every element of the system has an additive inverse is to say that for any x in the system, there is an element ^-x having the property that $x + {}^-x = 0$ and $^-x + x = 0$. It may be discerned from the addition table that $^-1 = 3$ (the additive inverse of 1 is 3). Also $^-3 = 1$, $^-2 = 2$, and $^-0 = 0$.

Subtraction in clock arithmetic is defined exactly as it was for whole numbers, as the operation opposite to addition. That is, for any elements x and y, $x - y$ is that number which when added to y gives x. In the arithmetic of a four-minute clock $3 - 1$ is the number p, if it exists, for which $p + 1 = 3$. The addition table shows that $p = 2$. Similarly $2 - 3$ is the number q, if it exists, for which $q + 3 = 2$. The table shows that q (or $2 - 3$) is 3.

EXERCISES

1. Construct addition and multiplication tables for an arithmetic of a five-minute clock and use them to answer the following questions about the system.

   (a) Is the set of numbers closed under addition? Multiplication? How can you tell?
   (b) Is addition a commutative operation? Is multiplication? How can you tell?
   (c) Does addition seem to be an associative operation? Does multiplication?
   (d) Is there an additive identity? If so what is it, and how can you tell?
   (e) Is there a multiplicative identity? If so, what is it, and how can you tell?
   (f) Which elements of the system have additive inverses? How can you tell?

2. Using the addition table from exercise 1, perform the following.

   (a) $2 + 4$ (b) $(3 + 2) + 3$ (c) $3 + (2 + 3)$
   (d) $3 + 4$ (e) $1 + 4$ (f) $(2 + 3) + 4$

3. In the system of exercise 1, what numbers do these symbols represent?

   (a) $^-4$ (b) $^-2$ (c) $^-0$ (d) $^-1$ (e) $^-3$

4. Using the addition table from exercise 1, perform the following.

(a) 2 − 3	(b) 2 + ⁻3	(c) 4 − 2	(d) 4 + ⁻2
(e) 1 − 4	(f) 1 + ⁻4	(g) 3 − 4	(h) 3 + ⁻4

5. Using Table 3–1, perform the following.

(a) 3 − 1	(b) 3 + ⁻1	(c) 1 − 3	(d) 1 + ⁻3
(e) 2 − 3	(f) 2 + ⁻3	(g) 0 − 3	(h) 0 + ⁻3

It may be seen that in the arithmetic of a four-minute clock or in that of a five-minute clock, it is possible to subtract any element from any other element. The systems of natural numbers and whole numbers do not have this property, nor are there additive inverses for the elements of those systems (except that the whole number 0 is its own additive inverse). In fact, since the system of natural numbers contains no additive identity, one could not even sensibly speak of additive inverses. The existence of additive inverses for all elements and the fact that all subtractions are possible are related, as may have been noted in the above exercises. Subtracting an element from another amounts to adding its additive inverse. For example, the subtraction $3 - 4$ is equivalent to the addition $3 + {}^-4$. This is universally true in clock arithmetics, and is also true in other mathematical systems to be studied later. It is thus worthy of some special note.

For any elements x and y in any clock arithmetic, $x - y = x + {}^-y$

The statement just made is not difficult to prove. First the definition of subtraction should be recalled and used. The number $x - y$ is, by definition of subtraction, that number which when added to y gives x. It can be shown that $x + {}^-y$ is that number by adding it to y, and proving that the result is x. If $x + {}^-y$ is added to y, the result may be symbolized as follows: $(x + {}^-y) + y$. Now, by using the associative law of addition and the definition of additive inverses, one may arrive at the fact that $(x + {}^-y) + y = x + 0$. How? It follows that the result is simply x. Why? Since $x + {}^-y$ gives x when added to y, the number $x + {}^-y$ is also the difference $x - y$, which was to be shown.

It may be noted here that the reasons given to support the assertions in the preceding proof are the existence of an identity, the existence of an additive inverse for each element, and the associative law of addition. Thus the proof holds not just for clock arithmetics, but rather holds in any mathematical system with these properties.

EXERCISES

1. Perform the following in the arithmetic of the five-minute clock.

(a) (4 − 2) − 3	(b) 4 − (2 − 3)	(c) 3 + ⁻(2 − 4)
(d) 2 − ⁻3	(e) ⁻4 − 1	(f) 3 − ⁻3

2. Write a complete proof of the theorem in boldface type above.

3. List carefully the properties that a system must have in order that the theorem of exercise 2 will hold true for that system.

The reader may find similarities between the notation '⁻3' and a familiar notation '−3' from elementary algebra. The similarity is not fortuitous, as will be seen later. In elementary algebra '−3' represents a number called "negative three," which happens to be the additive inverse of 3, or positive three. This is as far as the similarity goes, however, because in clock arithmetics there are no negative numbers, i.e., numbers less than 0. In fact, the numbers in a clock arithmetic are not ordered and thus no number is larger than any other. The number 3, in the arithmetic of the four-minute clock, may at first seem to be larger than 1, because there is some number which, when added to 1 gives 3. But there is also a number which when added to 3 gives 1. This is true of any pair of numbers; hence the set of numbers is not ordered.

4. MULTIPLICATIVE INVERSES AND DIVISION

Multiplicative inverses are analogous to additive inverses and are defined as follows.

A multiplicative inverse of an element x is a member of the system which when multiplied by x yields 1, the multiplicative identity.

In the arithmetic of the four-minute clock, some, but not all, elements have multiplicative inverses. This is apparent from Table 3–2, since the identity does not appear in the row or column headed 2. This means that there is no element which, when multiplied by 2, yields 1, the identity. On the other hand, 3 has a multiplicative inverse. Since $3 \cdot 3 = 1$, 3 is its own inverse. The number 1 is also its own inverse, since $1 \cdot 1 = 1$.

The multiplicative inverse of an element x will be represented by the symbol 'x^{-1}' (read "x inverse"). Thus for any element x for which x^{-1} exists,

$$x^{-1} \cdot x = 1 \quad \text{and} \quad x \cdot x^{-1} = 1.$$

From the table it is easily seen that while $3^{-1} = 3$ and $1^{-1} = 1$, the symbol 2^{-1} is meaningless for this system, since 2 has no multiplicative inverse. Multiplicative inverses are also called *reciprocals*.

Division, of course, is defined to be the opposite of multiplication. The quotient $2 \div 3$, or $\frac{2}{3}$, exists, since there is a number which when multiplied by 3 gives 2. On the other hand, $3 \div 2$, or $\frac{3}{2}$, does not exist because there is no number which when multiplied by 2 gives 3.

EXERCISES

1. In the arithmetic of a five-minute clock, which of these symbols are meaningless? For those that are not meaningless, what numbers do they represent?

    (a) 3^{-1} (b) 1^{-1} (c) 0^{-1} (d) 4^{-1} (e) 2^{-1}

2. Using the multiplication table for the five-minute clock, perform the following.

    (a) $2 \cdot 3$ (b) $4 \cdot 1$ (c) $0 \cdot 2$ (d) $3 \cdot 4$

    (e) $4 \cdot 3$ (f) $(2 \cdot 3) \cdot 4$ (g) $2 \cdot (3 \cdot 4)$ (h) $3 \cdot (1 \cdot 1)$

3. Using the multiplication table for the five-minute clock, perform the following.

    (a) $\frac{2}{3}$ (b) $2 \cdot 3^{-1}$ (c) $\frac{1}{4}$ (d) $1 \cdot 4^{-1}$

    (e) $\frac{4}{3}$ (f) $4 \cdot 3^{-1}$ (g) $\frac{2}{1}$ (h) $2 \cdot 1^{-1}$

It may be seen that in any of the clock arithmetics, certain divisions may be performed by multiplying by a reciprocal. This is somewhat parallel to the situation concerning subtraction and the existence of additive inverses. In fact, one may always divide by multiplying by a reciprocal, whenever that reciprocal exists, as stated in the following theorem.

In any clock arithmetic, if x is any element, and y is any element having a multiplicative inverse, then

$$\frac{x}{y} = x \cdot y^{-1}.$$

This theorem may be proved very much like the analogous theorem concerning additive inverses and subtraction. It is extremely important here, as in almost all proofs, to recall at the outset the pertinent definitions. In this case the definition of division and the definition of multiplicative inverse are vital. The details of a proof are left as an exercise.

EXERCISES

1. Write a proof of the theorem stated above in boldface type.

2. List carefully the properties that a system must have in order that the theorem of exercise 1 will hold true for that system.

3. In a system where all elements have multiplicative inverses, and have the properties listed in exercise 2, would all divisions be possible? If so, prove it, and compare the proof with the proof of the theorem about additive inverses and subtraction.

5. MODULAR ARITHMETICS

The reader who has noted that in studying the structure of four-minute clock arithmetic, no reference to the clock upon which it was based is necessary is to be congratulated. This mathematical system is not unusual in that respect. Generally speaking, once a mathematical system is completely defined, the physical model upon which it is based may be discarded, and the structure of the system studied from definitions alone.

Furthermore, the choice of a four-minute clock to illustrate a small mathematical system was arbitrary. Any clock would have served the purpose almost as well. An arithmetic of a twelve-hour clock could be constructed in a similar fashion, and in fact, for any natural number greater than 1, a similar arithmetic could be constructed, with or without reference to a clock. Mathematical systems of this sort are known as *modular arithmetics*. For the four-minute clock, the number 4 is known as the *modulus*, and the mathematical system is often known as *arithmetic modulo* 4, abbreviated *mod* 4. Note that arithmetic mod 4 contains four numbers, arithmetic mod 12 would contain twelve numbers, and so on. It might also be noted that if arithmetic mod 12 were constructed with reference to an ordinary clock, the symbol for the additive identity might be '12' or 'XII,' rather than '0.' This example illustrates the important point, to be elaborated further, that the structure of a mathematical system is not affected by a mere change of symbols.

EXERCISES

1.   Construct addition and multiplication tables for arithmetic mod 6, and then perform the following. Does it appear that multiplication is distributive over subtraction? Is subtraction an operation? An associative operation? Is the set closed under subtraction?

(a) $(3 + 5) + 4$ (b) $3 + (5 + 4)$ (c) $3 \cdot (4 + 5)$
(d) $(3 \cdot 4) + (3 \cdot 5)$ (e) $3 \cdot (4 \cdot 3)$ (f) $(3 \cdot 4) \cdot 3$
(g) $(3 - 5) - 1$ (h) $3 - (5 - 1)$ (i) $4 \cdot (3 - 5)$
(j) $(4 \cdot 3) - (4 \cdot 5)$ (k) $2 \cdot (1 - 3)$ (l) $(2 \cdot 1) - (2 \cdot 3)$

2.   Which of the following symbols are meaningless in arithmetic mod 6? For those that have meaning, what do they represent?

(a) $^-4$ (b) $^-0$ (c) $^-1$ (d) $^-3$
(e) 1^{-1} (f) 3^{-1} (g) 5^{-1} (h) 2^{-1}

3.   Using tables, perform the following in arithmetic mod 6, if possible. Is division an operation in arithmetic mod 6?

(a) $2 + 3$ (b) $4 + 5$ (c) $2 \cdot 4$ (d) $4 \cdot 3$
(e) $3 - 5$ (f) $1 - 5$ (g) $5 - 2$ (h) $4 \div 5$
(i) $1 \div 5$ (j) $3 \div 2$ (k) $4 \div 2$

4.   What does each of the following symbols represent in arithmetic mod 6? Generalize if you can.

(a) $^-(^-2)$ (b) $^-(^-1)$ (c) $^-(^-5)$ (d) $^-(^-0)$

5.   What does each of the following symbols represent in arithmetic mod 6?

(a) $^-1$ (b) $^-1 \cdot 2$ (c) $^-2$ (d) $^-1 \cdot 3$
(e) $^-3$ (f) $^-1 \cdot 0$ (g) $^-0$ (h) $^-1 \cdot 4$
(i) $^-4$ (j) $^-1 \cdot 5$ (k) $^-5$

6.   What does each of the following symbols represent in arithmetic mod 6?

(a) $^-2 + {}^-4$ (b) $^-(2 + 4)$ (c) $^-3 + {}^-5$ (d) $^-(3 + 5)$
(e) $^-1 + {}^-3$ (f) $^-(1 + 3)$ (g) $^-5 + {}^-4$ (h) $^-(5 + 4)$

7.   What does each of the following symbols represent in arithmetic mod 6?

(a) $^-3 \cdot 2$ (b) $3 \cdot {}^-2$ (c) $^-(3 \cdot 2)$
(d) $^-3 \cdot 5$ (e) $3 \cdot {}^-5$ (f) $^-(3 \cdot 5)$
(g) $^-2 \cdot 4$ (h) $2 \cdot {}^-4$ (i) $^-(2 \cdot 4)$

8.   What does each of the following symbols represent in arithmetic mod 6?

(a) $^-3 \cdot {}^-4$ (b) $3 \cdot 4$ (c) $^-2 \cdot {}^-5$ (d) $2 \cdot 5$
(e) $^-2 \cdot {}^-3$ (f) $2 \cdot 3$ (g) $^-4 \cdot {}^-5$ (h) $4 \cdot 5$

9.   What does each of the following symbols represent in arithmetic mod 5?

(a) $\frac{1}{3}$ (b) $\frac{2}{3}$ (c) $\frac{3}{3}$ (d) $\frac{1}{2}$ (e) $\frac{2}{2}$
(f) $\frac{3}{2}$ (g) $\frac{2}{4}$ (h) $\frac{3}{4}$ (i) $\frac{4}{3}$ (j) $\frac{0}{3}$

10.   What does each of the following symbols represent in arithmetic mod 5?

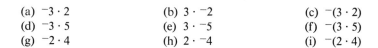

(a) $\frac{3}{2} \cdot \frac{4}{3}$ (b) $\frac{3 \cdot 4}{2 \cdot 3}$ (c) $\frac{1}{2} \cdot \frac{4}{3}$ (d) $\frac{1 \cdot 4}{2 \cdot 3}$

(e) $\frac{3}{4} \cdot \frac{1}{2}$ (f) $\frac{3 \cdot 1}{4 \cdot 2}$ (g) $\frac{4}{3} \cdot \frac{2}{3}$ (h) $\frac{4 \cdot 2}{3 \cdot 3}$

11. What does each of the following symbols represent in arithmetic mod 5?

(a) $\dfrac{3}{4}$ (b) $\dfrac{2}{2}$ (c) $\dfrac{3}{3}$ (d) $\dfrac{4}{4}$

(e) $\dfrac{3}{4}\cdot\dfrac{2}{2}$ (f) $\dfrac{3}{4}\cdot\dfrac{3}{3}$ (g) $\dfrac{3}{4}\cdot\dfrac{4}{4}$ (h) $\dfrac{3}{4}\cdot\dfrac{1}{1}$

12. What does each of the following symbols represent in arithmetic mod 5?

(a) $\dfrac{1}{3}+\dfrac{1}{3}$ (b) $\dfrac{1+1}{3}$ (c) $\dfrac{1}{3}+\dfrac{2}{3}$ (d) $\dfrac{1+2}{3}$

(e) $\dfrac{1}{4}+\dfrac{2}{4}$ (f) $\dfrac{1+2}{4}$ (g) $\dfrac{1}{4}+\dfrac{3}{4}$ (h) $\dfrac{1+3}{4}$

(i) $\dfrac{4}{3}+\dfrac{3}{2}$ (j) $\dfrac{4}{3}\cdot\dfrac{2}{2}+\dfrac{3}{2}\cdot\dfrac{3}{3}$ (k) $\dfrac{4\cdot2+3\cdot3}{3\cdot2}$

(l) $\dfrac{1}{4}+\dfrac{4}{3}$ (m) $\dfrac{1}{4}\cdot\dfrac{3}{3}+\dfrac{4}{3}\cdot\dfrac{4}{4}$ (n) $\dfrac{1\cdot3+4\cdot4}{3\cdot4}$

13. What does each of the following symbols represent in arithmetic mod 5?

(a) $\dfrac{2}{3}$ (b) $-\dfrac{2}{3}\left(\text{the additive inverse of }\dfrac{2}{3}\right)$

(c) $\dfrac{^{-}2}{3}$ (d) $\dfrac{2}{^{-}3}$ (e) $\dfrac{3}{4}$ (f) $-\dfrac{4}{3}$

(g) $\dfrac{^{-}3}{4}$ (h) $\dfrac{3}{^{-}4}$ (i) $\dfrac{1}{3}$ (j) $-\dfrac{1}{3}$

(k) $\dfrac{^{-}1}{3}$ (l) $\dfrac{1}{^{-}3}$

14. Recall that the division algorithm for whole numbers depends on the associative law of addition, the distributive law of multiplication over addition, and the possibility of subtracting. In arithmetic mod 5 these laws hold and all subtractions are possible. Therefore, the division algorithm is valid. Furthermore, since all subtractions are possible, any guess whatsoever may be made for a partial quotient. For example,

$$
\begin{array}{r}
3+2+1+1 \\
4{\overline{\smash{\big)}\,3}} \\
\underline{2} \\
1 \\
\underline{3} \\
3 \\
\underline{4} \\
4 \\
\underline{4} \\
0
\end{array}
$$

(a) Using random guessing of partial quotients, find $3\overline{\smash{\big)}2}$, mod 5, in five different ways.

(b) As in part (a), find $2\overline{\smash{\big)}3}$ in five different ways.

(c) In using the division algorithm with arithmetic mod 5, *need* the process end when a zero remainder is attained?

6. A MATHEMATICAL SYSTEM WITHOUT NUMBERS

The symmetries of a rectangle provide a simple example of a mathematical system without numbers. There are four symmetries in a rectangle. One is a symmetry with respect to a vertical axis, as shown in Fig. 3–2. Another is a symmetry with respect to a horizontal axis, a third is symmetry with respect to the center, and there is one other which must be considered for completeness. Each symmetry corresponds to a rotation which leaves the rectangle with its general appearance unchanged. The symmetry with respect to the vertical axis corresponds to a rotation of 180° about that axis. The symmetry with respect to the horizontal axis corresponds to a rotation of 180° about that axis. The symmetry with respect to the center corresponds to a 180° rotation in the plane of the rectangle, and the fourth symmetry to a rotation of 360°, or 0°, in the plane of the rectangle.

Attention will be focused on the rotations, and they will be named as follows:

H = rotation about horizontal axis,

V = rotation about vertical axis,

R = rotation of 180° in plane of rectangle,

I = leaving position unchanged, or rotation of 360° in plane of rectangle.

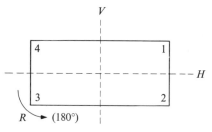

FIGURE 3–2

These four rotations and an operation to be defined will constitute a mathematical system. One operation will be defined, and it will be called "multiplication," even though it is quite different from multiplication of numbers. To multiply two elements of this mathematical system shall mean to perform first one rotation, then the other. For example, '$H \cdot V$' means to perform first the rotation about the horizontal axis, then the rotation about the vertical axis. To find the product, one decides what single rotation is equivalent to H followed by V. A moment's reflection shows that it is R, and thus $H \cdot V = R$. Table 3–3 is a multiplication table describing this operation. The reader may verify that it is correct by using a card or other object to represent the rectangle, marking its vertices, and rotating it.

TABLE 3–3

×	I	H	V	R
I	I	H	V	R
H	H	I	R	V
V	V	R	I	H
R	R	V	H	I

For example, to verify that $V \cdot H = R$, one would note that vertex 1 goes to position 4 in the rotation V. Then when H is performed that vertex goes to position 3. Thus $V \cdot H$ takes vertex 1 to position 3. Note then that R also takes vertex 1 to position 3. Likewise, R affects all four vertices in the same manner as $V \cdot H$, and therefore $V \cdot H = R$.

A brief study of this table will show that the set is closed under the operation, that the operation is commutative, that there is an identity element, and that for each element there is an inverse element. It may also be verified that the operation is associative.

Mathematical systems similar to that described above may be constructed for many geometric figures. In all such mathematical systems, one operation may be defined for which there is closure, associativity, an identity element, and for each element an inverse. The elements of any such system may be considered to be *transformations*. That is, they are rearrangements of the points of a geometric figure. It may be proved that any operation which consists of one transformation followed by another is an associative operation.*

EXERCISES

1. Make a table of "multiplication" for a mathematical system based on the symmetries of an isosceles triangle. [*Hint:* This system will contain just two elements: a rotation about the axis of the triangle and an identity element.]

2. Make a table of "multiplication" for a mathematical system based on the symmetries of an equilateral triangle, as shown in Fig. 3–3. Note that this system will contain 6 elements, which can be named as follows: flips about the axes F_1, F_2, and F_3, and rotations of 120° and 240° counterclockwise in the plane of the triangle. The 6th element, I, is a rotation of 0° or 360° in the plane. [*Caution:* The axes of the triangle are not to be considered as rotating with it, but rather as fixed in the plane.]

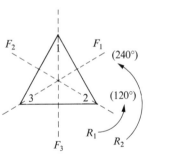

FIGURE 3–3   FIGURE 3–4

3. Make a table of "multiplication" for a mathematical system based on the symmetries of a square, as shown in Fig. 3–4. Note that this system will contain 8 elements, which can be named as follows: flips about horizontal, vertical, and diagonal axes, H, V, D_1, and D_2; counterclockwise rotations in the plane of 90°, 180°, and 270°, R_1, R_2, and R_3, respectively; and a rotation of 0°, or 360°, I.

4. Examine the table of exercise 1 and answer the following questions. (a) Is the set closed under the operation? (b) Is the operation commutative? (c) Is the operation associative? (d) Is there an identity element? (e) If the answer to (d) is yes, does every element have an inverse?

---

* For example, see McCoy, *An Introduction to Modern Algebra.*

5. Examine the table of exercise 2 and answer the same questions as for exercise 4.

6. Examine the table of exercise 3 and answer the same questions as for exercise 4.

7. In a table of an operation called "multiplication," we may find "squares." That is, if $X \cdot X = Y$, then Y may be called the square of X, and also X may be called a "square root" of Y. If an element is a square, it must appear on the diagonal of the table. (a) In the systems of exercises 1, 2, and 3, which elements are squares? For each square, name all of its square roots. (b) In arithmetic mod 5, determine which elements are squares, and name all the square roots of each.

8. Corresponding to the definition of squares and square roots of exercise 7, give a definition of cubes and cube roots. (a) From Table 3–3 determine which elements are cubes, and name all the cube roots of each. (b) In the system of exercise 2, determine which elements are cubes, and name all the cube roots of each.

9. How many elements are there in the system based on symmetries of a regular hexagon? A regular octagon?

10. How many elements are there in the system based on the symmetries of a circle?

11. Discuss the properties of the mathematical system consisting of the natural numbers under a single operation $\circ$, where "$a \circ b$" is defined to be the G.C.F. of a and b.

12. Consider the operation $\circ$ defined in exercise 11, together with ordinary multiplication, $\cdot$. (a) Is $\circ$ distributive over $\cdot$? (b) Is $\cdot$ distributive over $\circ$? (c) Prove your answers.

7. ABSTRACT MATHEMATICAL SYSTEMS

Although mathematical systems may arise from widely varying situations, it is not difficult to see that many of them have similar properties. For example, all of the systems based on symmetries of geometric figures have the following properties in common. The set is closed under the operation; that operation is associative; there is an identity element; and for each element there is an additive inverse. In modular arithmetics, considered only with respect to addition, the same properties are to be found. These examples are only a few of the mathematical systems enjoying these same properties. Since so many mathematical systems are similar in this respect, it is economical to study, in some detail, the properties that such systems have in common. This prompts an abstract definition of a class of mathematical systems with these properties. Other classes of systems with a different set of common properties can also be defined and studied in the abstract.

8. GROUPS

The name given to that class of mathematical systems closed under one associative operation, having an identity, and in which every element has an inverse, is *group*. The word *group* is used here in a technical sense, and in this context does not have its usual wider connotation. The abstract definition of a group is thus as follows.

A group is defined to be a set of elements G, together with one operation "$\circ$" satisfying the following conditions.

(i) G is closed under the operation $\circ$.

(ii) For any a, b, c in G, $a \circ (b \circ c) = (a \circ b) \circ c$.   (*cont.*)

(iii) There is in G an element i such that for any x in G,

$$i \circ x = x \circ i = x.$$

(iv) For every x in G, there is an element x^{-1} in G having the property that

$$x \circ x^{-1} = x^{-1} \circ x = i.$$

It should be noted that a system may have other properties besides these and still be a group. For example, in the modular arithmetics, the commutative law of addition holds. They are still groups, even though commutativity is not required by the definition of a group. In the modular arithmetics, there are two operations, while the definition of a group speaks of but one. The modular arithmetics are still groups under the operation of addition. They are not groups, however, under multiplication.

Groups which are commutative are of some special importance, and have been given the name "Abelian group," for the great Norwegian mathematician Niels Henrik Abel.

It should be noted also that the operation $\circ$ may be any operation whatever. In some instances it may be called "multiplication," in which case the group is called a "multiplicative group." In others the operation may be called "addition," and the group will be called an "additive group." In other instances the operation may be of a still different nature.

It should be noted that the natural numbers do not constitute a group under either addition or multiplication. Under addition there is closure and associativity, but there is no identity, and of course there are no inverses. Under multiplication there is closure, associativity, and an identity, but not all elements have inverses. The set of all symmetries of any geometric figure constitutes a group. All modular arithmetics under addition constitute groups, but no modular arithmetic under multiplication constitutes a group. In certain modular arithmetics under multiplication, if the additive identity is omitted from the set, a group is obtained. It may be noted that in these cases it is property (iv) which fails to hold for some arithmetics; that is, not all elements have multiplicative inverses. If, however, the modulus is a prime number, it may be seen that all elements except the additive identity have multiplicative inverses. To make a proper interpretation of symbolism, one should note that where the nonzero elements of a modular arithmetic constitute a group, the symbol '·' takes the place of '$\circ$.' When modular arithmetics under addition are considered as groups, the symbol '$+$' takes the place of '$\circ$' and '$-a$' takes the place of 'a^{-1}.'

The usefulness of the definition of *group* lies in its abstract nature. From the definition it must necessarily follow that any system which satisfies it has other properties not mentioned in the definition. Such properties may be deduced by regarding the parts of the definition as axioms, and proceeding to prove theorems from them. The theorem on p. 60 is an example. That theorem holds in any system which is a group, and hence is actually a theorem about groups in the abstract. This point, as well as the technique of proof, will be elaborated further later (Chapter 5). Once these consequences have been determined, they are known to apply to any mathematical system which is a group. Thus by studying groups in the abstract, one learns facts, not just about particular systems, but about many systems at once.

The theory of groups, which originated about the turn of the century, is now extensive and fills many volumes. The applications of group theory, both to mathematics itself and to the physical world, are of great importance. For example, it has been proved that there are exactly 17 basic designs for wall ornaments which are repetitive, such as found in wallpaper. It has also been shown that there can exist at most 33 different structures in crystals, 32 of which are known to exist in nature.

EXERCISES

1. The definition of a *group*, on page 67 may be satisfied in many different situations, and for many different kinds of operations. (a) Restate the group properties, interpreting '$\circ$' to be addition in modular arithmetic ('$\circ$' will be replaced by '$+$' and 'x^{-1}' by '^{-}x'). (b) Restate the group properties, interpreting '$\circ$' to be multiplication in modular arithmetic ('$\circ$' will be replaced by '$\cdot$' and 'x^{-1}' may be replaced by '$1/x$').

2. Show that arithmetic mod 5, under addition, constitutes a group.

3. Show that arithmetic mod 6, under multiplication, even when zero is deleted, does not constitute a group.

4. Which of the following constitute Abelian groups?

   (a) Arithmetic mod 6 under addition.
   (b) Arithmetic mod 5 under multiplication.
   (c) The symmetries of the rectangle.
   (d) The symmetries of the square.
   (e) The symmetries of the equilateral triangle.

5. Show that arithmetic mod 5, under multiplication, when zero is deleted, constitutes a group.

6. Why cannot any modular arithmetic under multiplication constitute a group unless zero is deleted?

7. Which of the following modular arithmetics, under multiplication, with zero deleted, constitute groups?

   (a) mod 7   (b) mod 8   (c) mod 9   (d) mod 10   (e) mod 11   (f) mod 12

8. Can you give a convincing argument that any modular arithmetic under multiplication, with zero deleted, is not a group if the modulus is not prime?

9. By using tables, find all solutions of each of the following equations in arithmetic mod 5.

   (a) $2 + x = 0$ (b) $4 + x = 3$ (c) $2 \cdot x = 1$
   (d) $4 \cdot x = 0$ (e) $0 \cdot x = 2$ (f) $0 \cdot x = 0$

10. By using Table 3–3, find all solutions of each of the following equations.

   (a) $V \cdot X = R$ (b) $H \cdot X = I$ (c) $V \cdot X = H$ (d) $R \cdot X = R$

11. By using tables, find all solutions of each of the following equations in arithmetic mod 6.

   (a) $2 \cdot x = 3$ (b) $2 \cdot x = 2$ (c) $3 \cdot x = 0$ (d) $3 \cdot x = 3$

9. FIELDS AND RINGS

As has been demonstrated in the previous sections, mathematical systems fall into categories. A definition of one of these, the *group*, has been given. There are many classifications of mathematical systems which could be mentioned. Two will be discussed briefly here.

The abstract mathematical system known as a *field* is exemplified by the modular arithmetics with prime modulus. In these systems two operations are considered, rather than one. For both operations there is closure; both are commutative and associative. There is an identity for each operation, and for one of the operations every element has an inverse. All elements but one have inverses for the other operation. The exception is the identity for the first operation. Moreover, a distributive law of the second operation over the first holds. This in effect constitutes the definition of a field. It is given more concisely below.

A *field* consists of a set *F*, containing at least two different elements, closed under two operations $+$ and $\cdot$ and satisfying the following conditions.

(i) *F*, together with $+$, constitutes an Abelian group.

(ii) *F*, with the identity of the group mentioned in (i) deleted, together with $\cdot$, constitutes an Abelian group.

(iii) For all *a*, *b*, *c* in *F*,

$$a \cdot (b + c) = (a \cdot b) + (a \cdot c).$$

The operations $+$ and $\cdot$ of any field are usually referred to as "addition" and "multiplication," respectively, even though they may bear little resemblance to these operations in mathematical systems commonly encountered. A *field* thus contains two groups. One of them, usually called the "additive" group, contains every element of the set. If the identity of the additive group is deleted, the remaining set constitutes the "multiplicative" group. Furthermore, the distributive laws must hold for all elements of the set.

Fields are of primary importance in elementary mathematics, because of the fact that the most useful number systems are fields. It is pointed out in later chapters that the number systems of ordinary algebra are fields.

It has already been stated that every modular arithmetic with prime modulus is a field. The modular arithmetics with composite modulus are not fields, but they illustrate another class of mathematical systems, called *rings*, defined below.

A *ring* consists of a set *R*, closed under two operations $+$ and $\cdot$, satisfying the following conditions.

(i) *R*, together with $+$, constitutes an Abelian group.

(ii) The operation $\cdot$ is associative.

(iii) For all *a*, *b*, *c* in *R*,

$$a \cdot (b + c) = (a \cdot b) + (a \cdot c) \qquad \text{and} \qquad (b + c) \cdot a = (b \cdot a) + (c \cdot a).$$

Note that the above definition is different from that of a field in that · is not necessarily commutative. It is thus necessary to state both a right and a left distributive law. There is not necessarily a multiplicative identity and no element is required to have a multiplicative inverse. If commutativity does hold in a ring, it is called a "commutative ring." If there is a multiplicative identity, the ring is said to have a "unity." Every modular arithmetic with composite modulus may be seen to be a commutative ring with unity. It should be noted that every mathematical system which is a field must also be a ring, and therefore the modular arithmetics with prime modulus are rings as well as fields.

As for groups, the power of the definitions of fields and rings lies in their abstract character. By considering the parts of the definitions as axioms and proving theorems from them, one may learn about a great many mathematical systems at once. This is the character of modern abstract algebra. The reader may have begun to suspect that in a group, for example, every equation $a \circ x = b$, where a and b are specific members of the group, has a solution. Such is actually the case, and it can be proved as a general theorem about groups. A proof will be found in Chapter 5. Similarly, it may have begun to appear that in any ring (such as the modular arithmetics), every product with a zero factor is zero. No amount of experimentation can verify that this is true, but a fairly simple proof, to be found in Chapter 5, establishes the fact.

EXERCISES

1. Show that arithmetic mod 5 is a ring.
2. Show that arithmetic mod 4 is a ring.
3. Show that arithmetic mod 5 is a field.
4. Show that arithmetic mod 4 is not a field.

CHAPTER *4*

Sentences, Sets,
and Relations

1. NAMES AND THINGS NAMED

In Chapter 1 the point was made that numerals are symbols for numbers, and therefore that numbers and symbols are not the same. In many cases no confusion results from not distinguishing a name from the object named. For example, from the sentence

The teacher wrote Cow on the board.

it is not difficult to realize that it was a symbol and not an animal which was written. However, the best English usage would probably require quotation marks around the word 'Cow' in order to show that the sentence is speaking about a symbol rather than the object represented by that symbol.

In elementary mathematics it has been traditional to ignore the distinction between a symbol and that which it represents. This practice has undoubtedly contributed to the confusion of many a student. In this book there is an earnest attempt to make the distinction, with the hope that the reader's attention will thereby be directed to concepts rather than symbols, and his use of language and symbols will be more precise than it would be otherwise. Quotation marks, usually single ones, are used to indicate that a symbol is being referred to. A symbol without quotation marks refers to the object named by that symbol. The following sentences illustrate correct use of quotation marks.

> Logic requires the use of symbols.
> 'Logic' has 5 letters.
> The jar had 'olives' on it.
> 'Mary' is half as long as 'Maryland.'

The following sentences illustrate incorrect usage.

> Logic requires the use of 'symbols.'
> 'Logic' has '5' letters.
> Logic has 5 letters.
> The jar had olives on it.
> Mary is half as long as 'Maryland.'
> 'Mary' is half as long as Maryland.
> There is land in 'Maryland.'

Quotation marks are sometimes omitted in phrases which themselves make it clear that a symbol is being referred to. For example, in

> the numeral 2,
>
> the letter x

quotation marks would be optional.

It should also be noted that a sentence does not name anything. It is a string of symbols, often making an assertion. Therefore a sentence need not be placed in quotation marks to indicate that it is being spoken of. For example, in

> The letter x is a variable in $x + 4 = 2$.

no quotation marks are needed around $x + 4 = 2$.

EXERCISES

Place quotation marks where needed in the following. (If the use is optional, include quotation marks.)

1. This page has 73 on it.
2. 7 is not a number.
3. Turned upside down 9 becomes 6.
4. 3 is a number, but 3 is a numeral.
5. If 35 is reversed it becomes 53.
6. The number 25 can be named with a 2 and a 5.
7. A name for 9 is $4 + 5$.
8. I don't mind being hit with a stick, but I don't like being hit with a stick.
9. 8/4 and $2 \cdot 1$ are two numerals for the same number.
10. The teacher wrote milk on the board.

REVIEW PRACTICE EXERCISES

1. Plot the following points on a graph.

    EXAMPLES: See Fig. 4–1.

    (a) (4, 6)   (b) (6, 4)   (c) (0, 3)   (d) (−5, −2)
    (e) (−5, 0)   (f) (0, −5)   (g) (3, −4)   (h) (−5, 3)
    (i) (6, 0)   (j) (0, −4)   (k) (8, 8)   (l) (0, 0)

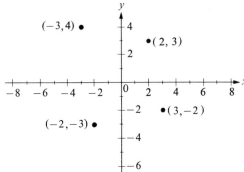

FIGURE 4–1

2. The graphs of the following equations are lines. Plot them using graph paper.

    EXAMPLE: To plot the graph of $y = 3x + 4$, find and tabulate some pairs of numbers, as follows.

x	0	−4	2	
y	4	−8	10	

    Plot these points and draw a line through them. See Fig. 4–2.

    (a) $y = x - 2$
    (b) $y = -2x + 3$
    (c) $3y + 2x = 5$
    (d) $4y - 5x = 6$

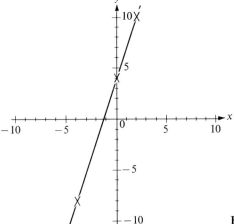

FIGURE 4–2

2. SENTENCES

Ideas are expressed by means of sentences. Therefore, a study of the language of reasoning must include a look at sentences. It is not necessary, however, to study all kinds of sentences, since ideas are expressed by those of a particular kind.

Statements. If a declarative sentence is true or false, but not both, it is called a *statement*. The following are examples of statements.

> New York is farther south than Chicago.
> Snow is white and grass is green.
> George Washington is King of the United States.
> $1 + 3 = 4$.
> $8 - 2 = 5$.

The following are not statements.

> Why did you come?
> Put on your shoes.
> He is president of the local Lions Club.
> That was long ago.
> $x + 14 = 15$.
> $p - q = 17$.

Variables and Constants. In the sentence $x + 14 = 15$, the letter x does not represent any specific number.* If '2' is substituted for 'x,' then a (false) statement is obtained. If '3/3' is substituted for it, then a (true) statement is obtained. With 'x' present and unspecified, $x + 14 = 15$ is neither true nor false, and hence is not a statement. A letter, or other symbol, which can represent various numbers is called a *variable*. Likewise 'He' is a variable in *He is president of the local Lions Club*. The sentence by itself is not true or false until the variable has been replaced by the name of a specific person, or it has somehow been indicated by context to whom 'He' refers, and therefore is not a statement. It is often the case that a sentence containing variables is neither true nor false, and is therefore not a statement.

In $x + 14 = 15$, the symbols 14 and 15 represent specific numbers. They are therefore not variables but are called *constants*. Letters as well as numerals may also be constants, provided that they are used to represent only one number through-out a particular discussion or argument. For example, if a discussion begins "Let

---

*According to a point of view held by some mathematicians, the letter x in a sentence like $x + 14 = 15$ represents a specific number, the number 1, because that number is the only one making the sentence true. The point of view presented in this book is a more recent one, and is believed by the author to be superior from the standpoint of both logic and pedagogy.

Difficulty arises in sentences like $x^2 = 1$, when the older point of view is taken. If 'x' is to represent a specific number, the one making the sentence true, then does it represent 1 or -1?

For a discussion of these points of view, the reader is referred to articles by E. G. Begle and H. Van Engen, *The Mathematics Teacher*, Vol. LIV, No. 3, March 1961, pp. 172–177.

$x = 35$," the 'x' represents one specific number throughout the discussion, and is thus a constant,* rather than a variable.

The word *sentence*, as used hereafter in this logical context, will refer to sentences which are either

(1) Statements,

or

(2) Sentences that will become statements when sensible substitutions are made for all of their variables.

The use of the word *sentence* in this restricted manner will focus attention on those kinds of sentences by which ideas are expressed.

Replacement sets. Replacements for variables of a sentence are always chosen with reference to some particular set. For example, the variable in $x + 14 = 15$ may be replaced by some numeral for a natural number. In this case the set of natural numbers is the replacement set. However, it might be agreed to use the set of all even numbers as the replacement set. The set of natural numbers less than 25 might also have been chosen. In many instances, context makes it clear what replacement set is intended, but in others it does not. When it is not clear what replacement set is intended, confusion and ambiguity may result. For one replacement set a sentence may have no replacement which makes it true, while for another replacement set there may be several which make it true.

Sets may be named by symbols such as the following: $\{3, 6, 4, 9\}$. The braces indicate that a set is being considered, and the symbols between them, separated by commas, are names for the members of the set. Sets may also be named by symbols such as this one:

$$\{x \mid x > 25\}.$$

Again the braces indicate that a set is being considered. Since the set is too large to enumerate, the conditions under which a number will belong to the set are specified, namely $x > 25$. The symbol is read, "The set of all x such that x is greater than 25."

It may be well to emphasize that variables are replaced by names of specific members of the replacement set, and not by members of the set itself. For example, the replacement set $\{1, 2, 3, 5, 12\}$ contains the numbers 1, 2, 3, 5, and 12. A variable may be replaced by a name, or *numeral*, for any of these numbers. There are many names which could be used for each number. For example, 1 can be named by '1,' '3/3,' '5 − 4,' etc. Although it is not possible to replace a variable by a *number*, but only by a name of a number, it is possible to speak of the replacements *for which a sentence becomes true*. For example, in $12 − x = 7$ with replacement set $\{2, 3, 5, 7, 9\}$, it may be said that 5 is a replacement which makes the sentence true. This is interpreted to mean that when any numeral for 5 is substituted for 'x' the sentence becomes true.

---

* If the replacement set for a variable should contain just one member, then that variable is a constant, according to the definition of a constant. Except for this trivial case, no variable is a constant.

Solution sets. Any replacement which makes a sentence true is called a *solution* of the sentence. The set of all solutions is known as its *solution set*. For example, consider the sentence $2 \cdot x = 8$, with replacement set $\{2, 3, 4, 5, 8, 11, 45\}$. The only member of the replacement set which makes the sentence true is 4. Therefore, the solution set is $\{4\}$, containing just one member. On the other hand, the sentence $y \cdot y = y$ with replacement set $\{0, 1, 2, 3\}$ has the solution set $\{0, 1\}$, containing two members.

The sentence $2 \cdot z = z + 1$ with replacement set $\{3, 5, 7, 9, 12, 21\}$ has no solutions whatever. Its solution set is then said to be *empty*, or the *empty set*. The empty set is designated by the symbol $\emptyset$.

EXERCISES

1.   Determine the variables in each of the following.

    (a) $5 + x = y + 1$ (b) She is ill.
    (c) He ate dinner.
    (d) For all natural numbers x and y, $y + x = x + y$.
    (e) The solution set is $\{y \mid y < 14\}$.

2.   Which of the following are statements? Which could become statements when replacements are made for the variables?

    (a) When he goes to school, he will have to study.
    (b) $2 + x = 5$ (c) Ocean water is salty.
    (d) The higher the thinner.   (e) Not this time, please.
    (f) $5 + 9 = 25$.   (g) Is it true that $4 + 5 = 9$?
    (h) For goodness sake.   (i) Come on over.
    (j) I like that white one.   (k) Nobody must enter this place.

3.   In each of the following a sentence and a replacement set for it are given. Determine the solution set in each case.

    (a) $2x = x + 4$ $\{0, 1, 2, 3, 4, 5\}$
    (b) $2w = w + 3$ $\{0, 1, 2, 3, 4, 5\}$
    (c) $4y = 3y + 2y$ $\{0, 1, 2, 3, 4, 5\}$
    (d) $2y < 5$ $\{0, 1, 2, 3, 4, 5\}$
    (e) $a^2 + 1 = a^3 + 1$ $\{0, 1, 2, 3, 4, 5\}$
    (f) $y + 2 = 2y - 4$ $\{p \mid p < 100\}$
    (g) $z - 4 = 3z - 14$ $\{t \mid t < 200 \text{ and } t > 25\}$

3. GRAPHS OF SENTENCES

When a sentence refers to an ordered set, such as the set of whole numbers, there is a natural way to picture, or *graph* that sentence. The replacement set is first pictured, in some fashion, and then that part of it which is the solution set is indicated. Figure 4–3, for example, is a graph of $y^2 = y$ with replacement set $\{0, 1, 2, 3\}$. Figure 4–4 is a graph of $x < 231$, where the replacement set is the set of whole numbers. A simplified picture is necessary in this case, since it is not possible to picture each member of the replacement set and it is not convenient to picture each member of

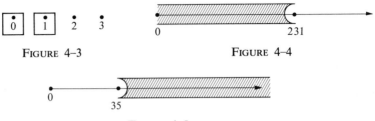

FIGURE 4–3   FIGURE 4–4

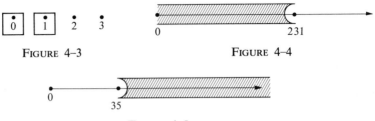

FIGURE 4–5

the solution set. The line with the arrowhead must be understood to represent the set of whole numbers. The solution set is shown by the shading. Note that the shaded region includes 0, but is concave about the point representing 231, to indicate that 231 is not in the solution set, but that all smaller whole numbers are. Figure 4–5 is a graph of $x > 35$.

If a sentence contains two variables, its solution set ordinarily consists of ordered pairs of numbers, and of course the replacement set would then also consist of ordered pairs of numbers. The solution set of $x + 2 = y$, for example, where the replacement set is the set of all ordered pairs of whole numbers, contains such ordered pairs as $(0, 2)$, $(1, 3)$, and $(250, 252)$. By convention, the numbers in the ordered pairs are taken to correspond with alphabetical order of the variables. In this case, the first number of an ordered pair is a replacement for 'x' and the second is a replacement for 'y,' since x precedes y in the alphabet. Figure 4–6 is a graph of $x + 2 = y$. Not all of the ordered pairs can be shown, but enough are shown to indicate the pattern. In this case, the points of the graph all lie on a line slanting upward to the right.

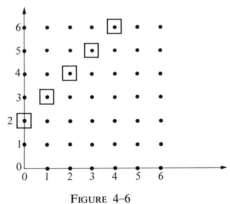

FIGURE 4–6

On occasion, a sentence with just one variable may have as its replacement set some set of ordered pairs. In this event, one variable may be considered to be "missing." The truth of such a sentence, upon making a replacement, does not depend upon the replacement for the missing variable. For example, the sentence $x < 3$ would become true for replacements $(1, 4)$, $(2, 35)$, $(0, 5)$, etc., if the replacement set is a set of ordered pairs (x, y).

EXERCISES

1. Plot graphs of the sentences of exercise 3(a) through (e) in the preceding set.

2. Plot a graph of each of the following sentences. The replacement set is the set of whole numbers.

    (a) $2x < 10$
    (b) $4x > 12$
    (c) $3x < x + 18$
    (d) $3 < x$ and $x < 350$

3. Plot a graph of each of the following sentences, where the replacement set consists of all ordered pairs of numbers taken from the set $\{0, 1, 2, 3, 4, 5\}$.

    (a) $x = y + 1$ (b) $x = y$ (c) $x < y$ (d) $x > y$
    (e) $x \leq y$ (f) $x \geq y$ (g) $x > y + 1$ (h) $2x + 1 < y$
    (i) $x > 3$ (j) $y < 3$

4. Plot a graph of each of the following sentences, where the replacement set consists of all ordered pairs of whole numbers.

    (a) $x = y$ (b) $x < y$ (c) $x > y$ (d) $x > y + 1$
    (e) $2x + 1 < y$ (f) $x = 5$ (g) $y = 7$ (h) $x < 4$
    (i) $y > 5$

4. VERBS

A sentence must have a verb, or predicate. Attention will be given here to a few of the verbs most commonly encountered in logic and mathematics.

"Is." The word *is*, in its various forms, is a verb which may cause difficulty, because it has several different meanings. There are three common meanings in logical contexts, listed and explained below.

I. x is B.

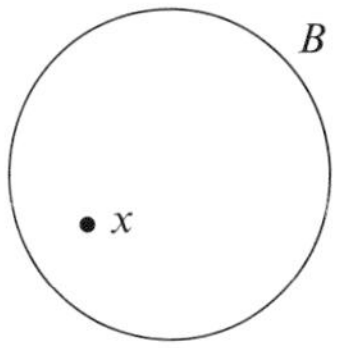

EXAMPLES: This animal is a cat.
              The number 6 is a multiple of 3.
              The fire engine is red.

FIGURE 4-7

In these examples the word "is" conveys the idea that the subject has a certain property. Each of the examples could be paraphrased to emphasize this point. For example, the second sentence could be paraphrased to: *The number 6 has the property of being a multiple of 3.*

It is convenient to consider sets here. For example, it is easy to consider the set of all red objects. Then every object which has the property of being red belongs to this set, and conversely every member of this set has that property. The third sentence could be paraphrased: *The fire engine belongs to the set of all red objects.* The other two sentences could be paraphrased: *This animal belongs to the set of all cats;* and *The number 6 belongs to the set of all multiples of 3.*

Thus the word "is" in this kind of sentence can be interpreted as indicating that the subject belongs to a certain set. This interpretation is most economical and most precise, and is to be preferred. Thus

$$x \text{ is } B$$

means x belongs to the set of all objects with property B. Figure 4–7 illustrates this use of "is," showing x as a member of B.

II. All A's are B's.

EXAMPLES: All men are mammals.
A horse is an animal.
All Cretans are liars.

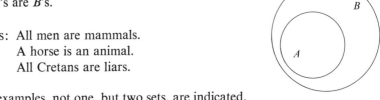

FIGURE 4–8

In these examples, not one, but two sets, are indicated. In the first, the set of all men and the set of all mammals; in the second, the set of all horses and the set of all animals; in the third, the set of all Cretans and the set of all liars. Each of these sentences asserts that one set is included in another, and could be paraphrased accordingly. For example, *The set of all horses is included in the set of all animals;* or *The set of all Cretans is included in the set of all liars.*

The word *is* (or *are*) used in this way can be interpreted in general as meaning that one set is included in another. Thus

$$\text{All } A \text{'s are } B \text{'s}$$

means the set of all A's is included in the set of all B's. Figure 4–8 illustrates this use of *is,* showing A included in B.

III. x is y.

EXAMPLES: George Washington was the first President of the United States.
The only even prime is 2.
Independence Day is July 4.

In these examples there is only one object or entity mentioned, and it is mentioned, or named, twice. 'George Washington' and 'the first President of the United States' are two names, or designations, of the same person. 'The only even prime' and '2' both name the same number, and 'Independence Day' and 'July 4' designate the same day.

The word *is* when used in this way may be called the *is of identity.* In these sentences one entity is named twice. They assert that the two names represent the same thing. Thus

$$x \text{ is } y$$

means 'x' and 'y' are two names of the same thing.

It should be noted that a sentence using the *is* of identity can be reversed without changing the meaning. For example, *Independence Day is July 4* means the same thing as *July 4 is Independence Day;* and *George Washington was the first President of the United States* means the same thing as *The first President of the United States was George Washington.* For the other uses of *is,* sentences cannot be reversed without changing their meaning.

In most instances the meaning of *is* becomes clear upon a moment's reflection. An awareness of the different meanings of this verb makes it easier to use language precisely.

Equality. The verb *equals* is probably encountered in mathematics more than any other. Although it has not always been used precisely, and at times has been given different meanings, its primary and correct usage is that of the *is of identity.* A sentence with = for its verb is called an *equation* or an *equality.*

The sentence $3 + 4 = 7$ asserts that '$3 + 4$' and '7' are two symbols for the same number. It is true. The sentence $5 = 6 + 3$ asserts that '5' and '$6 + 3$' are two symbols for the same number. It is false. The sentence $x - y = y + x - 4$ asserts that '$x - y$' and '$y + x - 4$' are symbols for the same number. It is neither true nor false unless the letters are being used to represent specific numbers.

This manner of considering the meaning of = is simple and direct. It is easy to see that any equation is reversible. This is an important point, since the habit of reading left-to-right tends to make it seem, for example, that

$$3 + 4 = 7 \qquad \text{and} \qquad 7 = 3 + 4$$

assert different ideas. The reader may recall from elementary algebra that in solving an equation, $x = 2$ would be considered a correct *answer,* or response, while $2 = x$ would seem strange. Since both sentences mean the same thing, either should be considered fully as correct as the other.

Misunderstanding or lack of adequate definition of = may lead to confusion on many points, and ordinary language usage sometimes tends to worsen rather than better the situation. For example, one may ask "What does $7 + 3$ equal?" The response usually desired is '10,' although '45/4.5' would also be correct. To speak of *two* numbers as being equal may also cause difficulty. If by *two* is meant two *different* numbers, then they cannot in any sense be equal. Instead of saying that two numbers are equal, it might be advisable to use language to the effect that two symbols represent the same number. Euclid's notion that "when equals are added to equals, the results are equal" does not make sense when applied to numbers instead of line segments. In effect, it would say that when a number is added to a number, the result is a number. This point will be discussed more fully later.

Verbs of inequality. A sentence using any of the following verbs is called an *inequality:*

$\neq$ means *is not equal to,*
$<$ means *is less than,*
$\leq$ means *is less than or equal to,*
$>$ means *is greater than,*
$\geq$ means *is greater than or equal to.*

The sentence $7 + 3 \neq 11 - 1$ asserts that '$7 + 3$' and '$11 - 1$' are not names for the same number. The sentence $5 + 2 < 3 + 4$ asserts that the number $5 + 2$ is less than the number $3 + 4$.

In addition to the symbols above, there are also verbs which indicate negations. Substitution of $\neq$ for $=$ in a sentence produces the negation of that sentence. A similar relationship holds between $<$ and $\not<$; $\leq$ and $\not\leq$; and so on.

EXERCISES

1. Which use of *is* is illustrated in each of the following?

   (a) Anderson is a fireman.

   (b) John Hancock was one of the signers of the declaration of independence.

   (c) The members of the first continental congress were colonists.

   (d) Five is a factor of 100.

   (e) Paul Bunyan is a character of fiction.

   (f) 'Babe' was the name of Bunyan's ox.

   (g) Philadelphia was the first capital of the United States.

   (h) The highest mountain in the world is Mt. Everest.

   (i) Joe Smith was not president of the United States.

   (j) No Indian has ever been president of the United States.

   (k) The greatest cowboy humorist of all time was Will Rogers.

   (l) The largest prime number less than 100 is 97.

   (m) All multiples of 4 are even numbers.

   (n) Powers of ten are multiples of 2.

   (o) The smallest multiple of both 3 and 7 is 21.

   (p) The sum of 3 and 5 is 8.

   (q) Division by zero is impossible.

   (r) Addition is an associative operation.

   (s) The solution set of $x = x + 1$ is the empty set.

   (t) The product of 2 and 4 is even.

   (u) The product of 2 and 4 is 8.

   (v) The smallest prime factor of 15 is 3.

   (w) A group is a mathematical system.

2. Determine which of the following sentences are true and which are false. Reverse each sentence and tell which sentences are then true and which are false.

   (a) $4 + 1 = 5$ (b) $6 - 3 = 5 + 6$ (c) $7 \cdot 5 \neq 30 + 4$
   (d) $4 + 15 \neq 20 - 1$ (e) $4 \cdot 5 < 21 + 2$ (f) $9 + 7 \not< 15 - 5$
   (g) $17 + 4 > 10 - 3$ (h) $75 \leq 70 + 5$ (i) $13 \leq 25 - 4$
   (j) $47 \geq 47 - 5$

3. Find and graph the solution set of each of the following inequalities. A replacement set is specified for each.

   (a) $x + 1 > 2$ $\{0, 1, 2, 3, 4\}$ (b) $2x < 8$ $\{0, \frac{1}{2}, 1, 3, 5, 9, 12\}$
   (c) $x \leq 2x$ $\{0, 1, 2, 3\}$ (d) $x - 4 \geq 5$ $\{8, 9, 10, 12, 15, 20\}$

4. Define =.

5. Discuss the difficulty of attempting to define = if one starts by saying "Two numbers are equal in case . . ."

6. Every equation has two members, or *sides*. Are they symbols or what the symbols represent? In view of your answer discuss the commonly used expression *adding the same thing to both sides of an equation*.

5. SETS

Symbolism for sets was introduced earlier in this chapter, and reference to sets has been made throughout the book. The importance of the set concept in clarifying mathematical ideas is great, and it is therefore helpful to use the language of sets. The reader may note that the word *set* has not been defined here, nor has it seemed necessary to explain what it means that *an element belongs to a set*. These ideas are intuitively clear, and hence can be left undefined.

Detailed study of mathematical theory of sets is beyond the scope of this book. Rather, a brief look at some of the basic concepts and symbolism is provided here.

Symbolism. Sets may be indicated as before, using braces, as follows:

$$\{0, 1, 3, 5, 25, 31\}, \qquad \{x|x + 2 < 5\}.$$

Letters are often used also to represent sets. For example, the set of natural numbers is often represented by 'N,' and the set of all prime numbers by 'P.'

Membership. The symbol $\in$ means *is a member of*, or *belongs to*. Thus the sentence $x \in A$ means *x is a member of the set A*, or *x belongs to set A*.

Set membership may be illustrated with a diagram as in Fig. 4–9. Here the interior of the closed curve represents a set A, and x is a point in that region. This therefore shows that $x \in A$.

Intersections. The set which contains just those elements common to several sets is called their *intersection*. The intersection of two sets A and B is indicated by the symbol

$$A \cap B.$$

Thus the symbol

$$\{0, 1, 3, 5, 25\} \cap \{2, 3, 4, 5, 6, 7, 9\}$$

represents the intersection of two sets, and is the set $\{3, 5\}$.

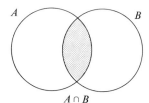

FIGURE 4–9   FIGURE 4–10

Set intersection is illustrated diagrammatically in Fig. 4–10. Here two sets, A and B, are pictured. The shaded region represents their intersection $A \cap B$.

The empty set. A set without members is known as the *empty set*, and is often named '$\emptyset$'. It may be described in various ways. For example, *The set of all green donkeys with glass hoofs* and *The set of all even prime numbers greater than 17* both describe the empty set

It is important to define a set without members for several reasons. It is often not clear whether or not a set contains members; for example, the set of all pairs of prime twins not yet found may be empty, but nobody knows for sure. Once a set without members is defined, it is guaranteed that every two sets have some set for their intersection. The following set, for example, is empty:

$$\{x | x \text{ is even}\} \cap \{y | y \text{ is odd}\}.$$

If there were no empty set, this would not be a set, and a certain lack of completeness would be felt, similar to that for numbers when zero is not used.

If two sets have a nonempty intersection, they are said to *intersect*. Two sets with an empty intersection are said to be *disjoint*.

Unions. Two sets A and B may be combined, forming a new set which contains the elements of A as well as those of B. The new set is called the *union* of A and B, and is represented by the symbol

$$A \cup B.$$

Thus the symbol

$$\{0, 5, 7, 13, 27\} \cup \{0, 2, 3, 4, 5\}$$

represents the union of two sets, and is the set

$$\{0, 2, 3, 4, 5, 7, 13, 27\}.$$

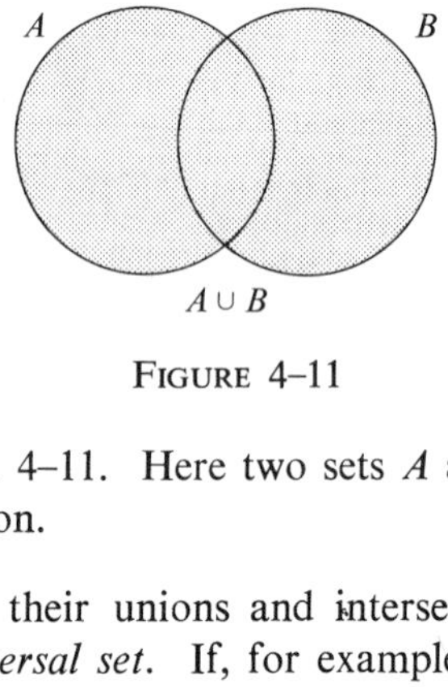

FIGURE 4–11

Set unions are illustrated diagrammatically in Fig. 4–11. Here two sets A and B are pictured. The shaded region represents their union.

Universal sets. In considering properties of sets, their unions and intersections and the like, it is important to keep in mind a *universal set*. If, for example, one considers sets such as the even numbers, the odd numbers, prime numbers, or multiples of 5, the universal set is probably the set of whole numbers. If one considers sets such as pigs, cows, chickens, or horses, the universal set is probably a set of animals. Every discourse has its universal set, even though it may not be specified clearly. One distinct advantage in viewing mathematics in terms of mathematical systems is that each discourse is clearly distinguished, and a universal set for each is clearly specified.

Figure 4–12 shows how a universal set may be illustrated. Pictured are the set of all plumbers and the set of all Methodists. The interior of the rectangle represents a universal set, which in this case might be the set of all people.

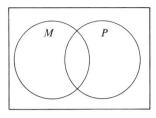

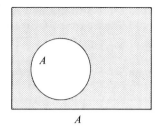

FIGURE 4–12   FIGURE 4–13

Complements. The *complement* of a set *A* is defined to be the set consisting of those members of the universal set which are not in *A*. For example, if the universal set is {3, 4, 5, 7, 9, 10, 12}, and *A* = {4, 7, 10}, then the complement of *A*, represented by the symbol

$$\overline{A},$$

is the set {3, 5, 9, 12}. It should be noted that for any set *A*, the union of *A* and $\overline{A}$ is the entire universal set, and the intersection of *A* and $\overline{A}$ is the empty set.

Set complements are illustrated diagrammatically as in Fig. 4–13. Pictured is a set. *A* in a universal set. The shaded region represents the complement of *A*, relative to this universal set.

Subsets. Given a set *A* with several members, it is possible to construct other sets using its members. For example, if *A* = {4, 5, 6}, the sets which can be constructed from its members are:

$$\{4, 5\}, \quad \{4, 6\}, \quad \{5, 6\},$$
$$\{4\}, \quad \{5\}, \quad \{6\},$$
$$\{4, 5, 6\}, \quad \emptyset$$

Each of these sets is a *subset* of *A*. Each is said to be *included in A*. The sentence, *P is a subset of Q*, or its equivalent, *P is included in Q*, is symbolized by

$$P \subset Q.$$

The sentence $Q \supset P$ is defined to mean the same thing.

It should be noted clearly that set *inclusion*, or *being* a *subset*, is different from set *membership*.* In the example just given, no subset *belongs* to the given set. Thus {4, 5} ∈ *A* is false, but {4, 5} ⊂ *A* is true. Also {6} ∈ *A* is false, while {6} ⊂ *A* is true. Thus 6 and {6} are different. The first is a number (the number 6), while the second is *the set containing just the number 6*.

Every set is considered to be a subset of itself. Any subset which is not also the entire set is called a *proper* subset. The empty set is a subset of every set.

---

* Set membership corresponds to the first use of the verb *is* (p. 79), while inclusion corresponds to the second use of *is*.

Set inclusion can be indicated diagrammatically as in Fig. 4–14. Here two sets *A* and *B* are shown (along with a universal set) for which $A \subset B$. That is, *A* is a subset of *B*. Note the difference between this and Fig. 4–9, showing set membership.

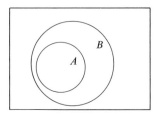

FIGURE 4–14

Equality for sets. If '*A*' and '*B*' represent sets, the sentence $A = B$ asserts that '*A*' and '*B*' are symbols representing the same set. Thus equality for sets is not different from equality for numbers. It is the *is of identity*.

Equality for sets may be stated in a different, but equivalent, fashion. It may be said that $A = B$ if and only if $A \subset B$ and $B \subset A$. To see that these are indeed equivalent, note that if *A* and *B* are the same set, then of course $A \subset B$ and $B \subset A$. Conversely, if $A \subset B$ and $B \subset A$, then every member of *A* must be a member of *B*; also every member of *B* is a member of *A*. Therefore *A* and *B* are the same set.

Cardinal numbers of sets. The cardinal number of a set is, roughly speaking, the number of elements belonging to it. Thus the cardinal number of the empty set is zero, and the cardinal number of the set of all natural numbers less than 7 is six. The cardinal number of the set of all even numbers is not a whole number, but is a kind of number not yet discussed here, known as an *infinite cardinal* number. For present purposes it will suffice to mention that two sets are defined to have the same cardinal number (finite or infinite) if and only if there is a one-to-one correspondence between the sets. The set of odd natural numbers and the set of even natural numbers have the same cardinal number, because there is a one-to-one correspondence between them. It can be exhibited as follows:

$$
\begin{array}{cccccccc}
1 & 3 & 5 & 7 & 9 & 11 & 13 & 15\dots \\
\updownarrow & \updownarrow & \updownarrow & \updownarrow & \updownarrow & \updownarrow & \updownarrow & \updownarrow \\
2 & 4 & 6 & 8 & 10 & 12 & 14 & 16\dots
\end{array}
$$

In this matching, or correspondence, each odd number corresponds to one and only one even number, and every even number corresponds to one and only one odd number. Thus the correspondence is one-to-one. It is also possible to find other one-to-one correspondences between these sets. Correspondences which are not one-to-one also exist. For example, the following is a many-to-one correspondence:

$$
\begin{array}{cccc}
1, 3, & 5, 7, & 9, 11, & 13, 15\dots \\
\downdownarrows & \downdownarrows & \downdownarrows & \downdownarrows \\
2 & 4 & 6 & 8 \quad \dots
\end{array}
$$

In this correspondence, each odd number corresponds to one and only one even number, but some even numbers correspond to more than one odd number. Thus the correspondence is many-to-one. Nevertheless *at least one* one-to-one correspondence exists between the sets, and hence they have the same cardinal number.

A definition of number. In Chapter 2 it was established that numbers are not numerals. They are not symbols, but *concepts* represented by symbols. This important distinction has been maintained, and will continue to be maintained, throughout this book. No definition of *number*, however, has been given. It is quite possible to treat the number concept as undefined. All of the manipulations and basic understandings necessary to them are possible without giving a definition of number. It is of interest, however, to discuss one formulation of a definition, essentially as it was given by Bertrand Russell.* For this definition the concept of a set and the concept of one-to-one correspondence are the essential notions.

A possible motivation for making this definition is provided by an analysis of how one learns to count. The child learns to recognize a set of 3 blocks, a set of 3 fingers, and a set of 3 spoons. At first these instances are separate concepts, but with maturation and practice, the child learns to place, mentally, any other set of 3 objects in a one-to-one correspondence with one of the known sets. This may be done by means of a counting process, but that is not essential. The essential thing is the establishing of a one-to-one correspondence. Thus the child eventually learns the abstract concept of *three* by learning to recognize any set for which there is a one-to-one correspondence with a given set known to have "3 members." If one could collect all the sets which are in one-to-one correspondence with a given set of "3 members," it would then seem that this collection would completely describe the concept of *three*. That collection is then defined to *be* the cardinal number 3.

Russell's definition of the cardinal number of a set is as follows:

The cardinal number of a set is the class of all sets which are in one-to-one correspondence with it.

Although this definition at first seems a bit strange, and although it is not necessary for a development of arithmetic, it does appear, upon reflection, to be philosophically satisfactory. It has the property of making precise and definite a rather vague notion, or abstract concept. In parallel with it one could define the abstract concept of *red* to be the set of all objects which have the property of "redness."

EXERCISES

1. If a universal set U is the set $\{0, 1, 2, 5, 7, 10\}$ and sets A, B, and C are defined as follows: $A = \{1, 2, 5, 10\}$, $B = \{0, 1, 7, 10\}$, $C = \{0, 1, 2, 5\}$, find the following.

(a) $A \cap B$ (b) $A \cap C$ (c) $B \cap C$ (d) $A \cap B \cap C$
(e) $A \cup B$ (f) $A \cup C$ (g) $B \cup C$ (h) $A \cup B \cup C$
(i) $A \cap (B \cup C)$ (j) $(C \cap A) \cup B$ (k) $(C \cap B) \cup B$ (l) $\overline{A}$
(m) $\overline{B}$ (n) $\overline{C}$ (o) $\overline{A \cap B}$ (p) $\overline{B \cup C}$
(q) $\overline{A \cap B \cap C}$ (r) $\overline{A \cap (B \cup C)}$

---

* See: Russell, B., *Introduction to Mathematical Philosophy*, 2nd ed., New York, The Macmillan Co., 1924.

2. Find all the subsets of each of the following.

(a) $\{p, q\}$ (b) $\{1, 2, 3\}$ (c) $\{1, 3, 9, 5\}$

3. Make a conjecture about the total number of subsets of a set with n members. Test your conjecture and see how thoroughly you can substantiate it.

4. Find a one-to-one correspondence between the set of even numbers and the set of odd numbers, which is different from that given in the text above.

5. Find a one-to-many relation between the set of even numbers and the set of odd numbers.

6. Find a one-to-one correspondence between the set of even numbers and the set of natural numbers.

7. Find a many-to-one correspondence between the set of even numbers and the set of natural numbers.

8. Draw a set diagram to represent each of the parts of exercise 1, beginning with a blank diagram (Fig. 4–15) for each part.

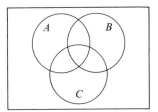

FIGURE 4–15

9. Using the set of whole numbers for a universal set, and given that

$$A = \{x | x < 150\},$$
$$B = \{y | y > 75\},$$

find the following.

(a) $A \cap B$ (b) $A \cup B$ (c) $\overline{A}$ (d) $\overline{B}$
(e) $\overline{A} \cap B$ (f) $\overline{A \cap B}$

10. Graph each of the sets of exercise 9 on a number line.

6. RELATIONS

The most fundamental concept in mathematics is that of a *set*. Sets are useful when considering properties of objects. To say that "a shirt is red," for example, is to say that the shirt belongs to the set of red objects. When comparing objects, the concept of a *relation* becomes important. To say that one shirt is larger than another is to speak in terms of a relation "is larger than" among objects of one set. Similarly, to say that one man is a brother of another is to speak in terms of a relation "is a brother of."

The relation concept is second in fundamental importance only to that of set. There are few situations, in mathematics or otherwise, in which the concept of a relation is not involved. Moreover, there are few ideas in mathematics, if any, which cannot be expressed in terms of relations or sets.

Relations may be denoted by upper-case letters, such as R. If two objects x and y are in the relation R with each other, this will be denoted by the sentence xRy.* If the letter R represents the relation "is older than," then the sentence xRy says that "x is older than y." If R is the relation "belongs to the same club as," then xRy says that x belongs to the same club as y." The negation of xRy is $x\not Ry$. Any relation must be considered with respect to some set. At times it is clear to what set a relation refers, in which case the set need not be specified. Otherwise, it is essential that the set be indicated.

Relations arising from comparisons of two objects are known as *binary* relations. All of the relations discussed above are binary. Certain relations involve three objects, rather than two. Such relations are called *ternary* relations. The relation "is between" is an example of a ternary relation. Relations of still higher orders may be considered, but attention here will be focused on binary relations.

It may happen that although a relation R involves some members of a set, it does not involve all of them. That is, there may be a member x of the set, for which there is no y such that either xRy or yRx. Then x is said not to be *involved* in the relation R.

There are many kinds of relations, and some of them occur often enough in mathematics that they deserve the special distinction of being named. Only a few important types will be considered here.

Reflexive relations. In many relations every element involved is in relation with itself. That is, if x is involved in the relation R, then xRx. Any such relation is said to be *reflexive*. Examples of reflexive relations are "is in the same family as" (every person who is in a family is in the same family as himself); "is congruent to" (every figure is congruent to itself).

Symmetric relations. A second important class of relations is that in which the elements x and y can be interchanged. A relation R is of this type if whenever xRy, it follows that yRx. Any such relation is said to be *symmetric*. Examples of symmetric relations are "is equal to" (if $x = y$, then $y = x$); "belongs to the same club as" (if x belongs to the same club as y, then y belongs to the same club as x).

Antisymmetric relations. An antisymmetric relation R is any relation for which the elements x and y, where x and y are different elements, cannot be interchanged. That is, a relation R is of this type if whenever xRy and $x \neq y$, it is not true that yRx. Examples of antisymmetric relations are "is less than" (if $x < y$, then $y \not< x$); "is less than or equal to" (if $x \leq y$ and $y \neq x$, then $y \not\leq x$); "is the father of" (if x is the father of y, then y is not the father of x).

Transitive relations. A relation R is called *transitive* if and only if it has the following property: For any x, y, and z in the set, if xRy and yRz, then xRz. Examples of transitive relations are "is greater than" (if for three numbers x, y, z, $x > y$ and $y > z$, then $x > z$); "has the same birthday as" (if x has the same birthday as y and y has the same birthday as z, then x has the same birthday as z).

---

* Sometimes this is denoted by 'Rxy.'

EXERCISES

1. Which of the following relations are reflexive? If necessary specify a set to which the relation refers.

(a) Votes the same way as
(b) Is parallel to
(c) $<$
(d) Is different from
(e) Is a divisor of
(f) Intersects
(g) Is perpendicular to
(h) Is a brother of
(i) $\cong$
(j) Is twice as large as
(k) Is a multiple of
(l) $\leq$
(m) Is similar to (geometric similarity)
(n) $=$
(o) Is on the same line as
(p) Is disjoint with (for sets)

2. Which of the relations mentioned in exercise 1 are symmetric?

3. Which of the relations mentioned in exercise 1 are antisymmetric?

4. Which of the relations mentioned in exercise 1 are transitive?

5. Which of the relations mentioned in exercise 1 are reflexive, symmetric, and transitive?

Equivalence relations.   Some relations are reflexive, symmetric, and transitive. Among these are equality, congruence, and similarity.   Such relations form an important class known as *equivalence relations*.

Since by definition any equivalence relation R is reflexive, symmetric, and transitive, it has properties similar to the equality relation, and behaves in a similar manner. That is,

(a) xRx, for all x involved.

Compare with: $x = x$ for all x (for the equality relation all x are involved).

(b) If xRy, then yRx.

Compare with: If $x = y$, then $y = x$.

(c) If xRy and yRz, then xRz.

Compare with: If $x = y$ and $y = z$, then $x = z$.

The properties indicated in (a) and (b) above, for equality, are generally taken for granted, since they are so obvious. The property indicated in (c) is not quite so obvious. It is, in effect, together with symmetry, Euclid's common notion "things equal to the same thing are equal to each other."

Still another important property of equality which is shared by other equivalence relations is that of *substitution*.   This follows from the fact that any equivalence relation on a set *partitions* that set. By a partitioning of a set S is meant a separation of S into disjoint subsets whose union is the set S itself, as shown in Fig. 4–16.

Given an equivalence relation R on a set S, a partitioning can be constructed as follows. Select any member x of set S. Find all elements y in S for which xRy. The set of all such y constitutes one subset, or *cell*, S_i, of the partitioning. Select any member x_1 of S, not in the first cell. Then find all elements y in S for which x_1Ry. The set of all such y constitutes another cell, S_j. Continue this process until all members of S have been placed in some cell.

The substitution property can now be explained as follows. All the members of any cell are "equivalent," with respect to the relation R, which produced the parti-

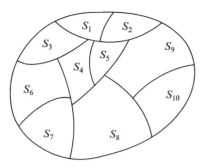

Fig. 4–16. A partitioning of a set.

tioning. In effect, they are indistinguishable in any context related only to the relation R. Therefore, any member of a cell, or *equivalence class*, may be used to represent the entire class in any appropriate context, and any member of a class may be replaced by any member of the same class in such contexts.

A geometric example may be of interest. The relation of similarity, $\sim$, is reflexive, symmetric, and transitive, and is hence an equivalence relation. It follows that this relation partitions the set of all geometric figures. One of the cells of the partitioning will contain a triangle whose sides have length 3, 4, and 5, respectively. That cell also contains every triangle similar to the given triangle. Within the context of similarity (where no mention is made of congruence, area, etc.), any triangle from the equivalence class will serve to represent the entire class. In fact, it is not uncommon to speak of "*the* 3-4-5 triangle" when considering properties of that entire class of triangles.

It remains to be shown that an equivalence relation on a set partitions that set. Consider Fig. 4–16 and the accompanying explanation of how the cells are obtained. It will be sufficient to show or verify that (a) any two cells are disjoint, and (b) that the union of all the cells is the set S. Part (b) is immediate, for the cells are constructed in such a way that each element of S belongs to some cell. Hence every element of S belongs to the union of all the cells, and the union of all the cells is S.

To prove part (a), consider any two distinct cells. The fact that the cells are distinct (different) means that there is at least one element m in one cell that is not in the other. The cells may conveniently be called S_m and S_n, the former containing m and the latter containing an element n. Thus $m\not\!Rn$. Now suppose that S_m and S_n were not disjoint, which means that their intersection would contain at least one element p. In that case, mRp, and also nRp. By symmetry it would follow that pRn, and by transitivity that mRn. But this contradicts the assumption that Sm and Sn are different (or $m\not\!Rn$). Thus it is not possible for two different cells to have a nonempty intersection. In other words, any two cells of the partitioning are disjoint.

EXERCISES

1. Which of the following relations, defined on the set of members of a mathematics class, are equivalence relations?

(a) has a birthday in the same month as   (b) has a higher grade average than
(c) sits in front of   (d) sits in the same row as
(e) is taller than   (f) was born in the same year as
(g) is older than   (h) will graduate in the same year as

2. For each equivalence relation of exercise 1 that applies to your mathematics class, construct a partitioning of the class by listing or describing all of the cells.

3. Consider the set of all polygons with six or fewer sides, and an equivalence relation, *has the same number of sides as*. Construct a partitioning of the set by listing or describing all of the cells.

4. On the set {2, 4, 6, 8} consider the equivalence relation of equality. Using this relation, construct a partitioning, listing all of the cells. What is peculiar about the partitioning produced by this relation?

5. How does the geometric relation of congruence, $\cong$, partition the set of all geometric figures. Compare this partitioning with that of the equality relation.

Order relations. Certain relations on a set allow the elements of that set to be arranged in order. For example, when a child arranges a set of sticks in order, from longest to shortest, he has an intuitive grasp of the relation "is longer than." A family lining up in "stairsteps" for a portrait does so according to the relation "is taller than." Any relation which orders a set will be called an *order* relation. It remains to see what properties characterize such a relation.

From the example of arranging sticks according to length, one sees that there are at least three properties which a relation R must have if it is to order a set. Namely:
(i) R must be *antisymmetric*. (Given two different sticks *only* one of them must be longer.)
(ii) R must be *transitive*. (If R were not transitive, then it could happen that a stick x is longer than y, and y is longer than z, but x is shorter than z. In such a situation one would not know how to arrange the three sticks x, y, and z.)
(iii) R must be *complete*, i.e., for any distinct elements x, y of set S, xRy or yRx. (Given two different sticks, one of them must be longer than the other. Otherwise they could not be given relative positions in the order.)

Conversely, if a relation R has the three properties just mentioned, then it orders a set in the sense that the members of a set could be listed in order by means of the relation R.

Thus any relation which is antisymmetric, transitive, and complete is called an *order relation*.

EXERCISES

1. Order the set of segments in Fig. 4–17 according to each of the following relations. Indicate the order by listing the numbers of the segments. (a) Use the relation "is longer than." (b) Use the relation "is shorter than." (c) Use the relation "has a larger number than." (d) Use the relation "is pictured to the right of."

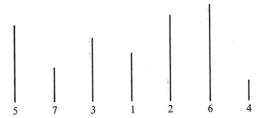

FIGURE 4–17   5   7   3   1   2   6   4

2. Consider the set of denominations of U.S. coins whose value is less than $1.00. (a) Order this set according to value. (b) Order this set according to diameter.

3. Show that the relation $>$ for whole numbers is an order relation.

4. Which of the following relations are order relations? Specify a set if necessary.

(a) Is greater than   (b) Is hotter than
(c) Is worse than   (d) Is greener than
(e) Is a divisor of   (f) Is twice as large as
(g) Is faster than   (h) Is a brother of

7. COMPOUND SENTENCES AND CORRESPONDING SETS

There is a striking parallel between sets and sentences. A simple open sentence, such as $x < 5$, referring to some number system, is very naturally associated with its solution set. Likewise, compound sentences formed by joining two or more sentences are naturally associated with their solution sets. Such compound sentences are used a great deal in mathematical discourse, and a study of them thus recommends itself.

Conjunctions. One of the simplest ways to form a compound sentence from two sentences is to join them by the word *and*. For example, if the sentence *The moon is full* is thus joined to *Five is a prime number*, the sentence

The moon is full and five is a prime number

is obtained. Any compound sentence of this type is called a *conjunction* of the two sentences.

Letters are often used as variables to represent sentences. Using such sentential variables, one may describe a conjunction of two sentences as being any sentence of the type

A and B.

To further simplify notation, the symbol $\land$ is often used in place of the word *and*. With this notation, a conjunction may be represented as

$A \land B.$

A conjunction $A \land B$ is considered true when both A and B are true. It is considered false if either or both of A and B are false, as shown in the following truth table.

A	B	$A \land B$
T	T	T
T	F	F
F	T	F
F	F	F

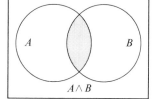

FIGURE 4–18

This is in accord with the ordinary English usage of the word *and*. The solution set of $A \wedge B$ is now easily seen to be the *intersection* of the solution set of A and the solution set of B. The sentential connective $\wedge$ therefore corresponds to set intersection $\cap$, as illustrated in Fig. 4–18. Pictured are the solution sets of A and B. The intersection of these sets is the solution set of $A \wedge B$.

Disjunctions. Another simple way to form a compound sentence from two sentences is to join them by the word *or*. The resulting sentence is called the *disjunction* of the two sentences. The symbol $\vee$ is often used in place of the word *or*. Thus a disjunction of sentences A and B may be represented as

$$A \vee B.$$

It is not as easy to decide when to call a disjunction true as it was for conjunctions, because the word *or* is used in two different ways in ordinary English. Consider these examples.

Do you expect to get an A in English or mathematics?

Shall we hang this picture on the north wall or the south wall?

The first question could be sensibly answered, in ordinary language, by the word *yes*. This would mean that the answerer expected to get an A in English, in mathematics, or both. On the other hand, since a picture cannot be hung on two walls at once, a *yes* answer to the second question would not be appropriate. Thus in English the word *or* is sometimes used in the exclusive sense, meaning one or the other, but not both; sometimes it is used in the inclusive sense, meaning one or the other, or both. Knowledge of the situation and inflections of voice usually make clear which meaning is intended. However, in legal contexts, where precise meaning is more important, it is common practice to use *and/or* for the inclusive *or*. In Latin there are different words, *vel* and *aout*, for the inclusive and exclusive *or*, respectively. The mathematical use of *or* is the inclusive one, meaning one or the other, or both, as shown in the accompanying truth table.

A	B	$A \vee B$
T	T	T
T	F	T
F	T	T
F	F	F

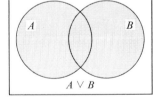

FIGURE 4–19

It is this use of the word that will be adopted here and throughout the book.

A disjunction $A \vee B$ is true if A is true, if B is true, and also when both A and B are true. It is false when A and B are both false. The sentential connective $\vee$ thus corresponds to set union, as illustrated in Fig. 4–19. Pictured are the solution sets of A and B. The union of these sets is the solution set of $A \vee B$.

Negations. A negation, or denial, of a sentence is again a sentence. For example, a negation of *roses are red* is the sentence *roses are not red*. A negation of *roses are* *not red* is *roses are red.* Negations may be stated in various ways. The following are also negations of *roses are red.*

It is false that roses are red.

It is not true that roses are red.

It is not profitable to consider the different possible ways of expressing negation as being essentially different, and therefore one may refer to *the* negation of a sentence. A bar over a sentence or over a sentential variable will indicate negation, as follows:

$$\overline{A}, \quad \overline{A \wedge B}, \quad \overline{A \vee B}.$$

In accordance with ordinary usage, the negation of a true sentence will be considered false, and the negation of a false sentence will be considered true, as the following truth table indicates.

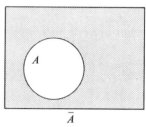

A	$\overline{A}$
T	F
F	T

$\overline{A}$

FIGURE 4–20

Negation thus corresponds to set complementation, as illustrated in Fig. 4–20. Pictured is the solution set of a sentence A. The complement of that set is the solution set of $\overline{A}$.

EXERCISES

1. In each of the following, construct the conjunction and the disjunction of the set of simple sentences. Decide, if you can, the truth value of each.

(a) July has 30 days.
    Christmas is December 25th.

(b) $2 + 5 = 4 + 3$.
    $9 - 5 = 2 \cdot 3$.

(c) The moon is larger than the earth.
    Rabbits multiply rapidly.

(d) Parallel lines do not intersect.
    Pastry is fattening.

(e) The first prime number is 4.
    8 is not a multiple of 2.

(f) $4 + 5 < 17$.
    $35 + 3 \neq 30 + 8$.
    $31 + 19 \geq 4 \cdot 6$

(g) $3 \cdot 5 = 14 + 1$.
    Most fire engines are red.
    The smallest prime number is 2.

(h) All eagles are reptiles.
    The United States of America
    is a dictatorship.
    $175 \nless 230$.

(i) $X + 2 < 14 \cdot 5$.
    $13 - 5Y = 45$.

(j) $2p = p$. $10q = q$.

2. Make a truth table for the conjunction $A \wedge B \wedge C$. [*Note:* There are 8 possible combinations of truth values of A, B, and C.]

3. Make a truth table for the disjunction $A \vee B \vee C$.

4. Write the negation of each of the following.

(a) The smallest prime number is 2.

(b) $a + b = 4$.

(c) $5 - 2 = 10$.

(d) $45 \cdot 2 \neq 30$.

(e) $3 + 7 \neq 10$.

(f) $17 < 35$.

(g) $173 \geq 315$.

(h) Mathematics is exact.

*(i) Some people are lazy.

*(j) All horses are animals.

Conditional sentences. A sentence such as *If A then B* is called a *conditional sentence*, or simply a *conditional*. Conditional sentences, it can be recognized, are extremely important in proofs. They may be symbolized as follows:

$$A \rightarrow B,$$

where '*A*' and '*B*' of course represent sentences. It should be understood that either or both may be compound sentences. The sentence *A* is called the *antecedent* of the conditional sentence, and *B* is called its *consequent*. The sentence $A \rightarrow B$ may be read "If *A* then *B*," or "*A* implies *B*."

In proofs it usually seems important that there be some connection between the antecedent and consequent of a conditional. However, it is often difficult to decide whether or not there is such a connection. For example, consider the following:

If Moscow has a cold winter, then the price of eggs in Indiana will be higher the following year.

At first glance it may seem that there is no connection between the antecedent, *Moscow has a cold winter*, and the consequent, *the price of eggs in Indiana will be higher the following year*. It would not be easy, however, to prove beyond any doubt that Moscow's weather conditions had nothing to do with those in the United States in such a way that they affected the productivity of poultry. A similar situation applies in mathematics. It is often impossible to tell whether or not there is any connection between antecedent and consequent of a conditional. Therefore, the consideration of conditionals is much better left on the same basis as that of conjunctions and disjunctions, that is, to agree how the truth values of $A \rightarrow B$ will be decided when those of *A* and *B* are known, even if they do not seem related. A sentence *A implies B* does not mean that *A* is the cause of *B*. Neither does it mean that it is easy to deduce *B* from *A*.

In ordinary language conditionals may take many forms. It is essential to be able to recognize them and to identify antecedent and consequent. The following exercises provide some practice. Although most of them should not prove difficult, it is advisable first to consider a word which may cause some trouble. The word is *only*. Its use in ordinary language is ambiguous, as the following sentences illustrate.

John takes pictures only when the sun is shining.
I get paid only when I have worked.

Experience makes one read into the second sentence an idea which it does not express, whereas the similar mistake is not likely in the first case. The first sentence is a conditional expressing the same idea as *If John takes pictures, then the sun is shining*. It does not convey the notion of *If the sun is shining, then John takes pictures*. Such behavior would be eccentric, to say the least. The second sentence is likewise a conditional, expressing the same idea as *If I get paid, then I have worked*. Experience tempts one to believe that this sentence also expresses the idea of *If I have worked, then I get paid*, when actually it does not. The word *only* almost always precedes, and thereby identifies, the consequent of a conditional, while the word *if* alone almost always identifies the antecedent.

EXERCISES

For each of the following, write a sentence of the *If then* type expressing the same idea as the given sentence. Identify the antecedent and the consequent of each.

1. This hat will be ruined if it rains.   2. Drivers who speed are fools.
3. School will be dismissed in case of snow.
4. $2x = 2y$ because $x = y$.
5. There is no factorization of n whenever n is a prime.
6. Triangles are not squares.   7. Triangles are polygons.
8. We must have money in order to survive.
9. Two lines intersect only if they are not parallel.
10. A natural number which is not odd is even.
11. A polygon has no diagonals only if it is a triangle.
12. Look before you leap.   13. He who hesitates is lost.
14. Birds of a feather flock together.   *15. Jack is a liar or I'm Humpty Dumpty.

In order to decide when to call a conditional true and when to call it false, it is advisable to study the use of the word *if* in ordinary language. Like *or* and *only* it is used in ambiguous fashion, and therefore some of its ordinary usages will have to be discarded in logical, or precise, discourse. An example of an *If then* sentence considered for truth and falsity may help.

If I get the bonus I shall take the family on vacation.

Suppose a neighbor makes this assertion. Under what circumstances would he be considered truthful, and in what cases would he be said to have lied? This consideration must, of course, be based on truth and falsity of antecedent and consequent of the sentence. There are four cases to consider.

(1) antecedent true: He gets the bonus.
     consequent true: He takes the family on vacation.

(2) antecedent true: He gets the bonus.
     consequent false: He does not take the family on vacation.

(3) antecedent false: He does not get the bonus.
     consequent true: He takes the family on vacation.

(4) antecedent false: He does not get the bonus.
     consequent false: He does not take the family on vacation.

In case (1) it is easy to agree that the neighbor kept his word, i.e., his assertion was true. In case (2) it is likewise easy to agree; this time that he lied, and his assertion was false. In case (3) where he does not get the bonus, but somehow decides to take the family on vacation anyway, it would be difficult to call him a liar. He did not actually say that if he did not get the bonus, then he would not take the family. Therefore, the assertion would be considered true. In case (4) it would likewise be difficult to make the point that the neighbor is a liar. He did not take the family on a trip, but then he did not get his bonus either. On the basis of this example, one would be led to decide that a conditional with false antecedent is true, regardless of the truth or falsity of the consequent.

It may seem a bit strange to call a conditional true whenever the antecedent is false. One tendency is to feel that a conditional with false antecedent is neither true nor false, i.e., that it does not apply. Closer inspection shows, however, that such a view is not tenable. In fact such sentences are not infrequently used to emphasize a point. For example,

> If you can sell the boss on this idea, then I'll eat my hat.

This sentence is actually intended to assert the impossibility of selling the boss. How does it do so? The consequent is clearly false, for no sane person eats hats. Therefore, for the conditional to be true, the antecedent must be false, that is, it is not possible to sell the boss.

In logic it is essential that every statement be either true or false. There can be none which are neither true nor false. This is another reason why conditionals with false antecedent cannot be ignored. The criteria for judging truth and falsity of conditionals is based on considerations such as those of the foregoing examples, as well as their use in mathematics, and is given in the following truth table.

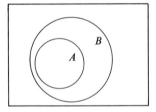

A	B	$A \rightarrow B$
T	T	T
T	F	F
F	T	T
F	F	T

FIGURE 4–21

The reader who still feels that this manner of considering conditionals is strange may be comforted by the fact that some of the best mathematical and philosophical minds of this century struggled for years with the problem. Today it is well established that the above truth table gives a definition which agrees with the way conditionals are actually used in mathematics and other precise discourse.

Whenever a conditional sentence $A \rightarrow B$ is true, the solution set of A must be a subset of the solution set of B. Figure 4–21 shows this relationship for a true conditional $A \rightarrow B$.

There are several ways of reading the conditional $A \rightarrow B$, some of which have already been mentioned. Two additional ones are in frequent use, and are included in the following list.

A is sufficient for B,   or A is a sufficient condition for B.

B is necessary for A,   or B is a necessary condition for A.

If A then B,   or A only if B.

The first of these verbalizations can be justified easily by noting that whenever a conditional is true and its antecedent is true, the consequent must also be true. In this sense, the truth of A guarantees the truth of B, or is *sufficient* for B, whenever A implies B. Similarly, whenever $A \rightarrow B$ is true, A is not true *unless* B is true. In this sense B is necessary for A whenever $A \rightarrow B$.

EXERCISES

Which of the following are true and which are false?

1. If $2 + 2 = 4$, then $5 = 5$.
2. If $3 \cdot 5 = 15$, then $8 - 4 = 12$.
3. If $17 - 5 = 3$, then $4 \cdot (5 + 3) = 32$.
4. If $1 = 2$, then 6 is a prime number.
5. If triangles are squares, then monkeys are birds.
6. If triangles are polygons, then $1 = 2$.
7. If wishes are horses, then the moon is made of cheese.
8. If Jefferson was the first president of the U.S., then John Adams was Socrates.
9. If $3 \cdot 5$ is a natural number, then 17 is prime.
10. If a mathematical system is a group, then it has an associative operation.
11. If a mathematical system is a field, then it has two commutative operations.
12. If a mathematical system is a ring, then each of its elements has an additive inverse.
*13. If $x = 2$, then $3x = 6$.

Converses. If the antecedent and consequent of a conditional sentence are interchanged, another conditional sentence, called the *converse* of the first, is formed. The converse of the conditional $A \rightarrow B$ is thus $B \rightarrow A$. It is important to recognize and remember that a conditional sentence may be true while its converse is false. For example, consider the sentence

If an animal is a dog, then it has four legs.

The sentence is true, but its converse,

If an animal has four legs, then it is a dog,

is false. A look at Fig. 4–21 also shows that the converse of a true conditional, $A \rightarrow B$, may be false. In order for the converse, $B \rightarrow A$, to be true, the solution set of B would have to be a subset of the solution set of A. This would mean that the solution sets are the same, since the solution set of A is already a subset of the solution set of B.

EXERCISES

Write the converse of each sentence of exercises 1 through 13, above.

Equivalent sentences. A conditional may be true while its converse is false. It may also happen that a conditional and its converse are both true. Whenever a conditional $A \rightarrow B$ and its converse $B \rightarrow A$ are both true, the sentences A and B are said to be *equivalent*. Knowing that sentences are equivalent is often of primary importance in mathematics and other logical discourse. Equivalence of sentences may be symbolized

$$(A \rightarrow B) \wedge (B \rightarrow A)$$

or more simply

$$A \leftrightarrow B.$$

If two sentences A and B are equivalent, this means that $A \rightarrow B$ and also $B \rightarrow A$. Since $A \rightarrow B$, the solution set of A must be a subset of the solution set of B, as shown in Fig. 4–19. Since $B \rightarrow A$, the solution set of B must be a subset of the solution set of A. The solution set of A must therefore be the same as the solution set of B. In other words, if sentences are equivalent, then they must have the same solution set. Conversely, if they have the same solution set, then they are equivalent, for if A and B have the same solution set, each is a subset of the other, and therefore $A \rightarrow B$ and $B \rightarrow A$ are both true. In elementary algebra, *equivalent equations* are sometimes defined to be equations with the same solution set. Equivalent equations are special kinds of equivalent sentences. Two equations (or other sentences) can be proved equivalent by showing that each implies the other. The following are examples of pairs of sentences which are equivalent:

$$x = 2, \qquad 2x = 4,$$

n is an even natural number,
n is a natural number with a factor of 2.

Any replacement which makes one sentence of a pair true also makes the other sentence true, and any replacement which makes one sentence false also makes the other false. This is clear from the fact that equivalent sentences have the same solution set.

Equivalence may be asserted verbally in a variety of ways, as follows.

A is equivalent to B.
A implies B, and conversely.
If A then B, and conversely.
A is a necessary and sufficient condition for B.
B is a necessary and sufficient condition for A.
A if and only if B (abbreviated A iff B).
B if and only if A.

All of these verbalisms are found in mathematical literature, and all of them convey the idea that $A \leftrightarrow B$.

Contrapositives. If the antecedent and consequent of a conditional sentence are negated and then interchanged, another conditional sentence, called the *contrapositive* of the first, is formed. The contrapositive of the conditional $A \rightarrow B$ is thus $\overline{B} \rightarrow \overline{A}$.

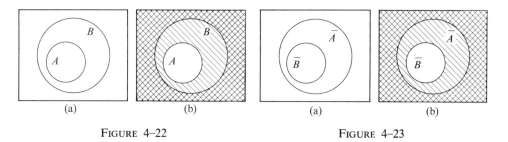

FIGURE 4–22   FIGURE 4–23

There is an important relationship between a conditional sentence and its contrapositive. If $A \rightarrow B$ is true, then its contrapositive $\overline{B} \rightarrow \overline{A}$ is also true. This is shown in Fig. 4–22. In part (a), the solution sets of A and B are related so that $A \rightarrow B$ is true. Part (b) shows the complements of these solution sets, and the fact that the solution set of $\overline{B}$ is a subset of the solution set of $\overline{A}$. Thus $\overline{B} \rightarrow \overline{A}$ is true whenever $A \rightarrow B$ is true.

It has been shown that $(A \rightarrow B) \rightarrow (\overline{B} \rightarrow \overline{A})$. It may be shown similarly that $(\overline{B} \rightarrow \overline{A}) \rightarrow (A \rightarrow B)$, as in Fig. 4–23. The sentences $A \rightarrow B$ and $\overline{B} \rightarrow \overline{A}$ imply each other, and are therefore equivalent. The important thing to remember, and to use in proofs, is that any conditional sentence is equivalent to its contrapositive. Thus either may be used in place of the other.

EXERCISES

Write the contrapositive of each sentence of exercises 1 through 13, p. 99.

8. NEGATIONS OF COMPOUND SENTENCES

It is easy to write a symbolic representation of the negation of any sentence by placing a bar over the symbolic representation of the sentence. For example, the negation of $A \wedge B \rightarrow (C \rightarrow D \vee A)$ is $\overline{A \wedge B \rightarrow (C \rightarrow D \vee A)}$. However, it is often desirable or convenient to find an equivalent sentence in which only individual sentential variables have the negation bar over them. The task is not difficult, even for quite complicated sentences, and one can proceed mechanically after a few basic principles are established.

The negation of any conjunction is equivalent to a certain disjunction, as proved in the following table.

A	B	$A \wedge B$	$\overline{A \wedge B}$	$\overline{A}$	$\overline{B}$	$\overline{A} \vee \overline{B}$
T	T	T	F	F	F	F
T	F	F	T	F	T	T
F	T	F	T	T	F	T
F	F	F	T	T	T	T

Note that the entries under $\overline{A \wedge B}$ and $\overline{A} \vee \overline{B}$ are identical, showing that the two sentences have identical truth values. Hence they have the same solution set. Thus the following theorem is proved:

$$\overline{A \land B} \leftrightarrow \overline{A} \lor \overline{B}.$$

This result provides a rule for negating conjunctions: Change the conjunction symbol to a disjunction symbol and also negate each of the individual sentences. The same rule applies for conjunctions having more than two parts. For example, $\overline{A} \lor \overline{B} \lor \overline{C}$ is a negation of $A \land B \land C$.

In a similar fashion it may be established that the negation of a disjunction is equivalent to a conjunction. For example, a negation of $A \lor B \lor C$ is $\overline{A} \land \overline{B} \land \overline{C}$. A proof is left to the reader.

The negation of the negation of a sentence is equivalent to the original sentence. That is, for any sentence, $A, \overline{\overline{A}} \leftrightarrow A$. Using this fact and the two rules just established, allows one to simplify rather complicated sentences, as in the following.

EXAMPLE. Simplify, by finding an equivalent sentence with negation bars only over individual sentential variables:

$$\overline{\overline{A \land B} \lor (C \land \overline{D}) \lor (\overline{C} \lor A)}.$$

The given sentence is the negation of a disjunction with three parts, and is hence equivalent to

$$\overline{\overline{A \land B}} \land \overline{C \land \overline{D}} \land \overline{\overline{C} \lor A}.$$

The first of the resulting parts is a double negation, and hence is equivalent to $A \land B$. The second is the negation of a conjunction, and hence equivalent to $\overline{C} \lor \overline{\overline{D}}$, and in turn to $\overline{C} \lor D$. Similarly, the third part is equivalent to $C \land \overline{A}$. Thus the given sentence simplifies to the following equivalent one:

$$(A \land B) \land (\overline{C} \lor D) \land (C \land \overline{A}).$$

The negation of a conditional may be thought to be again a conditional. The reader will do well to banish forever any such idea, for the negation of a conditional is *never* a conditional! It is in fact equivalent to a conjunction. The following truth table shows that the negation of $A \to B$ is equivalent to $A \land \overline{B}$.

A	B	$A \to B$	$\overline{A \to B}$	$\overline{B}$	$A \land \overline{B}$
T	T	T	F	F	F
T	F	F	T	T	T
F	T	T	F	T	F
F	F	T	F	F	F

Since the truth values for $\overline{A \to B}$ and $A \land \overline{B}$ are identical, these sentences have the same solution set and are therefore equivalent. A simple rule may thus be given for negating a condition sentence: Change the $\to$ to $\land$ and negate the consequent. That this is intuitively acceptable may be illustrated as follows. Bob says, "If Jim beats me at tennis, then I'll eat my hat," $(A \rightarrow B)$. Jim beats Bob at tennis, and asserts that Bob lied, $(\overline{A \rightarrow B})$. What he means is that Jim beat Bob at tennis *and* that Bob did not eat the hat, $(A \wedge \overline{B})$.

EXERCISES

1. Negate each of the conjunctions written for exercise 1 (a) through (f), p. 95.
2. Negate each of the disjunctions written for exercise 1 (a) through (f), p. 95.
3. Negate each of the conditional sentences of exercises 1 through 5, p. 99.

9. DEFINITIONS

In effect, most mathematical definitions are statements of intent to use a certain word or expression in a particular way. For example, in order to shorten writing or speaking, the word *triangle* is used to mean the same thing as *a polygon of three sides*. The definition may be stated by using the *is* of identity, as follows.

A *triangle* is *a polygon of three sides.*

Or, since any sentence with this verb is reversible, it could be stated

A *polygon of three sides* is a *triangle.*

Thus 'triangle' and 'a polygon of three sides' are two names of the same thing, and either can be used in place of the other at any time, without changing truth values, or otherwise changing the meaning of a sentence. Whenever a letter is assigned to a quantity, as is often done in solving a problem, a definition is being made. As an example, consider the following.

Let 's' represent the length of the side of a square. Here 's' and 'the length of the side of a square,' it has been agreed, are symbols which represent the same thing.

Definitions are sometimes given by conditional sentences. For example:

If a polygon has just three sides, then it is a triangle.

This practice is unfortunate, because the intent of the writer in such cases is always to convey equivalence, rather than implication. What is meant is the following.

A polygon is a triangle *if and only if* it has just three sides.

The student of mathematics must learn to read definitions which are stated as conditionals as if they were equivalences. It is important that definitions of this sort be equivalences rather than conditionals, because when the expression being defined is substituted for that which defines it, there must be no change in the truth value of the sentence in which it is substituted. A definition which is a conditional does not guarantee this.

The reader may ask why definitions need be stated as equivalences, when the *is* of identity serves so well. The answer is that not all definitions can easily be made in that way. For example, subtraction is defined in terms of addition by saying

$$x - y = z \quad \text{if and only if} \quad y + z = x.$$

In this case, an entire sentence, rather than a name, is being defined. It does not seem sensible to say that two sentences represent, or are names for, the same thing. Therefore, the equivalence appears necessary here. However, all definitions are, or should be, either equivalences or sentences using the *is* of identity.

In developing the theory for any mathematical system, it is impossible to define every word. To define a word requires other words, and the words used in the definition would then have to be defined, and so on endlessly. Thus it is absolutely necessary to leave some words undefined. The undefined (or *primitive*) words of a theory may be discussed, in order that one's intuition can be brought into play and a certain feeling about them established, but such discussions are not definitions.

As has already been stated, it is important that the student memorize definitions, and remember to use them. Many proofs are easy applications of one or two definitions, but would seem very difficult, or impossible, if the student ignores or forgets to use the appropriate definitions. Definitions are made to be used in a deductive development, and thus a good definition should contain no vague or contradictory terms, and where possible should introduce no new undefined terms. That is, unless it is absolutely necessary to introduce some new undefined terms, a definition should use no terms except those that have either been accepted among the undefined or have already been defined.

EXERCISES

1. Write a good definition of each of the following. Use the *is* of identity whenever possible.

(a) Circle, (b) Factor (of a natural number), (c) Parallel (lines), (d) Prime number, (e) Square, (f) Diagonal of a polygon, (g) Line segment, (h) Fraction, (i) Even number, (j) Numeral, (k) Intersection (of two sets).

2. Rewrite each of the definitions of exercise 1 in which the *is* of identity was used. This time state them as equivalences.

3. Make a list of the undefined terms from any geometry book.

4. Find three examples from mathematics textbooks of incorrectly stated definitions.

CHAPTER 5

Mathematical Reasoning and Creativity

1. INTRODUCTION

Human beings are expected to express themselves creatively in various fields, but it has not been generally thought that mathematics is one of these fields. That this is true reflects not the nature of mathematics, but rather the manner in which it has been presented. Most adults today probably think of mathematics as a collection of skills which may be used for calculating or problem solving, learned by rote, with little or no understanding, and which were always known, or at any rate discovered by the ancients. Nothing could be further from the truth. New mathematics is being created daily. In fact there has never been so much research in mathematics as there is today. Modern society has made it possible, and its needs demand it. More mathematics has been developed since 1900 than in all previous time.

That children can be creative in writing and art is not a new concept, but that they can be creative in mathematics is a relatively recent idea. Recent experiments in psychology and education, in which mathematicians have been involved, indicate that youngsters not only can exercise their imaginations mathematically far more than was supposed, but that younger children can do so as well as, or better than, older children and adults. It has been demonstrated, however, that when creativity is encouraged by a teacher, students exhibit high interest and enthusiasm, they can learn skills with better understanding and retention, and they are more able to see mathematics in better perspective.

It is not easy to give rules for creative activity or to specify what kind of reasoning is mathematical. By its very nature creativity cannot be limited too severely without being destroyed. It is possible, however, to describe the most common procedures which have been used by mathematicians and attempt to abstract from them some basic principles.

Reasoning, or drawing conclusions, can be classified in two categories, namely *inductive* reasoning and *deductive* reasoning. When a person makes observations and on the basis of his observations reaches conclusions, he is said to reason *inductively*. For example, a young child, on the basis of a very few observations, concludes that stoves are hot. Deductive reasoning, on the other hand, ordinarily proceeds from assumptions. It is usually by inductive reasoning that mathematical results are discovered. By deductive reasoning they are proved.

2. INDUCTIVE REASONING

The adult reader who has studied high-school plane geometry might well have gained the impression that mathematicians use deductive reasoning exclusively, since that subject is often developed with axioms, proofs, theorems, and corollaries; guessing or having hunches forbidden. It is unfortunate, but perhaps necessary, that when mathematics is published only the deductive aspect is shown. The mathematician must and does reason inductively before he can know what is worth trying to prove, and the mathematician without good intuition is not very creative. For every page of mathematics that appears in print, dozens of pages of unsuccessful attempts are discarded. Inductive reasoning is important for the student of mathematics also, whether or not he is headed for a mathematical career. Its practice makes him a better and more interested learner, besides giving him an appreciation of the real nature of mathematical activity.

Inductive reasoning is essential to mathematical creativity. To engage in it, one makes observations, gets hunches, guesses, or makes conjectures. There are many approaches which may be taken. Making lists of examples of a particular kind and looking for patterns in the list is one approach. Physical models may also be constructed to aid in "seeing" mathematical principles involved. In any event, one searches for patterns which may be generalizable.

Certain questions commonly found on intelligence tests require the use of inductive reasoning. A sequence of numbers is given and the subject is to find the next, or a missing, number in the sequence. For example, the next number in the sequence

$$2, 4, 6, 8$$

is probably 10. The next number in the sequence

$$1, 2, 4, 7, 11$$

is probably 16. To find the missing number the subject must, by inductive reasoning, find a pattern which is consistent throughout the sequence.

These problems furnish excellent examples of how people reason inductively. They also may be used to demonstrate that conclusions reached inductively must always be considered tentative. Guessing a missing number in a sequence is a kind of mind-reading trick. One must guess what was in the mind of the person who constructed the sequence. Another example will illustrate this. The next number in the sequence

$$1, 3, 5, 3$$

is not so easy to find. If the person who constructed it had in mind

$$1, 3, 5, 3, 1, 3, 5, 3, 1, 3, 5, 3, 1,$$

then the next number is 1. If he had in mind

$$1, 3, 5, 3, 1, 1, 3, 5, 3, 1, 1, 3, 5, 3, 1,$$

then the next number is also 1, but the following one is different. If he had in mind

$$1, 3, 5, 3, 5, 3, 5, 3, 5, 3, 5, 3,$$

then the next number is 5. If he had in mind

$$1, 3, 5, 3, 3, 5, 3, 3, 5, 3, 3, 5, 3, 3, 5, 3,$$

then the next number is 3. It should be clear that the number of possibilities is unlimited. If not, a look at a similar problem, using letters should be convincing. What is the next letter in the sequence *B, K, U, K*?

It is not difficult, in fact perhaps too easy, to "see" inductively that the sum of two odd numbers is even. One may proceed by finding sums of odd numbers:

$$3 + 5 = 8, \qquad 7 + 9 = 16,$$
$$17 + 5 = 22, \qquad 95 + 3 = 98.$$

On the basis of a very few such observations youngsters usually reach, inductively, the correct conclusion. This fact demonstrates that their ability to reason inductively is great. They should be encouraged to make such conjectures, but before their mathematical talent matures they must learn that while it is good to guess in such a fashion, their conclusions may not actually be true. They must learn to test conjectures and make proofs, and learn that verifying just a few cases seldom constitutes a proof.

By inductive reasoning, fully as valid as that just mentioned, it can be concluded that all natural numbers are less than 100. It is certainly true for 99 cases, a relatively large number.

A study of the following list may serve further to illustrate the process of inductive reasoning.

$$3 + 7 = 10, \qquad 13 + 17 = 30,$$
$$1 + 9 = 10, \qquad 11 + 19 = 30,$$
$$3 + 17 = 20, \qquad 5 + 5 = 10,$$
$$5 + 15 = 20.$$

This list may illustrate a general principle. If that principle were stated, however, the reader would immediately be denied the opportunity to discover the principle for himself. Induction is often the process by which some discovery is made, and if the conclusion is already at hand, discovery is impossible. The teacher of mathematics can profit by keeping this point in mind. The reader may well make lists of his own and study them to gain a further grasp of the inductive process.

EXERCISES

1. In each of the following sequences, find a probable rule, and on the basis of that rule, find the next few members.

(a) 2, 3, 5, 7, 11, 13   (b) 2, 4, 11, 23
(c) 9, 8, 10, 9, 11   (d) 3, 4, 6, 8, 12, 14
(e) 6, 4, 6, 8, 6, 8, 10   (f) 1, 3, 4, 1, 5, 4, 9, 5, 14, 9

2. Study the following, experiment as you see fit, add to the lists if you wish, and tell as much as you can about what you find.

(a) 1
    1 + 3
    1 + 3 + 5
    1 + 3 + 5 + 7

(b) 1 + 2 + 1
    1 + 4 + 4
    1 + 6 + 9
    1 + 8 + 16
    1 + 10 + 25

(c) 1
    1 + 8
    1 + 8 + 27
    1 + 8 + 27 + 64
    1 + 8 + 27 + 64 + 125

(d) 1   = 0 + 1
    2 + 3 + 4   = 1 + 8
    5 + 6 + 7 + 8 + 9   = 8 + 27
    10 + 11 + 12 + 13 + 14 + 15 + 16   = 27 + 64

(e)   1
           1   1
          1   2   1
        1   3   3   1
      1   4   6   4   1

3. A line segment joining two vertices of a polygon may be a side of the polygon. If not, it is called a "diagonal." A triangle has no diagonals, and any quadrilateral has just two. By experimenting as you wish, see if you can find a probable general rule or formula for finding the number of diagonals of any polygon.

4. A circle separates a plane into two regions, the inside and the outside. Two circles separate a plane into three regions if they do not intersect; four if they do (a maximum of four regions). Three circles separate a plane into a maximum of eight regions. Thus if n is the number of circles and N the maximum number of regions into which a plane is separated, the relation is as follows:

n	N
1	2
2	4
3	8

(a) From this table, make a conjecture about the case of four circles. Test your conjecture, and revise it if necessary.
*(b) See if you can, by conjecture, find a general rule, or formula, relating n and N for any natural number n.

3. DEDUCTIVE REASONING

By using inductive reasoning one may find probable general truths or principles. However, inductive reasoning does not, in most mathematics, provide certainties, but only plausibilities or probabilities. Before principles are established as certain, they must be *proved*.

The arguments used in proofs most often proceed from some basic principles which are known or assumed, and the conclusions reached apply generally, rather than in only a few specific cases. Such arguments are deductive. Deductive reasoning is thus necessary for most proofs, and its study is therefore essential for anyone who would understand the nature of mathematics.

What is a proof? It should now be clear that in most mathematical systems, even a very large number of examples does not ordinarily constitute a proof. There are, however, cases in which a proof can be given by examples.

In small mathematical systems such as modular arithmetics, proofs may be given by listing examples, since it is possible to demonstrate a principle for all possible cases in the system.

A disproof is also a proof. The principle, "All prime numbers are odd," can be proved false (thereby proving true the statement, "At least one prime number is even") by finding a single example. Showing that there is one prime number, 2, which is even, constitutes the proof in this case. Such proofs are often called "proofs by counterexample," and are of considerable importance.

Proofs by example are important, but they are not the most important type. Of most importance are the deductive proofs, or arguments, which apply not just to specific instances, but which hold in general.

The reader who has studied high-school geometry is familiar with the arguments which are called *proofs* in that subject. It may be recalled that they are usually written in a formal fashion, with numbered assertions and reasons. There are, however, other kinds of arguments called *proofs* both in mathematics and elsewhere. Proofs in law are an example of the latter.

It is not rare in mathematical history that a proof which was universally accepted in its day has later been shown, on the basis of better knowledge, to be inadequate or incorrect. Thus an argument which was once called a *proof* may not be considered to be a proof today.

The reader will note that "proof" has not yet been defined here, and that there are obvious obstacles to giving such a definition. To find a satisfactory definition, one must look for those aspects common to the arguments which are or have been called *proofs*, and such common aspects are not numerous. It is much easier to say what a proof *is not* than to say what it *is*. The only common aspect readily apparent, and indeed the only aspect which shows itself to be common upon more intensive scrutiny, seems to be that an argument must be *convincing* to be called a proof.

If it can be agreed that a proof is simply a convincing argument, then it is clear that the nature of proof must vary from time to time, from culture to culture, and from one group of people to another. Most deductive proofs, however, seem to have in common a very general pattern, to the effect that some knowledge is assumed, and on the basis of that knowledge a conclusion is reached. Such proofs, moreover, are powerful because of their generality. Instead of applying only to a few special cases, they usually apply to an infinite number of cases. In later sections of this chapter some of the principles of formal deduction will be discussed.

As a person grows toward mathematical maturity, he must learn how to reason both inductively and deductively. The deductive reasoning can be informal in the earlier stages, becoming gradually more formal. The ultimate in deductive formality is characterized by stating, in advance, all assumptions that are to be used, together with the rules for drawing deductive conclusions. Euclid attempted to do this in his thirteen books of "Elements" of geometry, where he listed axioms, postulates, and common notions, and attempted to deduce all the rest of geometry without reference to any other knowledge or assumptions.

Informal deduction. Deductive arguments which do not proceed from explicitly stated assumptions may be very convincing, and therefore be regarded as proofs. The nature of proofs of this sort can perhaps best be illustrated by some examples or arguments produced by children in early adolescence.

The sum of any two even numbers is even. This has been proved as follows by a junior high school boy:

> "Every even number can be *broken up* into twos, because by definition an even number has the factor 2. So if we take two even numbers, we can break them both up into twos. Then put all these twos together and you have a number which can be broken up into twos. It will be an even number."

The sum of the angles of any plane triangle is 180°. This has been proved as follows by a junior high school girl:

> "In any triangle if I turn a pencil, then it moves through the angles. As in this triangle (Fig. 5–1), I start with the pencil on side *BC* and turn it to side *AB*. It has then turned through angle *B*. Then I turn it to side *AC* and it turns through angle *A*. Then I turn it once more, to side *BC*, and it has turned through angle *C*. When this is finished, the pencil is on the side where it started, but pointed the other way. So the pencil turned 180° altogether, and the sum of the three angles must be 180°."

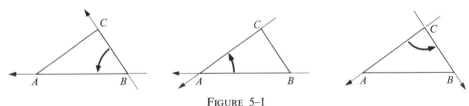

FIGURE 5–1

It should be noted that the arguments just illustrated are deductive, since they apply *in general*, and not only to a few specific cases. The assumptions in these arguments are hidden, and therefore the convincing nature of these proofs depends on the fact that they appeal strongly to common intuition. The essential difference between informally deductive proofs, such as these, and more formal proofs is that in the latter the assumptions are explicitly stated.

REVIEW PRACTICE EXERCISES

Solve these equations.

1. $4x + 2 = 5$
2. $3x - 6 = 7$
3. $-4x + 4 = 2x - 6$
4. $3.2x - 5.1 = 1.2x + 4.9$
5. $-7.3x + 4.2 = 3.2x - 7.1x - 7$
6. $35x - 750 = 87$
7. $47y - 13 = 63y + 5$
8. $95y + 6 = 37y - 7y + 2$

4. SOME RULES OF INFERENCE

In the preceding sections the discussion of the nature of proof was rather general and the reader searching for a formulalike description of mathematical proof may have been disappointed. Unfortunately no such description can be given. There is no formula, or recipe, for producing mathematical proofs. The producing of mathematical proofs is a creative activity and the ingenuity of the prover is often called upon. There are, however, certain principles, or rules, that can be helpful, and the present task is to discuss a few of them.

An example of a proof. The following proof of a theorem about groups will be used in discussing rules of inference. The definition of a group should be recalled.

A group consists of a set G, closed under one binary operation $\circ$, and satisfying the following:

(i) The operation $\circ$ is associative, i.e., for any a, b, $c \in G$, $a \circ (b \circ c) = (a \circ b) \circ c$.

(ii) There is an identity element in G, i.e., there is an element i such that for any x in G, $i \circ x = x \circ i = x$.

(iii) Every element in G has an inverse, i.e., for every x in G, there is an element x^{-1} in G for which $x \circ x^{-1} = x^{-1} \circ x = i$.

In the following proof, the underlying assumptions are precisely the properties listed in the definition of a group, and no others. Hence the theorem holds in any mathematical system which is a group.

Theorem. For any elements a, x, and y in a group G, if $a \circ x = a \circ y$, then $x = y$. This theorem is sometimes referred to as a *left cancellation law*, meaning that a symbol appearing on the left on both sides of an equation may be dropped. The word *cancellation* is perhaps unfortunate for pedagogical reasons, since the process of *cancelling* gives rise to so many errors and to so much lack of understanding.

Proof

ASSERTIONS	REASONS
1. $a \circ x = a \circ y$	1. Hypothesis
2. $a^{-1} \circ (a \circ x) = a^{-1}(a \circ y)$	2. Operating on the left with a^{-1}, which exists, since every element of a group has an inverse.
3. $(a^{-1} \circ a) \circ x = (a^{-1} \circ a) \circ y$	3. Assertion 2, Associativity
4. $i \circ x = i \circ y$	4. Assertion 3, Property of inverses
5. $x = y$	5. Assertion 4, Identity property
6. If $a \circ x = a \circ y$, then $x = y$.	6. Assertions 1–5

The rule of conditional proof. One rule of inference illustrated by this proof concerns the manner of proving a theorem stated as a conditional $A \rightarrow B$. One assumes the antecedent, A, as an hypothesis and then shows that B, the consequent, follows. It is then concluded that $A \rightarrow B$. In this case, the theorem is $a \circ x = a \circ y \rightarrow x = y$; hence the antecedent, $a \circ x = a \circ y$, is used as hypothesis. It is shown that $x = y$ follows, and the theorem itself finally concluded. This is a common way of proving a theorem stated by a conditional sentence, known as the rule of conditional proof.

> **Rule of Conditional Proof (C.P.).   From an argument which shows that B follows from an hypothesis A, one may infer $A \rightarrow B$.**

Introduction of hypotheses. In the preceding proof, an hypothesis was introduced at the outset, for a specific purpose. The question now arises concerning circumstances under which hypotheses may be introduced. An hypothesis, it should be emphasized, is nothing more than an assumption of a temporary nature, introduced into a proof in order that the proof may be accomplished. Thus whenever the prover's purposes are served by the introduction of any assumption, or hypothesis, he may introduce it. Here, then, is a second rule of inference.

> **An hypothesis may be introduced into a proof at any place.**

It should be kept in mind that hypotheses need not be true. In fact the hypothesis used in the preceding example is an open sentence, and is neither true nor false. In certain proofs (proofs by contradiction) an hypothesis believed to be false is introduced in order to obtain a contradiction. The prover may use any hypothesis at all, be it true or false, whenever it suits his purpose.

Principle K. In arriving at Assertion 2 of the preceding proof, an operation is performed "on both sides of an equation," to use a common metaphor. From the equation $a \circ x = a \circ y$, the equation $a^{-1} \circ (a \circ x) = a^{-1} \circ (a \circ y)$ is obtained. This procedure may be reminiscent of elementary algebra, where from an equation $3x = x + 1$, one obtains a new equation $2 \cdot (3x) = 2 \cdot (x + 1)$ by "multiplying both sides by 2," so to speak.† A procedure like this is valid in any circumstance where there is an operation and closure under that operation. This may be seen as follows:

Consider any set S closed under a binary operation $*$. Now consider any equation $a = b$ referring to S. This sentence says that 'a' and 'b' are two symbols representing the same member of S. If this is true, then for any c which is a member of S, '$a * c$' and '$b * c$' must represent a single member of S. This is so because $*$ is an operation and S is closed under it. Closure guarantees the existence of $a * c$ and $b * c$. The fact that $*$ is an operation guarantees that '$a * c$' represents a *unique* member of S. Similarly, '$b * c$' represents a unique member of S. Now if it is true that 'a' and 'b' represent the same thing ($a = b$), then '$a * c$' and '$b * c$' must likewise represent one member of S. In other words, *if $a = b$, then $a * c = b * c$.*

---

† This way of speaking is clearly metaphoric, since *sides* of equations are symbols, not numbers, and one does not multiply symbols. Multiplication associates a unique *number* with a given ordered pair of *numbers*, and is not an operation performed upon symbols.

From any equation $a = b$, then, the equation $a * c = b * c$ may be inferred, when $*$ is any operation and the set in question is closed with respect to it. This procedure, or principle, is used so often in proofs that it deserves a name. It is called Principle K.

> **Principle K. From an equation $a = b$, the equation $a * c = b * c$ may be inferred, provided that $*$ is an operation and a, b, and c are members of a set closed under $*$.**

Other rules of inference. There are other commonly used rules of inference that are not used in the preceding proof. They will be discussed and listed. One of these provides a way of drawing inferences from conditionals. From $A \rightarrow B$ alone one cannot infer anything, but if A is also known to hold, then B may be inferred. This should be clear if one remembers that for $A \rightarrow B$ to be true B cannot be false when A is true. Thus if $A \rightarrow B$ and A are both true, it follows that B must be true. This rule of inference is known as the rule of *modus ponens*.

> **Modus Ponens. From a conditional $A \rightarrow B$ and A, one may infer B.**

If two sentences are equivalent, then either may be substituted for the other without changing the truth or falsity of any sentence in which the substitution is made. This is easy to see, since equivalent sentences are sentences that are true or false together (having the same solution set). Another rule, called the *rule of substitution*, has in effect just been stated.

> **Rule of Substitution. If sentences A and B are equivalent, i.e., if $A \rightarrow B$ and $B \rightarrow A$, then either sentence may be substituted for the other.**

It should be recalled that every conditional sentence is equivalent to its contrapositive. By applying the rule of substitution one may therefore replace any conditional sentence by its contrapositive. This is done rather often in practice. In fact, it is often easier to prove the contrapositive of a theorem than the theorem itself; this is permissible and valid by the rule of substitution.

There are still a great many other rules of inference. Almost all of those not yet mentioned are rather obvious from an intuitive standpoint, and they can be derived from the basic rules already listed, and hence are not so fundamental. It is not necessary to learn a longer list of rules of inference. It will suffice, for present purposes, to list one such rule, called the *transitive law of implication*, as an example.

> **Transitive Law of Implication. From conditionals $A \rightarrow B$ and $B \rightarrow C$, one may infer that $A \rightarrow C$.**

This rule may be derived using the rule of conditional proof and modus ponens. Details will not be considered here.

REVIEW PRACTICE EXERCISES

Simplify

1. $^-(^-3)$	2. $^-1 \cdot {}^-2$	3. $3 \cdot {}^-4$
4. $^-(^-x)$	5. $^-x \cdot {}^-y$	6. $x \cdot {}^-y$
7. $^-1 \cdot 3$	8. $^-1 \cdot x$	9. $^-1 \cdot 3x^2$

10. $3x \cdot {}^-x^2$ 11. ${}^-5y \cdot {}^-6y^2$ 12. $\dfrac{1}{x} \cdot \dfrac{1}{y}$

13. $x^{-1} \cdot y^{-1}$ 14. $\dfrac{1}{x^2} \cdot \dfrac{1}{y^2}$ 15. $x^{-2} \cdot y^{-2}$

16. 1^{-1} 17. $1 \cdot 1^{-1}$ 18. $\dfrac{1}{1}$

19. $(3x)^{-1} \cdot (2x)^{-1}$ 20. $(4y)^{-1} \cdot (2x)^{-1}$ 21. $(3y)^{-1} \cdot (5y)^{-1}$

5. WRITING STYLES

The parallel column format used in the proof of the previous section may be familiar to the reader from high school courses. This style of writing makes it fairly easy to check each step in a proof, but is usually more difficult to write than the less formal narrative style used by experienced mathematicians. The latter is illustrated below, where the cancellation law for groups is proved in narrative style.

Theorem. For any elements a, x, and y in a group G, if $a \circ x = a \circ y$, then $x = y$.

Proof. Suppose, as hypothesis, that $a \circ x = a \circ y$. Since a^{-1} exists, $a^{-1} \circ (a \circ x) = a^{-1} \circ (a \circ y)$, by Principle K. By associativity it follows that $(a^{-1} \circ a) \circ x = (a^{-1} \circ a) \circ y$. But $a^{-1} \circ a = i$, the identity element of the group; hence $i \circ x = i \circ y$, and therefore $x = y$. By Rule C.P. it follows that if $a \circ x = a \circ y$, then $x = y$, which was to be shown.

It should be noted that the narrative style contains all the essential structure shown in the parallel column style proof. Assertions are made and supporting reasons are given for them. The narrative style is less rigid, however, and allows the writer to use and develop his own writing talents. Vital parts of a proof may thus be given greater emphasis than trivial parts, according to the writer's own inclination and literary ability. It is to be expected that no two persons will write identical narrative proofs.

EXERCISES

1. Write a parallel column proof of the *right cancellation law* for groups: For any elements a, x, and y in a group G, if $x \circ a = y \circ a$, then $x = y$.

2. Write a narrative proof of the right cancellation law.

6. SOME FURTHER THEOREMS ABOUT GROUPS

Several interesting and basic theorems about groups are relatively simple, and will be discussed here. Theorems will be numbered, and for completeness the theorems already proved (the right and left cancellation laws) will be included.

Theorem I. For any elements a, x, and y in a group G, if $a \circ x = a \circ y$, then $x = y$.

Theorem II. For any elements a, x, and y in a group G, if $x \circ a = y \circ a$, then $x = y$.

The next theorem about solutions of equations has implications for the solving of equations in elementary algebra, and it illustrates the basic logical principles involved.

Theorem III. Every equation $a \circ x = b$, where a and b are elements of a group G, has one and only one solution (for x) in G.

Before proceeding with a proof, we should note that there are two parts, a conditional and its converse. For an element s to be a solution, it must make $a \circ x = b$ true when 's' is substituted for 'x.' Thus the sentence *if $x = s$, then $a \circ x = b$* asserts that s is a solution. Its converse, *if $a \circ x = b$, then $x = s$*, asserts that there can be no solution except s; in other words, s is the only possible solution. Both parts are to be proved. For reasons that will become apparent, it is convenient to prove the second part first.

Proof

ASSERTIONS	REASONS
Part A	
1. $a \circ x = b$	1. Hypothesis
2. $a^{-1} \circ (a \circ x) = a^{-1} \circ b$	2. Assertion 1, Principle K
3. $(a^{-1} \circ a) \circ x = a^{-1} \circ b$	3. Assertion 2, Associativity
4. $i \circ x = a^{-1} \circ b$	4. Assertion 3, Property of inverses
5. $x = a^{-1} \circ b$	5. Assertion 5, Identity property
6. If $a \circ x = b$, then $x = a^{-1} \circ b$.	6. Assertions 1–5 (Rule C.P.)
Part B	
1. $x = a^{-1} \circ b$	1. Hypothesis
2. $a \circ x = a \circ (a^{-1} \circ b)$	2. Assertion 1, Principle K
3. $a \circ x = (a \circ a^{-1}) \circ b$	3. Assertion 2, Associativity
4. $a \circ x = i \circ b$	4. Assertion 3, Property of inverses
5. $a \circ x = b$	5. Assertion 4, Identity property
6. If $x = a^{-1} \circ b$, then $a \circ x = b$.	6. Assertions 1–5 (Rule C.P.)

The unique solution of the equation $a \circ x = b$ has been shown to be the element $a^{-1} \circ b$. The reader may note a similarity between Part A of this proof and a procedure often learned in beginning algebra for finding solutions of equations. For example, the following steps might be used to find the solution of $\frac{2}{3}x = \frac{5}{9}$:

$$\frac{2}{3}x = \frac{5}{9},$$
$$\frac{3}{2} \cdot \frac{2}{3}x = \frac{3}{2} \cdot \frac{5}{9},$$
$$x = \frac{3}{2} \cdot \frac{5}{9}, \quad \text{or} \quad \frac{5}{6}.$$

The rationale for obtaining step 2 here is often stated "if equals are multiplied by equals, the results are equal." Note that such verbiage is inconsistent with the approach of this book. Rather, Principle K has been used. Traditionally, associativity is not mentioned, nor is the identity for multiplication (the number 1). Note also that the above sequence of steps does not guarantee that $\frac{5}{6}$ is a solution of the equation, but only that it is the only *possible* solution. The converse may be established in cases of this kind by substituting '$\frac{5}{6}$' in the original equation to see if it indeed makes a true statement. Thus the "checking" of equations, as usually performed, is logically very important, and not just a procedure for detecting errors.

It should be noted carefully that when $a \circ x = b$ is taken as hypothesis (in Assertion 1, part A) the sentence is *assumed*, temporarily, to be true, even though it is in fact neither true nor false as it stands, (since it contains the variable 'x'). The sentence of Assertion 5 is likewise neither true nor false, since it also contains the variable 'x.' However, *the sentence of Assertion 6 is true!* The rule of conditional proof has been used, and the resulting sentence is a conditional. It is true for all replacements for the variable. In particular, this establishes that any replacement making $a \circ x = b$ true also makes $x = a^{-1} \circ b$ true. Thus if there is a solution of $a \circ x = b$, it must be $a^{-1} \circ b$.

It may be noted also that the word *solution* is used traditionally in at least three different ways. The above list of steps might be called a "solution" of the equation. The sentence $x = \frac{5}{6}$ might be described as a solution, and the number $\frac{5}{6}$ might also be called a solution. In this book only the latter meaning of the word is used.

The next theorem is similar to Theorem III. In the statement of that theorem the variable x appeared on the right of 'a.' Since groups are not necessarily commutative, a second theorem is required for equations in which the variable is on the left.

Theorem IV. Every equation $x \circ a = b$, where a and b are elements of a group G, has one and only one solution in G.

Proof of this theorem is left as an exercise.

The definition of a group states that there is an identity element i. It does not say that it is unique, i.e., that there is only one. According to the definition, there might possibly be more than one identity element. The next theorem shows that in fact there cannot be.

Theorem V. In any group G, there is only one identity element.

The plan of proof is to use two different symbols to represent identities, and then to show that the two symbols are in fact names of the same element. Thus any two symbols representing identities must represent a single element, and there is at most one identity. In other words, it is to be proved that

$$\text{If } i_1 \text{ and } i_2 \text{ are identities, then } i_1 = i_2.$$

Proof. Suppose (as hypothesis) that i_1 and i_2 are identity elements. Then by definition of identity element, $i_1 \circ x = x$ for all x in the group, in particular when $x = i_2$. Thus $i_1 \circ i_2 = i_2$. Similarly, $x \circ i_2 = x$ for all x in the group, in particular when $x = i_1$. Thus $i_1 \circ i_2 = i_1$, and therefore $i_1 \circ i_2 = i_1 = i_2$. It follows that if i_1 and i_2 are identity elements, then $i_1 = i_2$.

The definition of a group states that there is, for each element, an inverse element. It does not say that the inverse is unique. There cannot, in fact, be more than one inverse for a given element of a group, as the next theorem states.

Theorem VI. In a group G, for each x in G there is only one inverse.

It is intuitively clear that the identity element of any group must be its own inverse. The next theorem states this fact.

Theorem VII. In any group, the identity is its own inverse, that is, $i^{-1} = i$.

The next theorem establishes an interesting fact, namely that the inverse of a product is the product of the inverses, but taken in reverse order. This fact is probably not so clear intuitively, since most familiar mathematical systems are commutative.* In a commutative system, of course, order does not matter.

Theorem VIII. For any x, y in a group G, $(x \circ y)^{-1} = y^{-1} \circ x^{-1}$.

When a theorem is stated by a conditional sentence, $A \to B$, it is most naturally proved using the rule of conditional proof, taking A as hypothesis. Not all theorems are stated by conditional sentences, however. For example, Theorems III through VIII are not. In such cases, how does one proceed? The proof of Theorem III shows one way. The theorem was restated, in such a way that the restatement was a conditional sentence. For some theorems, that procedure would not be fruitful, and another method of attack should be used. That method consists of looking for some statement known to be true, and from which the desired result will follow. The true statement is used in much the same way as an hypothesis, and in most other respects, the proof would be similar to any other kind of direct proof. An outline of a proof of Theorem VIII will illustrate.

Outline of Proof. For any x, y in a group G, $(x \circ y)^{-1} \circ (x \circ y) = i$. This is true because $x \circ y$ exists in G by closure, hence has an inverse. The product of any element and its inverse is the identity. Now using Principle K, with y^{-1} on the right, and associativity, one obtains $y \circ y^{-1}$, the identity, on the right; a simplification is thus possible. A similar simplification is possible after using Principle K with x^{-1} on the right.

The statement used to start this proof is true, as shown in the proof outline above, but the reader may be wondering how one arrives at such a statement. In other words, how can a student find such a statement for himself when he wishes to accomplish a proof? There is no easy answer. Anybody, student or otherwise, must expect to spend considerable effort before finding an opening statement that will work. There are a few hints that one can give himself, however. In this case, the theorem refers to a product of inverses and the inverse of a product. Since these are involved, one would quite naturally consider using, in some fashion, such expressions as $(x \circ y)^{-1}$ or $a^{-1} \circ b^{-1}$. These expressions show the inverse of a product and a product of inverses, respectively. Since inverses are involved, one should also expect to use the definition of inverses in some way. If one should write a sentence to explain the meaning of '$(x \circ y)^{-1}$,' according to the definition of

---

* A simple example may help to educate the intuition. A man performs the (noncommutative) operation of putting on his socks and then his shoes. The inverse consists of performing the inverses in reverse order, i.e., taking off his shoes and then taking off his socks.

inverses, for example, he would have precisely the opening statement of the preceding outline. This illustrates that for any theorem not stated by a conditional sentence, the nature of the entities to which it refers usually gives some clue as to what kind of opening statement might work in a proof. This also illustrates the importance of memorizing definitions and remembering to use them in proofs.

The next theorem states that the inverse of the inverse of an element is the element itself.

Theorem IX. For any x in a group G, $(x^{-1})^{-1} = x$.

A proof of this theorem is left as an exercise.

EXERCISES

1. Write a narrative style proof of Theorem III.

2. Write a narrative style proof of Theorem IV.

3. Prove Theorem VI. [*Hint:* A proof may be somewhat similar to the proof of Theorem V.]

4. Prove Theorem VII. [*Hint:* Remember, in looking for an opening statement, to consider what kinds of things are involved and their definitions.]

5. Write a complete proof of Theorem VIII.

6. Prove Theorem IX.

7. Modular arithmetics constitute groups under addition. The symbol used for the operation is $+$ and the inverse of an element x is denoted ^-x. Restate the theorems about groups of this section using this symbolism instead of '$\circ$' and 'x^{-1},' thus showing how these group theorems apply to modular arithmetics.

8. Modular arithmetics with prime modulus constitute groups under multiplication if 0 is not included. The symbol $\cdot$ is used for the operation and 'x^{-1}' may be used to denote the multiplicative inverse of an element x. Restate the theorems about groups of this section using this symbolism, thus showing how these group theorems apply to modular arithmetics.

9. Is the theorem stated on page 60 a theorem about groups? Explain.

10. Is the theorem stated on page 62 a theorem about groups? Explain.

REVIEW PRACTICE EXERCISES

Simplify

1. $^-(^-3y)$

2. $^-x + {}^-y$

3. $^-3x + {}^-5y$

4. $^-7y + {}^-8x^2$

5. $^-x + {}^-y^2$

6. $^-7y + {}^-8y + {}^-9z$

7. $3x + {}^-3x$

8. $7y + {}^-7y$

9. $^-8x^2 + 8x^2$

10. $3 \cdot 3^{-1}$

11. $x \cdot x^{-1}$

12. $y^{-1} \cdot y$

13. $3y \cdot (3y)^{-1}$

14. $x^{-1} + {}^-x^{-1}$

15. $(4y^2)^{-1} \cdot 4y^2$

16. $(7y - 5x + 2) \cdot (3x - 3x)$

17. $0 + (7y - 5)$

18. $\dfrac{0}{4x + 2}$

19. $\dfrac{x}{2y} \cdot \dfrac{x}{y}$

20. $\dfrac{3x}{4} \cdot \dfrac{x}{5y}$

7. SOME THEOREMS ABOUT FIELDS AND RINGS

The definitions of rings and fields, as given earlier, use the definition of an Abelian group. A *ring* is defined as follows.

A *ring* is any mathematical system consisting of a set R, closed under two binary operations, $+$ and $\cdot$, such that the following hold:

(i) R, together with $+$, constitutes an Abelian group.

(ii) The operation $\cdot$ is associative.

(iii) For any a, b, and c in R,

$$a \cdot (b + c) = (a \cdot b) + (a \cdot c) \qquad \text{and} \qquad (b + c) \cdot a = (b \cdot a) + (c \cdot a).$$

A *field* is likewise defined in terms of Abelian groups, as follows:

A *field* is any mathematical system consisting of a set F, containing at least two elements, and closed under two binary operations $+$ and $\cdot$, such that the following hold:

(i) F, together with $+$, constitutes an Abelian group.

(ii) F, with the identity of the group in (i) deleted, together with $\cdot$, constitutes an Abelian group.

(iii) For any a, b, and c in F,

$$a \cdot (b + c) = (a \cdot b) + (a \cdot c).$$

Since several theorems have already been proved about groups, much is also already known about fields and rings. It is sufficient to replace certain symbols used in the group theorems by the corresponding ones for the additive group of a field or a ring, or the multiplicative group of a field. When considering an additive group, the 'o' becomes '$+$' and 'x^{-1},' becomes '^{-}x' (the notation used for additive inverses in modular arithmetics). When considering a multiplicative group, the 'o' becomes '$\cdot$,' and 'x^{-1}' remains 'x^{-1}.' Thus in a field or ring, additive inverses are to be indicated '^{-}x' and multiplicative inverses 'x^{-1}.' The identity of the additive group will be represented by '0,' and the identity of the multiplicative group by '1.'

Making appropriate replacements of symbols results in the following knowledge about fields and rings. In the following theorems it should be kept in mind that every field is also a ring. Therefore, any theorem about rings holds also for fields.

The cancellation laws. For any a, x, y in a ring R,

$$a + x = a + y \rightarrow x = y \qquad x + a = y + a \rightarrow x = y.$$

For any nonzero a, x, y in a field F,

$$a \cdot x = a \cdot y \rightarrow x = y \qquad x \cdot a = y \cdot a \rightarrow x = y.$$

For this theorem a, x, y are assumed nonzero, so that they are in the multiplicative group. The theorem would still be true if x and y were not assumed to be nonzero. (See Theorem I below.)

Unique solutions of certain equations. Every equation $a + x = b$, referring to a ring R, has one and only one solution in R. Every equation $a \cdot x = b$, referring to a field F, but where a, x, b are nonzero, has one and only one solution in F. (This theorem actually holds even if x and b are not assumed to be nonzero.)

Uniqueness of identities and inverses. There is only one additive identity in any ring. Each element of a ring has a unique additive inverse. There is only one multiplicative identity in any field (unless 0 should also be a multiplicative identity. Theorem I below shows that it is not). Each nonzero element of a field has a unique multiplicative inverse.

Inverses of products and sums. In any ring, the additive inverse of a sum is the sum of the inverses of the summands, that is,

$$^-(x + y) = {}^-x + {}^-y.$$

(Note that this follows from Group Theorem VIII and commutativity. Theorem VIII guarantees that $^-(x + y) = {}^-y + {}^-x$, and commutativity allows the order of the summands to be changed.)

In any field, the multiplicative inverse of a product of nonzero factors is the product of the inverses of the factors, that is,

$$(x \cdot y)^{-1} = x^{-1} \cdot y^{-1}.$$

(This follows in a manner exactly analogous to that above.)

Inverses of inverses. In any ring, the additive inverse of the additive inverse of any element is that element, that is,

$$^-({}^-x) = x.$$

In any field, the multiplicative inverse of the multiplicative inverse of any nonzero element is that element, that is,

$$(x^{-1})^{-1} = x.$$

(Note that both of these facts are merely applications of Group Theorem IX.)

In all of the foregoing, the operations called *addition* and *multiplication* were considered separately. The following theorems about rings and fields show how the distributive law of multiplication over addition underlies the relation between the two operations.

The ring and field definitions say that there is closure under multiplication, implying in particular that one may multiply any element by zero. The product of zero and any element of F is zero. This is not stated as part of the definition, since it is Theorem I.

Theorem I. For any element a in a ring R, $a \cdot 0 = 0$.

It should be noted that in this theorem, the operation of *multiplication* is involved, while it is the *additive* identity with which one is concerned. This should be a clue to the fact that the distributive law will be important in the proof. As always, one should remember to use the appropriate definitions. In this case the definition of additive identity is the only one that seems germane at the outset. Although this kind of analysis should help in getting started on a proof, there will usually be a good deal of trial and error remaining. In this text it is not possible to illustrate the kind of trial and error that might be involved. Instead, a proof will now be given.

Proof. Since 0 is the additive identity, $0 + 0 = 0$. Now for any a in R, $a \cdot (0 + 0) = a \cdot 0$, by Principle K. By distributivity, it follows that $(a \cdot 0) + (a \cdot 0) = a \cdot 0$, or, using again the fact that 0 is the additive identity, $(a \cdot 0) + (a \cdot 0) = (a \cdot 0) + 0$. Now, using Group Theorem I (cancellation law), the desired result, $a \cdot 0 = 0$, is obtained.

The second ring theorem is almost identical with the first.

Theorem II. For any element a in a ring R, $0 \cdot a = 0$.

Since a ring need not have commutative multiplication, this theorem does not follow from Theorem I. The proofs, however, are very similar. The proof of Theorem II is left as an exercise.

The next theorem is necessary for later theorems, and is not particularly interesting in itself.

Theorem III. In any field, $0 \neq 1$.

For a proof it suffices to note that 1 is a member of the multiplicative group, but that 0 is not. Therefore $0 \neq 1$.

In the definition of a field, 0 was excluded from the multiplicative group. The question arises, however, whether 0 might have a multiplicative inverse even though it is not in that multiplicative group. If that could happen, division by 0 would be possible in some cases. This theorem answers the question.

Theorem IV. In any field, 0 has no multiplicative inverse.

This theorem will be proved by contradiction. It will be assumed, as hypothesis, that 0 does have a multiplicative inverse. The task will then be to show that something false follows from the hypothesis.

Proof. Suppose that in a field there is an element 0^{-1} which is a multiplicative inverse of 0. Then $0^{-1} \cdot 0 = 1$. By Ring Theorem I, however, $0^{-1} \cdot 0 = 0$, and therefore $0 = 1$. This violates Theorem III; hence this hypothesis must be false, and it follows that 0 has no multiplicative inverse.

Theorem V. For any elements a, b in a ring, $^-a \cdot b = {}^-(a \cdot b)$.

Again in this theorem, multiplication and addition are involved together. To be considered is a *product* of an element and the *additive* inverse of an element. The distributive law will therefore be of central importance. Note that '$^-a \cdot b$' indicates that the inverse of a should be found and multiplied by b, while '$^-(a \cdot b)$' indicates that the product $a \cdot b$ is to be found and then its additive inverse taken.

Proof. By definition of additive inverses, $^-a + a = 0$, for any a. It then follows that for any b, $(^-a + a) \cdot b = 0 \cdot b$, using Principle K. By Theorem II, $0 \cdot b = 0$; hence $(^-a + a) \cdot b = 0$. Now by the distributive law, $^-a \cdot b + a \cdot b = 0$, for any a, b. By Principle K, it now follows that $[^-a \cdot b + a \cdot b] + {}^-(a \cdot b) = 0 + {}^-(a \cdot b)$. By associativity of addition it follows that $^-a \cdot b + [a \cdot b + {}^-(a \cdot b)] = {}^-(a \cdot b)$, and by properties of inverses and the additive identity, that $^-a \cdot b = {}^-(a \cdot b)$, which was to be shown.

Theorem V establishes that given any two elements of a ring, finding their product and then its additive inverse gives the same result as taking the additive inverse of just one of them and then finding the product. This theorem has implications for "rules of signs" when multiplying numbers. In the number systems of ordinary algebra, to be discussed later, there are some positive and some negative numbers, as well as zero. Theorem V, among other things, guarantees that the product of a positive and a negative number is negative. For, if a and b are taken positive, then $a \cdot b$ is positive, ^-a is negative, and $^-(a \cdot b)$ is negative. This theorem also applies, of course, to modular arithmetics, even though they do not contain either positive or negative numbers.

Theorem VI also applies to modular arithmetics in particular, and can be applied to rings or fields of numbers used in ordinary algebra to show that the product of two negative numbers must be positive. Further, it shows that the product of two numbers is the same as the product of their additive inverses, whether the numbers are positive, negative, or zero. A proof of Theorem VI will be left as an exercise.

Theorem VI. For any elements a and b in a ring, $^-a \cdot {}^-b = a \cdot b$.

The following theorem has interesting and important applications. For one thing, it answers a question that was raised about symbolism in modular arithmetics in Chapter 3.

Theorem VII. For any a, c in a field, and for any nonzero b, d, in the field,

$$(a \cdot b^{-1}) \cdot (c \cdot d^{-1}) = (a \cdot c) \cdot (b \cdot d)^{-1}.$$

With the notation of exercise 10, p. 63, this theorem would be stated as follows:

$$\frac{a}{b} \cdot \frac{c}{d} \qquad \frac{a \cdot c}{b \cdot d} \qquad \text{(where } b \neq 0 \text{ and } d \neq 0\text{).}$$

From this notation it becomes apparent that Theorem VII says something about multiplying using fractional symbolism: That in any field, if a fractional symbol a/b means $a \cdot b^{-1}$, then to multiply two elements represented by such fractional symbols, one may "multiply numerators and multiply denominators," as in elementary arithmetic. This theorem holds also for the systems of rational and real numbers (which are *fields*) to be discussed in later chapters.

EXERCISES

1. Prove Theorem II.

2. Prove Theorem VI. [*Hint:* Begin with $^-b + b = 0$, and multiply by ^-a.]

3. Prove Theorem VII.

4. Prove: In a field, if $a \neq 0$, then $a \cdot x = a \cdot y \rightarrow x = y$.

5. From arithmetic mod 5, find three examples to illustrate Theorem V.

6. From arithmetic mod 5, find three examples to illustrate Theorem VI.

7. From arithmetic mod 5, find three examples to illustrate Theorem VII.

8. Use arithmetic mod 6 (which is a ring but not a field) to show that the cancellation law of multiplication (exercise 4) does not hold in every ring.

CHAPTER **6**

The Number System of Ordinary Arithmetic

1. INTRODUCTION

Except for the systems of natural numbers and whole numbers, none of the more important number systems has yet been considered here. The numbers used in ordinary arithmetic and those used in the various phases of elementary algebra have not yet been considered as mathematical systems. In this and the following chapters the most important number systems will be considered as mathematical systems. They will, in effect, be *created*, or reconstructed here. For each, a set of elements will be determined, operations in that set defined, and properties of the system deduced or determined.

It is especially worthy of note that a number system may be constructed according to some physical idea, i.e., in effect, abstracted from some physical situation. It is not necessary that number systems be constructed in this fashion (and some are not), but if they are, they are certain to find immediate application. Once definitions in the abstract are given, the properties of a mathematical system can be determined without further reference to the physical situation upon which they are based, except perhaps to indulge in some inductive reasoning in order to get ideas about what may be proved. When the structure of a number system is delineated sufficiently, it

124

may then be used in applications to problems arising from the physical situation which inspired the creation of the system. It usually happens that a number system finds applications to other situations as well.

The study of ordinary arithmetic quite naturally begins with a consideration of natural numbers and whole numbers, but the need soon arises for halves, thirds, and other fractions, and their study is also important. In ordinary arithmetic, as it usually has been regarded, the numbers used are the whole numbers as well as numbers which can be called *fractions* (numbers which are not whole numbers). No negative numbers are considered.

The notion of a fraction arises from situations in which objects are actually, or conceptually, cut into pieces. For example, a pie may actually be cut into six pieces, called sixths. In measurement, an inch is often conceptually divided into four parts, called fourths, or into sixteen parts, called sixteenths. The numbers of arithmetic are abstracted from physical situations such as these, in which objects are actually or conceptually cut into pieces.

2. DIVIDING OBJECTS

Before making a formal construction of the number system of ordinary arithmetic it is important to consider the types of physical situations from which it is to be abstracted. Some simple diagrams will illustrate how the definitions of this system are motivated.

REVIEW PRACTICE EXERCISES

Multiply

1. $\frac{3}{8} \cdot \frac{5}{7}$
2. $\frac{4}{3} \cdot \frac{8}{5}$
3. $\frac{5}{9} \cdot \frac{2}{3}$
4. $\frac{18}{5} \cdot \frac{3}{7}$
5. $\frac{6}{5} \cdot \frac{8}{7}$
6. $\frac{9}{8} \cdot \frac{9}{5}$
7. $\frac{4}{5} \cdot \frac{2}{2}$
8. $\frac{9}{5} \cdot \frac{4}{4}$
9. $\frac{3}{8} \cdot \frac{7}{7}$
10. $\frac{9}{9} \cdot \frac{5}{8}$
11. $\frac{13}{13} \cdot \frac{14}{9}$
12. $\frac{16}{16} \cdot \frac{5}{9}$

Simplify

EXAMPLE: $\dfrac{24}{18} = \dfrac{6 \cdot 4}{6 \cdot 3} = \dfrac{6}{6} \cdot \dfrac{4}{3} = \dfrac{4}{3}$

13. $\frac{18}{12}$
14. $\frac{25}{35}$
15. $\frac{64}{100}$
16. $\frac{36}{81}$
17. $\frac{75}{300}$
18. $\frac{39}{75}$
19. $\dfrac{3x}{2x}$
20. $\dfrac{4x^2 y}{2xy^2}$
21. $\dfrac{x(x+2)}{y(x+2)}$

Symbols and interpretations. When an object is divided into n parts, all of which are the same size, each of those parts is called *one nth* of the object, and may be symbolized '$1/n$.' For example, if an object is so divided into four parts, each is $\frac{1}{4}$ of the object as pictorialized in Fig. 6–1. If three of the fourths shown in the figure are selected, the amount can be represented by '$3 \cdot \frac{1}{4}$' (three of the parts called *fourths*), as shown in Fig. 6–2. With a similar interpretation of symbols, '$\frac{1}{4} \cdot 3$' should represent an amount which is $\frac{1}{4}$ of three objects, as shown in Fig. 6–3.

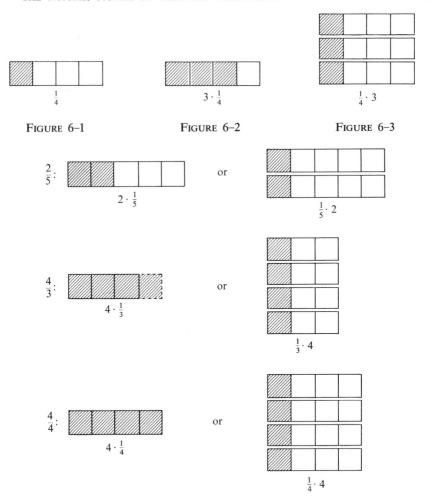

FIGURE 6–1   FIGURE 6–2   FIGURE 6–3

FIGURE 6–4

Evidently the amounts shown in Figs. 6–2 and 6–3 are the same. It is therefore common practice to write '$\frac{3}{4}$' to represent either $3 \cdot \frac{1}{4}$ or $\frac{1}{4} \cdot 3$. The dual interpretation of fractional symbols is further illustrated in Fig. 6–4.*

Apparently similar interpretations can be given for any symbols of the type m/n, where 'm' and 'n' are symbols for natural numbers. That is, 'm/n' may represent an amount determined by dividing an object into n parts and taking m of them, or by dividing a collection of m objects into n parts and taking one of them. Note that all of the following cases are admissible:

$$m = n, \quad m < n, \quad m > n.$$

* It is common in elementary arithmetic to use circular diagrams, rather than bar diagrams. The latter have the advantage of illustrating easily the dual interpretation of fractional symbols.

Note also that some kind of *operation* is beginning to emerge from the foregoing considerations. Taking $m \cdot (1/n)$ is equivalent to taking $(1/n) \cdot m$. The symbol '·' looks as if it might come to represent an operation when an abstract number system is formulated, and that it may be commutative.

A symbol $0/n$, where 'n' represents a natural number, can be interpreted to represent an amount determined by dividing an object into n parts and taking none of them. It would thus represent a zero amount.* A symbol such as '$n/0$' does not find sensible interpretation along similar lines, for it is nonsense to speak of dividing an object into *zero* parts. (If it is not divided at all, then one might say that it is divided into *one* part, but not into *zero* parts.)

Already the foregoing examples suggest that any mathematical system based on these ideas must deal with *pairs* of whole numbers, such as (m, n), or m/n. The first number of the pair may be any whole number, and the second number may be any whole number different from zero.

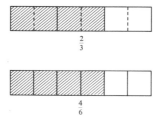

FIGURE 6–5

It is easily shown that different ordered pairs of whole numbers under the previous interpretation can represent the same amount, for example '$\frac{2}{3}$' and '$\frac{4}{6}$,' as in Fig. 6–5. The object represented by the first diagram of Fig. 6–5 can be divided into sixths by dividing each of the thirds in half. Thus four of the sixths is the same amount as two of the thirds. Evidently, doubling both of the whole numbers represented in a symbol m/n produces another symbol which represents the same amount under the interpretation being considered. Thus the symbols $\frac{1}{2}$, $\frac{2}{4}$, $\frac{4}{8}$, $\frac{8}{16}$, and $\frac{16}{32}$ would all represent the same amount. Similarly, tripling both whole numbers represented in a fractional symbol m/n would produce another symbol representing the same amount. Thus the symbols $\frac{2}{3}$, $\frac{6}{9}$, $\frac{18}{27}$, and $\frac{54}{81}$ would all represent the same amount. Finally, it may be noted that multiplying both numbers represented in a symbol 'm/n' by any single natural number produces another symbol which would represent the same amount. In general, then,

$$\frac{\text{'}m\text{'}}{n} \text{ and } \frac{\text{'}m \cdot p\text{'}}{n \cdot p} \text{ represent the same amount,}$$

where 'm' represents any whole number and 'n' and 'p' represent any natural numbers.

* It might be said to represent *nothing* but this is misleading. A *zero amount* is an important concept—it is "quite something." It has been demonstrated that when children are taught that "zero means nothing" they suffer for it later. Zero is a number, a very important number; it is far from being a mere nothing.

The symbols $\frac{3}{6}$ and $\frac{2}{4}$ also represent the same amount, even though there is no natural number n such that $2 \cdot n = 3$. This may be seen by dividing each of the sixths into four parts, and dividing each of the fourths into six parts. The first amount is then seen to be $3 \cdot 4$, or 12, twenty-fourths, and the second amount $2 \cdot 6$, or 12, twenty-fourths. In this example, the second member of the first ordered pair was multiplied by the first member of the other. Then the first member of the first ordered pair was multiplied by the second member of the other. The products were compared and found to be the same. This is, in effect, a means of testing which can be applied generally, and can be demonstrated as follows.

Compare a/b and c/d. Since b and d are both natural numbers (zero being excluded), 'a/b' and '$(a \cdot d)/(b \cdot d)$' represent the same amount. Similarly, 'c/d' and '$(c \cdot b)/(d \cdot b)$' represent the same amount.

Since the set of natural numbers is closed under multiplication and the operation is commutative, $b \cdot d = d \cdot b$ and $c \cdot b = b \cdot c$. Thus

$$\frac{c \cdot b}{d \cdot b} = \frac{b \cdot c}{b \cdot d}.$$

Therefore, the symbols $(a \cdot d)/(b \cdot d)$ and $(b \cdot c)/(b \cdot d)$ both represent dividing an object into $b \cdot d$ parts. In the first case $a \cdot d$ of those parts are taken, and in the second case $b \cdot c$ parts are taken. The amounts will be the same if and only if the number of parts taken is the same in each case, that is, if and only if $a \cdot d = b \cdot c$. Thus the general conclusion is:

Two symbols 'a/b' and 'c/d' represent the same amount *if and only if* $a \cdot d = b \cdot c$.

Symbols such as $\frac{2}{2}$, $\frac{5}{5}$, $\frac{3}{3}$, and $\frac{15}{15}$ can easily be seen to represent the whole of an object. For example '$\frac{3}{3}$' would be interpreted to mean dividing an object into three parts and taking all of them, or to mean dividing a collection of three objects into three parts and taking one of them. In either case a *unit*, or *entire object*, is represented.

REVIEW PRACTICE EXERCISES

Simplify

1. $\frac{4}{5} + \frac{2}{5}$ 2. $\frac{4}{5} + \frac{2}{3}$ 3. $\frac{7}{9} + \frac{1}{9}$

4. $\frac{5}{12} + \frac{7}{18}$ 5. $\frac{9}{8} + \frac{7}{12}$ 6. $\frac{7}{15} + \frac{3}{25}$

7. $\frac{5}{17} - \frac{2}{17}$ 8. $\frac{3}{8} - \frac{1}{12}$ 9. $\frac{4}{5} - \frac{2}{3}$

10. $\frac{9}{8} - \frac{7}{12}$ 11. $\frac{7}{15} - \frac{3}{25}$ 12. $\frac{12}{15} - \frac{8}{35}$

13. $\dfrac{3}{x} + \dfrac{2}{y}$ 14. $\dfrac{3x}{2y} + \dfrac{x}{y^2}$ 15. $\dfrac{(x-2)}{x+4} + \dfrac{x^2}{x-2}$

Operations. It has been remarked (p. 127) that from the notions of dividing objects, some sort of operation begins to emerge. That operation is, of course, the familiar *multiplication* in ordinary arithmetic. The question now arises as to what interpretation might be given to symbols like $\frac{2}{3} \cdot \frac{3}{4}$. Continuing the same agreements about

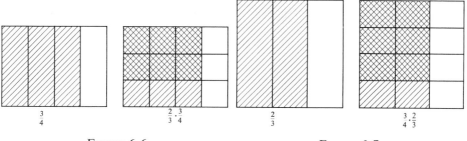

FIGURE 6–6   FIGURE 6–7

dividing objects and the resulting symbol interpretations, and interpreting the symbol '·' as before, the symbol $\frac{2}{3} \cdot \frac{3}{4}$ would have an interpretation as shown in Fig. 6–6. An object is first divided into four parts and three are taken. This amount is $\frac{3}{4}$. Then that amount is divided into three parts and two are taken. The latter amount is $\frac{2}{3}$ of $\frac{3}{4}$. It is easily noted how this amounts to dividing the original object into twelve parts and taking six of them. The symbol '$\frac{3}{4} \cdot \frac{2}{3}$' would have the interpretation shown in Fig. 6–7, where an object is first divided into thirds, taking two of them and the result divided into fourths, taking three of them. Again, this amounts to dividing the original object into twelve parts, taking six of them.

Thus according to this interpretation, the symbols $\frac{3}{4} \cdot \frac{2}{3}$ and $\frac{2}{3} \cdot \frac{3}{4}$ represent the same amount. They also represent the same amount as '$\frac{1}{2}$.' The symbol $\frac{6}{12}$, which can be obtained by multiplying the first members of the ordered pairs and then the second members of the ordered pairs, also represents the same amount. Similarly, for any 'a/b' and 'c/d' it can be seen that '$(a/b) \cdot (c/d)$' and '$(a \cdot c)/(b \cdot d)$' represent the same amount. This is the familiar rule of arithmetic, to *multiply numerators and multiply denominators*. Accordingly, it appears that any symbol n/n, where n is any natural number, would act as an identity for multiplication, since for any a/b, '$(a/b) \cdot (n/n)$' represents the same amount as 'a/b.'

The notion of *addition* for natural numbers is one of combining sets of objects. That same notion can be applied to situations in which objects are actually or conceptually divided. For example, the symbol $\frac{1}{2} + \frac{2}{3}$ has the interpretation shown in Fig. 6–8. It can be seen that the symbols $\frac{1}{2}$ and $\frac{3}{6}$ represent the same amount, and also that '$\frac{2}{3}$' and '$\frac{4}{6}$' represent a single amount. The "sum" can be represented by the

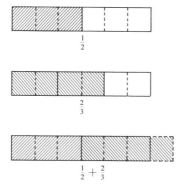

FIGURE 6–8

symbol '$\frac{7}{6}$.' This procedure brings to mind a familiar rule of arithmetic, namely, to *find a common denominator and add the numerators.* Such a rule can be derived from the interpretations being considered. A variation of this rule can be determined, as follows.

Consider '*a/b*' and '*c/d*,' where *a* and *c* are any whole numbers and *b* and *d* are any natural numbers. Thus '$(a \cdot d)/(b \cdot d)$' represents the same amount as '*a/b*,' also '$(c \cdot b)/(d \cdot b)$' represents the same amount as '*c/d*.' The amounts represented are therefore $a \cdot d$ $(b \cdot d)$ths, and $c \cdot b$ $(b \cdot d)$ths. Combining the objects produced $(a \cdot d + b \cdot c)$ of these $(b \cdot d)$ths. Thus '$(a/b) + (c/d)$' and '$(a \cdot d + b \cdot c)/(b \cdot d)$' present the same amount.

EXERCISES

1. By diagrams similar to those used in the preceding text, show interpretations of the following.

   (a) $2 \cdot \frac{1}{3}$ (b) $\frac{1}{3} \cdot 2$ (c) $5 \cdot \frac{1}{4}$ (d) $\frac{1}{4} \cdot 5$

2. By diagrams show comparisons of the following.

   (a) $\frac{4}{5}$ and $\frac{8}{10}$ (b) $\frac{2}{3}$ and $\frac{3}{5}$ (c) $\frac{3}{4}$ and $\frac{4}{3}$ (d) $\frac{2}{3}$ and $\frac{3}{3}$

3. Test the following pairs of symbols to see if both represent the same amount.

   (a) $\frac{2}{3}$ and $\frac{14}{21}$ (b) $\frac{5}{3}$ and $\frac{15}{9}$ (c) $\frac{4}{35}$ and $\frac{12}{105}$ (d) $\frac{21}{85}$ and $\frac{39}{160}$

4. Since $3 \cdot 4 = 2 \cdot 6$, the following pairs of symbols represent the same amount: $\frac{3}{2}$ and $\frac{6}{4}$, $\frac{3}{4}$ and $\frac{2}{4}$, $\frac{4}{2}$ and $\frac{6}{3}$, $\frac{4}{6}$ and $\frac{2}{3}$. Make similar statements from: (a) $2 \cdot 8 = 4 \cdot 4$ (b) $6 \cdot 4 = 3 \cdot 8$.

5. Two symbols *a/b* and *c/d* represent the same amount if and only if $a \cdot d = b \cdot c$. See if you can determine a similar short method of telling when one symbol represents a larger amount than another.

6. Use diagrams to interpret each of the following symbols.

   (a) $\frac{3}{4} \cdot \frac{4}{7}$ (b) $\frac{2}{5} \cdot \frac{2}{3}$ (c) $\frac{1}{2} + \frac{2}{5}$ (d) $\frac{3}{4} + \frac{2}{3}$

3. DEFINING THE SYSTEM

A number system, based on the notions just discussed, will now be defined formally and its properties developed.

Selecting the set. It seems clear that a number system based on the ideas of the preceding section must, in some way, involve ordered pairs of whole numbers. One possibility worth considering is to let each ordered pair of whole numbers (a, b), where $b \neq 0$, represent a number of arithmetic. In this way the ordered pair $(1, 3)$ would actually be defined to *be* the number ordinarily known as '$\frac{1}{3}$.'* Such a procedure would have the distinct advantage of making very definite what is meant by a *number.* In elementary arithmetic it is not usually made clear what is meant

---

* For the purposes of constructing a number system, the notation (a, b) is preferable to *a/b* because the familiarity with the latter is apt to lead one to make unwarranted assumptions.

by a number. Even if the distinction between numbers and symbols is made, the notion of *number* itself is vague.

If a number is defined to be an ordered pair, an important difficulty soon presents itself. If the ordered pair $(1, 3)$ is to represent a number, then the ordered pair $(2, 6)$, being a different ordered pair, should represent a different number, whereas experience in dividing objects urges that such not be the case. Furthermore, there is an unlimited number of ordered pairs which should be identified with $(1, 3)$, in fact every ordered pair in which the second member is three times the first.

This set contains such ordered pairs as $(1, 3)$, $(2, 6)$, $(3, 9)$, $(100, 300)$, $(210, 630)$, and $(13, 39)$. The difficulty can be overcome by designating this infinite set of ordered pairs as a *number* in the new system. The number *one-third* would thus be the set

$$\{(a, b)|3 \cdot a = 1 \cdot b\},$$

that is, it would be the set of all ordered pairs of whole numbers (a, b), where $b \neq 0$, and for which $3 \cdot a = 1 \cdot b$. (Or, the second member is three times the first.) To simplify notation, square brackets will be used. The number *one-third* will be denoted by '$[1, 3]$,' or by '$[2, 6]$,' etc. One may select any ordered pair of whole numbers in the set $\{(a, b)|3 \cdot a = 1 \cdot b\}$ and write square brackets instead of parentheses. Under this agreement, '$[1, 3]$' represents the set

$$\{(a, b)|3 \cdot a = 1 \cdot b\},$$

whereas '$(1, 3)$' represents one of the members of that set. Similarly the number *two-thirds* is the infinite set

$$\{(a, b)|3 \cdot a = 2 \cdot b\},$$

which may be named '$[2, 3]$' or '$[4, 6]$,' or '$[12, 18]$,' etc. Of course '$(2, 3)$,' '$(4, 6)$,' '$(12, 18)$,' etc., each represent single members of the infinite set.

In general, any number of arithmetic will be defined to be such an infinite set of ordered pairs of whole numbers. It should be noted that two ordered pairs (a, b) and (c, d) belong to the same set (number of arithmetic) if and only if $a \cdot d = b \cdot c$, and that this is in accordance with experience in dividing objects.

The preceding discussion may bring to mind the partitioning of a set by an equivalence relation, as discussed in Chapter 4. The set to be partitioned in this case is the set of all ordered pairs of whole numbers, (a, b), where $b \neq 0$. Two ordered pairs (a, b) and (c, d) are to be identified with each other if and only if $a \cdot d = b \cdot c$. A relation is in effect thereby defined, i.e.,

$$(a, b) \ R \ (c, d) \text{ if and only if } a \cdot d = b \cdot c.$$

This relation R is in fact an equivalence relation, being reflexive, symmetric, and transitive. Proof of this fact is left to the reader. Since R is an equivalence relation, it does partition the set of all ordered pairs into disjoint and exhaustive subsets. Each of these subsets is to be called a number in this new number system of ordinary arithmetic, and the set of numbers for the new system can now be defined precisely. The set of numbers will be called 'A.'

Definition 1. A is the set of all equivalence classes of ordered pairs of whole numbers (a, b), where b ≠ 0 and where (a, b) and (c, d) belong to the same class if and only if a · d = b · c.

Equality. The notion of equality is that of logical identity throughout this book. Thus equality for the numbers of arithmetic is not different from equality for sets or whole numbers. The sentence $[2, 3] = [4, 6]$ asserts that '$[2, 3]$' and '$[4, 6]$' are two names of the same number. In effect, it is a shorter way of saying

$$\{(a, b)|3 \cdot a = 2 \cdot b\} = \{(a, b)|6 \cdot a = 4 \cdot b\}.$$

The latter is clearly a sentence about sets, asserting that the two symbols represent the same set.

It should be remembered that the truth of a sentence $[a, b] = [c, d]$ may be tested by using Definition 1. To do this, one tests the truth of $a \cdot d = b \cdot c$, the latter sentence referring to the system of whole numbers. For example, $[2, 3] = [4, 6]$ because $2 \cdot 6 = 3 \cdot 4$. Similarly $[5, 9] = [60, 108]$ because $5 \cdot 108 = 9 \cdot 60$. It should also be noted that when a sentence $[a, b] = [c, d]$ is true, it follows that (a, b) and (c, d) belong to the same equivalence class. Conversely of course, if (a, b) and (c, d) belong to the same equivalence class, then it is true that $[a, b] = [c, d]$.

EXERCISES

1. The symbol '$[5, 7]$' represents the set $\{(a, b)|7 \cdot a = 5 \cdot b\}$. In a similar way, describe

    (a) [7, 11]   (b) [13, 4]   (c) [61, 2]   (d) [8, 43]

2. Is it true that $[7, 11] = [28, 44]$? Prove your answer by applying Definition 1.

3. Find two members of each of the following numbers (sets). In each case prove that your selections are valid by using Definition 1.

    (a) [8, 11]   (b) [13, 4]   (c) [61, 2]   (d) [8, 43]

4. Which of the following sentences are true and why?

    (a) $[5, 4] = [10, 8]$ (b) $[6, 8] = [12, 25]$
    (c) $(5, 12) = (10, 25)$ (d) $(5, 10) = (10, 24)$
    (e) $(3, 5) = [6, 12]$ (f) $(3, 5) = [6, 10]$
    (g) $(10, 12) \in [5, 6]$ (h) $(5, 6) \in [10, 12]$
    (i) $[4, 5] \in [8, 10]$ (j) $[4, 5] \in (8, 10)$
    (k) $(3, 4) \in (6, 8)$

5. Prove that the relation R defined in the preceding text is an equivalence relation.

4. DEFINING THE OPERATIONS

Now that the set of elements of this mathematical system has been defined, the next task is to define operations, after which their properties will be determined. The definitions will of course be made in accordance with experience.

Multiplication. Experience with dividing objects gave rise to the notion that '$\frac{2}{3} \cdot \frac{5}{7}$' and '$(2 \cdot 5)/(3 \cdot 7)$' represent the same amount. This experience motivates a definition of multiplication of arithmetic numbers as follows.

Definition 2. **For any numbers of arithmetic $[a, b]$ and $[c, d]$,**

$$[a, b] \odot [c, d] = [a \cdot c, b \cdot d].$$

The multiplication sign on the left has been circled to distinguish it from those on the right. The latter indicate multiplications in the system of whole numbers, already known, whereas the multiplication on the left is for arithmetic numbers, being defined here. The definition says in effect to multiply first members and multiply second members (numerators and denominators, respectively).

Theorem I. The set of numbers of arithmetic is closed under $\odot$.

Proof. Given any numbers of arithmetic $[a, b]$, $[c, d]$, $[a, b] \odot [c, d] = [a \cdot c, b \cdot d]$ by Definition 2. By Definition 1, a, b, c, d are whole numbers. Since the set of whole numbers is closed under '$\cdot$,' $a \cdot c$ and $b \cdot d$ are whole numbers. By Definition 1, $b \neq 0$ and $d \neq 0$. Therefore, $b \cdot d \neq 0$, and $[a \cdot c, b \cdot d]$ fulfills the conditions of Definition 1. It is therefore a number of arithmetic.

It is not yet clear that $\odot$ is an operation, since it has not been shown that results are unique. The ordered pairs used in multiplying, (a, b) and (c, d), according to the definition, may be chosen at random from the sets. If (a', b') had been chosen from the same set as (a, b) and (c', d') from the same set as (c, d), the name obtained for the result would have been '$[a' \cdot c', b' \cdot d']$,' and it is not obvious that

$$[a \cdot c, b \cdot d] = [a' \cdot c', b' \cdot d'].$$

Theorem II. In the set of numbers of arithmetic, $\odot$ is an operation. That is, if $[a, b] = [a', b']$ and $[c, d] = [c', d']$, then $[a \cdot c, b \cdot d] = [a' \cdot c', b' \cdot d']$.

Proof. Consider any numbers $[a, b]$ and $[c, d]$, and suppose that $[a, b] = [a', b']$ and $[c, d] = [c', d']$. In other words, (a, b) and (a', b') are in the same equivalence class, and similarly (c, d) and (c', d') are in the same equivalence class. By Definition 1 this is equivalent to saying that

(i) $a \cdot b' = b \cdot a'$

and

(ii) $c \cdot d' = d \cdot c'$.

It is to be shown that $[a \cdot c, b \cdot d] = [a' \cdot c', b' \cdot d']$ follows, or equivalently (by Definition 1) that

(iii) $a \cdot c \cdot b' \cdot d' = b \cdot d \cdot a' \cdot c'$.

Now (iii) follows from (i) and (ii) by Principle K, multiplication, and commutativity and associativity of multiplication of whole numbers. The final conclusion is that if $[a, b] = [a', b']$ and $[c, d] = [c', d']$, then $[a \cdot c, b \cdot d] = [a' \cdot c', b' \cdot d']$, which was to be shown.

Multiplication of numbers of arithmetic is of course an operation on infinite equivalence classes. When two of these classes are multiplied according to Definition 2 the result is a unique equivalence class, regardless of the names used. To perform a multiplication of two numbers, of course, one uses any particular ordered pair from each class. Using Definition 2 directly, one finds a particular ordered pair in the product. One ordered pair of the product, however, is enough to identify it.

Addition. Experience with dividing objects leads one to define addition of arithmetic numbers as follows.

Definition 3. For any numbers of arithmetic $[a, b]$ and $[c, d]$,

$$[a, b] \oplus [c, d] = [a \cdot d + b \cdot c, b \cdot d].$$

Again the sign of operation on the left has been circled, since it is different from those on the right. The former is addition in the system of numbers of arithmetic, being defined, while the latter are operations in the system of whole numbers.

There is obviously closure under $\oplus$, for reasons analogous to those given for closure under $\odot$. It is a question whether or not $\oplus$ is actually an operation, since it remains to be shown that results are unique. They in fact are, but the proof is left as an exercise. These statements are Theorems III and IV, respectively, for arithmetic numbers.

Theorem III. The set of numbers of arithmetic is closed under $\oplus$.

Theorem IV. In the number system of arithmetic, $\oplus$ is an operation (i.e., results are unique).

EXERCISES

1.   (a) Find the product $[3, 7] \odot [5, 2]$.   (b) Choose an ordered pair of $[3, 7]$ other than $(3, 7)$, an ordered pair of $[5, 2]$ other than $(5, 2)$. Use them to find the product, and show that the results are the same, i.e., that the same equivalence class is obtained as the product. [*Hint:* Remember to use Definition 1.]

2.   (a) Find the product $[6, 5] \odot [3, 2]$. (b) As in exercise 1, find other ordered pairs in each number and find the product. Then show that the results are the same.

3.   (a) Find the sum $[5, 3] \oplus [3, 2]$. (b) As in exercise 1, find other ordered pairs in each number and find the sum. Then show that the results are the same.

4.   (a) Find the sum $[3, 12] \oplus [8, 2]$. (b) As in exercise 1, find other ordered pairs in each number and find the sum. Then show that the results are the same.

5.   Prove Theorem III.

*6.   Prove Theorem IV.

5. FURTHER PROPERTIES OF THE SYSTEM

Now that two operations have been defined and closure has been established, the next step is to find what properties those operations enjoy.

Multiplication. From experience in dividing objects, one is led to expect that multiplication will be commutative and associative, and also that there is a multiplicative identity, and for most numbers, multiplicative inverses.

Theorem V. (Commutativity) For any numbers of arithmetic $[a, b]$ and $[c, d]$, $[a, b] \odot [c, d] = [c, d] \odot [a, b]$.

Proof. For any two numbers of arithmetic, $[a, b]$ and $[c, d]$, $[a, b] \odot [c, d] = [a \cdot d, b \cdot d]$, by Definition 2. Similarly, $[c, d] \odot [a, b] = [c \cdot a, d \cdot b]$, by Definition 2. It remains to show that the products are the same. By Definition 1 they are the same if $a \cdot d \cdot d \cdot b = d \cdot a \cdot d \cdot b$. By commutativity and associativity of multiplication for whole numbers this last equation is clearly true; hence it follows that $[a \cdot c, b \cdot d] = [c \cdot a, d \cdot b]$ and in turn it follows that $[a, b] \odot [c, d] = [c, d] \odot [a, b]$, which was to be shown.

Theorem VI. (Associativity) For any numbers of arithmetic $[a, b]$, $[c, d]$, and $[e, f]$, $\{[a, b] \odot [c, d]\} \odot [e, f] = [a, b] \odot \{[c, d] \odot [e, f]\}$.

Theorem VII. The number $[a, a]$ where $a \neq 0$, is a multiplicative identity, i.e., for any number of arithmetic $[c, d]$, $[a, a] \odot [c, d] = [c, d]$.

Theorem VIII. Every number of arithmetic $[a, b]$, where $a \neq 0$, has the multiplicative inverse $[b, a]$, i.e., for every $[a, b]$, where $a \neq 0$, $[a, b] \odot [b, a] = [n, n]$, for some nonzero whole number n.

Proofs of the preceding theorems are left as exercises. Theorem VIII speaks about every $[a, b]$, where $a \neq 0$. The complement of that set is the set of all $[a, b]$, for which $a = 0$. The latter consists of a single number, since all ordered pairs $(0, x)$ are in the same equivalence class. This is seen by noting that $[0, x] = [a, b]$ if and only if $0 \cdot b = x \cdot a$, and that since $x \neq 0$, a must be zero. The equivalence class in which every ordered pair has 0 for its first member is the arithmetic number zero.

Evidently the set of all nonzero numbers of arithmetic under multiplication constitutes an Abelian group. Therefore, several things are at once known about the system. For example, the multiplicative identity is unique, and each nonzero arithmetic number has a unique inverse (Theorems V and VI for groups).

EXERCISES

1. Prove Theorem VI.

2. Prove Theorem VII.

3. Prove Theorem VIII.

4. Rewrite Theorems I, III, VII, VIII, and IX for groups, using the symbolism of this section, thus showing how those theorems apply to the nonzero numbers of arithmetic.

5. What is the multiplicative inverse of each of the following?

    (a) $[2, 3]$ (b) $[9, 5]$ (c) $[0, 5]$ (d) $[m, n]$

6. Prove: For any number of arithmetic $[a, b]$,

$$[a, b] \odot [0, n] = [0, n].$$

7. Prove: For any numbers of arithmetic $[m, n]$, $[p, q]$

$$[m, n] \odot [p, q] = [0, t]$$

if and only if

$$[m, n] = [0, t] \text{ or } [p, q] = [0, t].$$

Addition. As one would expect, addition for numbers of arithmetic is commutative and associative, and zero is an additive identity. Additive inverses, however, do not exist, except for the number zero itself.

Theorem IX. (Commutativity) For any numbers of arithmetic $[a, b]$ and $[c, d]$, $[a, b] \oplus [c, d] = [c, d] \oplus [a, b]$.

This theorem can be proved in a manner analogous to that of Theorem V.

Theorem X. (Associativity) For any numbers of arithmetic $[a, b]$, $[c, d]$, and $[e, f]$, $\{[a, b] \oplus [c, d]\} \oplus [e, f] = [a, b] \oplus \{[c, d] \oplus [e, f]\}$.

Theorem XI. The number $[0, a]$ is an additive identity, i.e., for any number of arithmetic $[c, d]$, $[c, d] \oplus [0, a] = [c, d]$.

Theorem XII. If for numbers of arithmetic $[a, b]$ and $[x, y]$, $[a, b] \oplus [x, y] = [0, n]$, then $a = 0$ and $x = 0$. (In other words, only the arithmetic number zero has an additive inverse.)

Outline of Proof. Suppose, as hypothesis, that $[a, b] \oplus [x, y] = [0, n]$. By Definition 3, $[a, b] \oplus [x, y] = [a \cdot y + b \cdot x, b \cdot y]$, and hence $[a \cdot y + b \cdot x, b \cdot y] = [0, n]$. Then by Definition 1, $(a \cdot y + b \cdot x) \cdot n = b \cdot y \cdot 0 = 0$. Now $n \neq 0$, by Definition 1; hence $a \cdot y + b \cdot x$ must be zero, because for a product of whole numbers to be zero, at least one of the factors must be zero. In order that $a \cdot y + b \cdot x$ be zero, both $a \cdot y$ and $b \cdot x$ must be zero, because if a sum of whole numbers is zero, all of the summands must be zero. Now $y \neq 0$ and $b \neq 0$, by Definition 1, and therefore $a = 0$ and $x = 0$. In conclusion, if $[a, b] \oplus [x, y] = [0, n]$, then $a = 0$ and $x = 0$, which was to be shown.

Theorem XIII. (Distributivity) For any numbers of arithmetic $[a, b]$, $[c, d]$, and $[e, f]$, $[a, b] \odot \{[c, d] \oplus [e, f]\} = \{[a, b] \odot [c, d]\} \oplus \{[a, b] \odot [e, f]\}$.

EXERCISES

1. Prove Theorem IX.
2. Prove Theorem X.
3. Prove Theorem XI.
4. Prove Theorem XII.
5. Prove the converse of Theorem XII.
6. Prove Theorem XIII.

6. FRACTIONAL SYMBOLS FOR NUMBERS OF ARITHMETIC

Symbolism. The notation '$[a, b]$' is preferred to 'a/b' for purposes of developing the properties of the number system of ordinary arithmetic, but the more familiar fractional notation is preferable for discussing calculations. Thus the symbol 2/3 will now mean the same as '$[2, 3]$,' i.e., $2/3 = \{(a, b) | 2 \cdot b = 3 \cdot a\}$. Similarly '3/1' will mean the same as '$[3, 1]$,' and so on.

The temptation naturally arises to write '3' to mean the same as '3/1.' Such a procedure is common in ordinary arithmetic, but it is questionable at this point, since '3' is clearly a symbol for a whole number, while '3/1' is a symbol for a number of arithmetic, which is an equivalence class of ordered pairs of whole numbers. The convenience of the simpler symbolism prompts an attempt to somehow justify the procedure.

Isomorphism. The numbers of arithmetic such as 3/1, 5/1, 95/1, and so on (numbers which contain an ordered pair of whole numbers with second member 1) can be shown to act exactly like the whole numbers. In this case, one is justified in using whole-number symbols for them. It is important first to examine the meaning of the phrase *act exactly like the whole numbers.*

In the first place there are one-to-one correspondences between the sets of whole numbers and the arithmetic numbers $a/1$. The most natural one can be exhibited as follows:

$$
\begin{array}{cccccccccc}
0 & 1 & 2 & 3 & 4 & 5 & 6 & 7 & 8 & 9 \ldots \\
\updownarrow & \updownarrow & \updownarrow & \updownarrow & \updownarrow & \updownarrow & \updownarrow & \updownarrow & \updownarrow & \updownarrow \\
0/1 & 1/1 & 2/1 & 3/1 & 4/1 & 5/1 & 6/1 & 7/1 & 8/1 & 9/1 \ldots
\end{array}
$$

There are other correspondences between these sets, but this is the most important one. If these sets could not be matched in such a one-to-one fashion, they could not behave in an identical manner. Multiplications in one set, moreover, must be "exactly like" those in the other set. Similarly, additions must be alike in the two sets. This means, for example, that if two whole numbers are multiplied and the corresponding arithmetic numbers are multiplied, the two results must be corresponding numbers. To check one case, consider

$$2 \cdot 3 = 6$$

(a calculation in the system of whole numbers). Now 2 corresponds to 2/1 and 3 corresponds to 3/1, so the corresponding calculation in arithmetic numbers is

$$\frac{2}{1} \odot \frac{3}{1} = \frac{2 \cdot 3}{1 \cdot 1}, \quad \text{or} \quad \frac{6}{1}.$$

The two results, 6 and 6/1, correspond.

This example hints that the multiplication for one set could easily be performed in the other and the answer found by selecting the element corresponding to the result. If such is the case for every multiplication, then the two systems under that operation are essentially indistinguishable. The systems are said to be *isomorphic.* In practice the principal difference between them is a difference in symbolism, and the isomorphism renders the difference relatively unimportant.

It will now be proved that the two sets under multiplication are isomorphic, i.e., for any whole numbers a, b, the product, $a \cdot b$ corresponds to the product of the corresponding arithmetic numbers,

$$\frac{a}{1} \odot \frac{b}{1}.$$

Proof. For any a, b, a corresponds to $a/1$, and b corresponds to $b/1$. The product of a and b is $a \cdot b$. The product of $a/1$ and $b/1$ is

$$\frac{a}{1} \odot \frac{b}{1}, \quad \text{or} \quad \frac{a \cdot b}{1 \cdot 1}, \quad \text{or} \quad \frac{a \cdot b}{1};$$

$a \cdot b$ corresponds to $a \cdot b/1$. Thus the systems are isomorphic.

In a similar way it may be shown that the two systems are isomorphic under addition. Then, since only the two basic operations are defined for each, they are simply said to be *isomorphic* (under both operations). This, then, is what was meant by saying that the arithmetic numbers $a/1$ "act exactly like the whole numbers."

EXERCISES

1. Show that the set of whole numbers under addition is isomorphic to the set of all even whole numbers $(0, 2, 4 \ldots)$ under the same operation. [*Hint:* Find a one-to-one correspondence such that sums of corresponding elements correspond.]

2. Using the isomorphism established in exercise 1, perform the following calculations for even whole numbers by performing the corresponding operations in the system of whole numbers.

(a) $12 + 26$ (b) $62 + 350$
(c) $88 + 120$ (d) $490 + 324$

3. Prove that the set of whole numbers under addition is isomorphic to the set of all arithmetic numbers $a/1$ under addition.

Further simplification of symbolism. It has been established that a subsystem of the system of numbers of arithmetic is isomorphic to the system of whole numbers. It is therefore natural to agree to simplify symbolism accordingly. That is, any whole number which can be represented by a symbol '$a/1$' can also be represented by 'a' alone. Thus

$$3/1 = 3, \quad 8/4 = 2/1 = 2, \quad \text{and} \quad 16/4 = 4/1 = 4.$$

In particular it should be noted that the multiplicative identity can be represented by the symbol '1,' and the additive identity by the symbol '0.'

It will also be convenient to drop the circles around the symbols of operation. This is permissible since a multiplication like $\frac{3}{7} \cdot \frac{5}{11}$ cannot be interpreted as multiplication of whole numbers, whereas a multiplication like $4 \cdot 5$ or $\frac{8}{2} \cdot \frac{10}{2}$ can be interpreted as multiplication of whole numbers or of arithmetic numbers without making any difference.

EXERCISE

Restate all the theorems proved thus far about the numbers of arithmetic, but using fractional symbolism and the agreements about simplifying notation discussed above.

REVIEW PRACTICE EXERCISES

Divide

1. $\frac{3}{5} \div \frac{4}{3}$

2. $\frac{9}{8} \div \frac{5}{9}$

3. $\frac{17}{6} \div \frac{3}{8}$

4. $\frac{15}{8} \div \frac{9}{12}$

5. $\frac{13}{15} \div \frac{39}{5}$

6. $\frac{18}{7} \div \frac{25}{12}$

7. $\dfrac{3x}{2y} \div \dfrac{x^2}{3}$

8. $\dfrac{x-2}{x^2} \div \dfrac{x}{x+4}$

9. $\dfrac{x^2-4}{x} \div \dfrac{x-5}{2x}$

7. CALCULATIONS USING FRACTIONAL SYMBOLS

The numbers of arithmetic can be symbolized, or named, not only by the familiar fractional symbols being used here, but also by other kinds of numerals. In Chapter 1 it was shown that decimal (base ten) numerals could be used, or that numerals based on numbers other than ten could be used. The choice of symbolism for numbers of arithmetic is usually made to suit one's convenience in a particular situation. It is, of course, essential to be able to convert from one kind of symbolism to another.

Multiplication. Rules for calculating in the number system of ordinary arithmetic, using fractional numerals, have to some extent already been developed, since ordered pair notation was used in stating and proving the theorems. For example, to multiply two numbers of arithmetic, using fractional numerals, one first selects numerals 'a/b' and 'c/d' to represent the numbers. Then the numerators, a and c, are multiplied, and the denominators, b and d, are multiplied, to obtain $(a \cdot b)/(c \cdot d)$, according to Definition 2. A specific example of such a calculation is

$$\frac{14}{5} \cdot \frac{3}{11} = \frac{14 \cdot 3}{5 \cdot 11} = \frac{42}{55}.$$

Change of symbol. The number 1 is the multiplicative identity, according to Theorem VII. It can be named by any fractional symbol a/a, having the same natural number for numerator and denominator. Thus some of the symbols for the number 1 are

$$\tfrac{3}{3}, \quad \tfrac{11}{11}, \quad \tfrac{1000}{1000}, \quad \tfrac{17}{17}.$$

Suppose it is desired to find a fractional numeral for $\frac{2}{3}$, having a denominator of 9. This can be accomplished by multiplication by the identity, as follows:

$$\tfrac{2}{3} = \tfrac{2}{3} \cdot \tfrac{3}{3} = \tfrac{6}{9}.$$

The symbol $\frac{3}{3}$ was chosen for the identity, in order that the denominator in the final result would be 9.

The procedure above can be reversed. Given a symbol such as $\frac{6}{9}$, it is often desirable to find a simpler numeral for the number represented. In this case the numerator and denominator of the symbol $\frac{6}{9}$ would be factored:

$$\frac{6}{9} = \frac{2 \cdot 3}{3 \cdot 3}.$$

Using Definition 2 (but in reverse), one obtains

$$\frac{2 \cdot 3}{3 \cdot 3} = \frac{2}{3} \cdot \frac{3}{3}.$$

By Theorem VII, $\frac{3}{3}$ is the identity for multiplication, and therefore

$$\tfrac{2}{3} \cdot \tfrac{3}{3} = \tfrac{2}{3}.$$

The same principle can be used repeatedly to handle more complex situations.*

EXAMPLE. Find the simplest fractional numeral for $\frac{90}{84}$:

$$\frac{90}{84} = \frac{2 \cdot 3 \cdot 3 \cdot 5}{2 \cdot 2 \cdot 3 \cdot 7} = \frac{2 \cdot 3 \cdot 3 \cdot 5}{2 \cdot 3 \cdot 2 \cdot 7} =$$

(here commutativity and associativity are used with the denominator)

$$\frac{2}{2} \cdot \frac{3}{3} \cdot \frac{3 \cdot 5}{2 \cdot 7} = \frac{3 \cdot 5}{2 \cdot 7} = \frac{15}{14}.$$

EXAMPLE. Multiply $\frac{5}{6}$ by $\frac{9}{25}$ and find the simplest fractional numeral for the result.

$$\frac{5}{6} \cdot \frac{9}{25} = \frac{5 \cdot 9}{6 \cdot 25} = \frac{1 \cdot 3 \cdot 3 \cdot 5}{2 \cdot 3 \cdot 5 \cdot 5} = \frac{3 \cdot 5}{3 \cdot 5} \cdot \frac{1 \cdot 3}{2 \cdot 5} = \frac{3}{10}.$$

Note the use of the factor 1 in the numerator here. This allows for complete pairing of factors in numerator and denominator. Note also that the simplest fractional numeral for a number of arithmetic is the one whose numerator and denominator have no prime factor in common.

In many situations where multiplication has been performed, it is desirable to use the simplest fractional numeral for the result. In others it is found more convenient to use some other symbol. For example, the numeral $\frac{8}{3}$ has no common prime factors in numerator and denominator, and therefore it is the simplest fractional numeral for the number it names. In many cases such a symbol is the most useful. If it were the answer to a problem in which a number of sixths is to be determined, however, the numeral $\frac{16}{6}$ would be more convenient. In still other cases the numeral $2\frac{2}{3}$ is better. Generally speaking, the user of the symbolism should decide which kind of symbol is most useful.†

---

* The reader may be accustomed to "canceling" in situations such as these. Although habits of some standing are not easy to eradicate, it is advisable to try to forget about canceling, at least for the moment. Canceling is a process usually veiled in mystery, and its use probably causes more errors than any other single process. Hopefully it may one day disappear from the schoolroom.

† The ideas of this paragraph run contrary to a common practice in the teaching of arithmetic. Students are often taught arbitrary rules, to the effect that answers *must* be in lowest terms, and that no symbol in which the numerator exceeds the denominator is allowed. While this makes for a uniformity which may be desirable in a classroom situation, it obscures the important point that different situations may call for different symbolism, and that the simplest symbol is not always the most useful.

REVIEW PRACTICE EXERCISES

Add

1. $4\frac{1}{8}$
    $3\frac{1}{2}$
    $2\frac{3}{4}$

2. $5\frac{2}{3}$
    $7\frac{1}{8}$
    $9\frac{1}{2}$

3. $7\frac{1}{8}$
    $9\frac{2}{3}$
    $10\frac{3}{4}$

Multiply

4. $(4\frac{1}{2})(2\frac{1}{4})$

5. $(3\frac{1}{8})(2\frac{2}{3})$

6. $(5\frac{1}{4})(7\frac{1}{8})$

Division. By Theorem VIII every nonzero number of arithmetic a/b has a multiplicative inverse b/a. Therefore, division is always possible, except by zero. In fact, the nonzero numbers of arithmetic constitute a group under multiplication. Therefore, to divide by an arithmetic number is to multiply by its inverse, or reciprocal. For example, '$\frac{2}{3} \div \frac{5}{7}$' indicates the product $\frac{2}{3} \cdot \frac{7}{5}$. This brings to mind the mysterious rule *invert the divisor and multiply*, often taught to children. The ideas in the succeeding development provide simpler, more understandable means of explaining division using fractional symbols.

The division symbol '$\div$' is not generally useful, except for typographic convenience. It is ordinarily better to use fractional symbols to indicate division. The division $\frac{2}{3} \div \frac{5}{7}$ is thus symbolized by

$$`\frac{2/3}{5/7}.\text{'}$$

Since this division is possible, the symbol represents a number of arithmetic, and is therefore a numeral, i.e., a name for a number.

To multiply using symbols of this sort, one is naturally inclined to multiply numerators and multiply denominators, since that is the procedure used with the standard fractional numerals. Thus

$$\frac{2/3}{5/7} \cdot \frac{5/9}{3/7}$$

could be represented as

$$`\frac{\frac{2}{3} \cdot \frac{5}{9}}{\frac{5}{7} \cdot \frac{3}{7}}.\text{'}$$

This is indeed the case, but it seems far from obvious that such a procedure is valid. A proof is needed. For this case it can be checked by noting first that

$$\frac{2/3}{5/7} = \frac{2}{3} \cdot \frac{7}{5}.$$

Similarly,

$$\frac{5/9}{3/7} = \frac{5}{9} \cdot \frac{7}{3}.$$

The product in question is then

$$\left(\frac{2}{3}\cdot\frac{7}{5}\right)\cdot\left(\frac{5}{9}\cdot\frac{7}{3}\right).$$

By commutativity and associativity of multiplication it is also

$$\left(\frac{2}{3}\cdot\frac{5}{9}\right)\cdot\left(\frac{7}{5}\cdot\frac{7}{3}\right), \quad \text{or} \quad \left(\frac{2}{3}\cdot\frac{5}{9}\right)\cdot\left(\frac{7\cdot7}{5\cdot3}\right).$$

The number can then be symbolized

$$\frac{\frac{2}{3}\cdot\frac{5}{9}}{5\cdot3} \quad \text{or} \quad \frac{\frac{2}{3}\cdot\frac{5}{9}}{\frac{5}{7}\cdot\frac{3}{7}}.$$

Exercise 5 below asks the reader to provide a general proof.

Any fractional symbol with the same nonzero numerator and denominator represents the number 1, whether it is a standard symbol for an arithmetic number such as $\frac{3}{3}$, or a symbol to indicate division of arithmetic numbers such as

$$\frac{3/5}{3/5}.$$

Thus all of the following symbols are numerals for the multiplicative identity:

$$\frac{\frac{3}{2}}{\frac{3}{2}}, \quad \frac{\frac{1}{3}}{\frac{2}{6}}, \quad \frac{\frac{3}{1}}{\frac{9}{3}}, \quad \frac{\frac{4}{5}}{\frac{4}{5}}, \quad \frac{2\frac{1}{3}}{\frac{7}{3}}, \quad \frac{0.6}{\frac{3}{5}}.$$

Division can now be accomplished by the simple process of multiplying by 1, as in the following example:

$$\frac{\frac{2}{3}}{\frac{7}{5}} = \frac{\frac{2}{3}}{\frac{7}{5}}\cdot\frac{\frac{5}{7}}{\frac{5}{7}} = \frac{\frac{2}{3}\cdot\frac{5}{7}}{\frac{7}{5}\cdot\frac{5}{7}} = \frac{\frac{2}{3}\cdot\frac{5}{7}}{1} = \frac{10}{21}.$$

The symbol used for the identity has the reciprocal of the divisor for both numerator and denominator. This procedure provides a simple means of explaining simply the rule of "invert and multiply."

A variation of the above procedure is illustrated in the following:

$$\frac{\frac{2}{3}}{\frac{7}{5}} = \frac{\frac{2}{3}}{\frac{7}{5}}\cdot\frac{15}{15} = \frac{\frac{2}{3}\cdot15}{\frac{7}{5}\cdot15} = \frac{10}{21}.$$

In this case the symbol used for the identity has a numerator and denominator of 15, which is the least common multiple of the denominators 3 and 5.

A simple fractional symbol such as $\frac{2}{3}$ is often interpreted to mean division, in this case $2 \div 3$. It is not difficult to see that such interpretation is valid if one recalls that '2' is a simplification of '$\frac{2}{1}$' and '3' is a simplification of '$\frac{3}{1}$.' The quotient $\frac{2}{1} \div \frac{3}{1}$ is also the product $\frac{2}{1}\cdot\frac{1}{3}$, which is $\frac{2}{3}$. Any fractional symbol a/b can thus be interpreted to mean division of a by b.

EXERCISES

1. For each number, multiply by 1 to find a fractional symbol having the denominator indicated.

     (a) $\frac{5}{9}$ (54)   (b) $\frac{18}{7}$ (49)   (c) $\frac{4}{17}$ (85)

     (d) $\frac{13}{22}$ (132)   (e) $\frac{75}{8}$ (72)   (f) $\frac{9}{34}$ (306)

2. For each number, multiply by 1 to find a fractional symbol having the numerator indicated.

     (a) $\frac{3}{5}$ (33)   (b) $\frac{7}{12}$ (70)   (c) $\frac{19}{21}$ (76)

     (d) $\frac{14}{9}$ (154)   (e) $\frac{45}{13}$ (315)   (f) $\frac{31}{47}$ (186)

3. By factoring numerator and denominator and "removing factors of 1," find the simplest fractional numeral for each number.

     (a) $\frac{30}{63}$ (b) $\frac{45}{210}$ (c) $\frac{35}{105}$ (d) $\frac{91}{455}$ (e) $\frac{45}{13}$ (f) $\frac{231}{1001}$

4. Multiply and simplify the following.

     (a) $\frac{3}{2} \cdot \frac{10}{7} \cdot \frac{21}{9}$ (b) $\frac{12}{11} \cdot \frac{14}{3} \cdot \frac{22}{35}$ (c) $\frac{32}{14} \cdot \frac{17}{25} \cdot \frac{21}{34} \cdot \frac{15}{64}$ (d) $\frac{27}{49} \cdot \frac{18}{13} \cdot \frac{26}{9} \cdot \frac{49}{36}$

5. Prove: For any numbers of arithmetic a/b, p/q, and any nonzero numbers of arithmetic c/d, r/s,

$$\frac{\dfrac{a}{b}}{\dfrac{c}{d}} \cdot \frac{\dfrac{p}{q}}{\dfrac{r}{s}} = \frac{\dfrac{a}{b} \cdot \dfrac{p}{q}}{\dfrac{c}{d} \cdot \dfrac{r}{s}}$$

[*Hint:* Note the similarity between this and Field Theorem VII.]

6. Divide and simplify, using the procedure of multiplying by 1.

     (a) $\dfrac{\frac{3}{7}}{\frac{9}{5}}$ (b) $\dfrac{\frac{7}{11}}{\frac{6}{13}}$ (c) $\dfrac{\frac{13}{12}}{\frac{5}{11}}$ (d) $\dfrac{\frac{72}{15}}{\frac{8}{30}}$ (e) $\dfrac{\frac{135}{216}}{\frac{54}{12}}$ (f) $\dfrac{\frac{312}{180}}{\frac{156}{135}}$

7. Prove that it is valid to interpret 'a/b' as $a \div b$, by showing that

$$\frac{a}{1} \div \frac{b}{1} = \frac{a}{b}.$$

8. Prove: For any natural numbers a, b, c, and d,

$$\frac{a}{b} \div \frac{c}{d} = \frac{a \div c}{b \div d}.$$

Addition. Definition 3 translated to fractional symbolism shows that for any numbers of arithmetic a/b and c/d,

$$\frac{a}{b} + \frac{c}{d} = \frac{a \cdot d + b \cdot c}{b \cdot d}.$$

Stated thus, the definition shows how to add using fractional symbols, and can be applied directly.

EXAMPLE 1.

$$\frac{3}{5} + \frac{7}{9} = \frac{3 \cdot 9 + 5 \cdot 7}{5 \cdot 9} = \frac{27 + 35}{45} = \frac{62}{45}.$$

EXAMPLE 2.

$$\frac{2}{3} + \frac{5}{6} = \frac{2 \cdot 6 + 3 \cdot 5}{3 \cdot 6} = \frac{12 + 15}{18} = \frac{27}{18}.$$

EXAMPLE 3.

$$\frac{2}{7} + \frac{3}{7} = \frac{2 \cdot 7 + 3 \cdot 7}{7 \cdot 7} = \frac{14 + 21}{49} = \frac{35}{49}.$$

In Example 3 both symbols have the same denominator. The reader will recall a rule for adding which says to "add numerators and retain the common denominator." Thus $\frac{2}{7} + \frac{3}{7} = \frac{5}{7}$. That such a procedure is valid can be proved as follows.

Theorem XIV. For any numbers of arithmetic a/c and b/c,

$$\frac{a}{c} + \frac{b}{c} = \frac{a + b}{c}.$$

Proof. By Definition 3,

$$\frac{a}{c} + \frac{b}{c} = \frac{a \cdot c + b \cdot c}{c \cdot c}.$$

By the distributive law for whole numbers, $a \cdot c + b \cdot c = (a + b) \cdot c$. Thus

$$\frac{a \cdot c + b \cdot c}{c \cdot c} = \frac{(a + b) \cdot c}{c \cdot c}.$$

Applying Definition 2,

$$\frac{(a + b) \cdot c}{c \cdot c} = \frac{a + b}{c} \cdot \frac{c}{c}.$$

Since c/c is the multiplicative identity, as guaranteed by Theorem VII,

$$\frac{a + b}{c} \cdot \frac{c}{c} = \frac{a + b}{c}.$$

Thus

$$\frac{a}{c} + \frac{b}{c} = \frac{a + b}{c},$$

as was to be shown.

When denominators are the same, as in Example 3, the direct application of the definition is not the most efficient way to add. Rather, it is more convenient to use Theorem XIV. In certain other cases, as in Example 2, it is likewise more convenient to use Theorem XIV. It is necessary, however, to find symbols having a common denominator before using this method. This may be accomplished by multiplying by the identity, as follows.

EXAMPLE.

$$\tfrac{2}{3} + \tfrac{5}{6} = \tfrac{2}{3} \cdot \tfrac{2}{2} + \tfrac{5}{6} = \tfrac{4}{6} + \tfrac{5}{6} = \tfrac{9}{6}.$$

In more complex cases, the symbol to be used for the identity is not so easily discerned. In that event it is helpful to find prime factorizations of the denominators, as in the following example. The symbol for the identity is then chosen so that the common denominator becomes the least common multiple (L.C.M) of the denominators.*

EXAMPLE.

$$\frac{13}{70} + \frac{11}{21} = \frac{13}{2 \cdot 5 \cdot 7} + \frac{11}{3 \cdot 7} = \frac{13}{2 \cdot 5 \cdot 7} \cdot \frac{3}{3} + \frac{11}{3 \cdot 7} \cdot \frac{2 \cdot 5}{2 \cdot 5} = \frac{39 + 110}{2 \cdot 3 \cdot 5 \cdot 7} = \frac{149}{210}.$$

The meaning of commonly used symbols such as $2\frac{2}{3}$ becomes clear if the missing plus sign is written, to obtain

$$2 + \tfrac{2}{3}, \quad \text{or} \quad \tfrac{2}{1} + \tfrac{2}{3}.$$

It is now a simple matter to find a single fractional symbol for the number. One needs only to accomplish the addition:

$$2\tfrac{2}{3} = \tfrac{2}{1} + \tfrac{2}{3} = \tfrac{2}{1} \cdot \tfrac{3}{3} + \tfrac{2}{3} = \tfrac{8}{3}.$$

Addition using symbols of this type also becomes clearer when the missing plus signs are written, as follows:

$$\begin{array}{c} 4 + \tfrac{3}{5} \\ 2 + \tfrac{1}{5} \\ 7 + \tfrac{4}{5} \\ \hline \end{array} \quad \text{or} \quad (4 + \tfrac{3}{5}) + (2 + \tfrac{1}{5}) + (7 + \tfrac{4}{5}).$$

By associativity and commutativity, the sum can also be named as

$$(4 + 2 + 7) + (\tfrac{3}{5} + \tfrac{1}{5} + \tfrac{4}{5}),$$

and then $13 + \tfrac{8}{5}$. Now

$$\frac{8}{5} = \frac{5 + 3}{5},$$

and thus by Theorem XIV, $\tfrac{8}{5} = \tfrac{5}{5} + \tfrac{3}{5}$, or $1 + \tfrac{3}{5}$. Therefore

$$13 + \tfrac{8}{5} = 13 + (1 + \tfrac{3}{5}) = (13 + 1) + \tfrac{3}{5} = 14 + \tfrac{3}{5}.$$

Similarly, multiplication using symbols such as $2\frac{2}{3}$ becomes more understandable when the missing plus signs are written.

EXAMPLE 1.

$$5 \cdot 2\tfrac{2}{3} = 5 \cdot (2 + \tfrac{2}{3}).$$

It is now apparent that the distributive law can be applied, obtaining

$$5 \cdot 2 + 5 \cdot \tfrac{2}{3}, \quad \text{or} \quad 10 + \tfrac{10}{3}, \quad \text{or} \quad 13 + \tfrac{1}{3}.$$

---

* The terminology "L.C.M. of the denominators" is more descriptive than "least common denominator," and is therefore to be preferred.

EXAMPLE 2.

$$2\tfrac{1}{4} \cdot 3\tfrac{1}{3} = (2 + \tfrac{1}{4}) \cdot (3 + \tfrac{1}{3}).$$

The distributive law is now applied more than once:

$$[(2 + \tfrac{1}{4}) \cdot 3] + [(2 + \tfrac{1}{4}) \cdot \tfrac{1}{3}] = 2 \cdot 3 + \tfrac{1}{4} \cdot 3 + 2 \cdot \tfrac{1}{3} + \tfrac{1}{4} \cdot \tfrac{1}{3}$$
$$= 6 + \tfrac{3}{4} + \tfrac{2}{3} + \tfrac{1}{12}$$
$$= 6 + \tfrac{3}{4} \cdot \tfrac{3}{3} + \tfrac{2}{3} \cdot \tfrac{4}{4} + \tfrac{1}{12}$$
$$= 6 + \tfrac{9}{12} + \tfrac{8}{12} + \tfrac{1}{12}$$
$$= 6 + \tfrac{18}{12}, \quad \text{or} \quad 6 + \tfrac{3}{2}, \quad \text{or} \quad 7 + \tfrac{1}{2}.$$

Subtraction is of course the opposite of addition. To subtract

$$\frac{a}{b} - \frac{c}{d},$$

one looks for a number which when added to c/d gives a/b. The usual procedure in subtracting, however, is to first find symbols with the same denominator and then subtract the numerators. For example,

$$\tfrac{2}{3} - \tfrac{3}{5} = \tfrac{2}{3} \cdot \tfrac{5}{5} - \tfrac{3}{5} \cdot \tfrac{3}{3} = \tfrac{10}{15} - \tfrac{9}{15} = \tfrac{1}{15}.$$

It remains to be shown that this procedure is a valid one. It must be proved that for any a/c and b/c (where $b < a$) that

$$\frac{a}{c} - \frac{b}{c} = \frac{a-b}{c}.$$

A proof consists of showing that when

$$\frac{a-b}{c}$$

is added to b/c the result is a/c. Details are left to the reader.

EXERCISES

1. Add, by direct application of Definition 3.
   (a) $\tfrac{3}{5} + \tfrac{4}{7}$ (b) $\tfrac{7}{5} + \tfrac{9}{11}$ (c) $\tfrac{7}{12} + \tfrac{5}{6}$
   (d) $\tfrac{3}{8} + \tfrac{5}{8}$ (e) $\tfrac{1}{2} + \tfrac{2}{3} + \tfrac{4}{5}$ (f) $\tfrac{3}{5} + \tfrac{4}{3} + \tfrac{1}{2} + \tfrac{2}{5}$

[*Hint* for (e), (f): The definition must be applied more than once.]

2. Add, using the common denominator approach.
   (a) $\tfrac{2}{5} + \tfrac{4}{15}$ (b) $\tfrac{13}{30} + \tfrac{8}{3}$ (c) $\tfrac{7}{50} + \tfrac{41}{210}$
   (d) $\tfrac{5}{14} + \tfrac{9}{77}$ (e) $\tfrac{4}{15} + \tfrac{6}{35} + \tfrac{10}{21}$ (f) $\tfrac{7}{165} + \tfrac{3}{140} + \tfrac{2}{385}$

3. Subtract.
   (a) $\tfrac{7}{9} - \tfrac{5}{9}$ (b) $\tfrac{5}{8} - \tfrac{1}{4}$ (c) $\tfrac{7}{30} - \tfrac{6}{35}$ (d) $\tfrac{11}{35} - \tfrac{3}{28}$

4. Explain the method you used in exercise 3, and justify it on the basis of the theory developed in this chapter.

5. Symbolize each of the following numbers as a sum.

EXAMPLE. $\frac{4}{5} = \frac{1}{5} + \frac{3}{5}$ or $\frac{2}{5} + \frac{2}{5}$.

(a) $\frac{3}{4}$ (b) $\frac{5}{7}$ (c) $\frac{5}{3}$ (d) $\frac{13}{9}$ (e) $\frac{3}{2}$ (f) $\frac{18}{7}$

6. Symbolize each of the following numbers as a product.

EXAMPLE. $\dfrac{10}{21} = \dfrac{2 \cdot 5}{3 \cdot 7} = \dfrac{2}{3} \cdot \dfrac{5}{7}$ or $\dfrac{2}{7} \cdot \dfrac{5}{3}$.

(a) $\frac{12}{15}$ (b) $\frac{9}{14}$ (c) $\frac{21}{15}$ (d) $\frac{16}{27}$

7. In the system of natural numbers, the fundamental theorem of arithmetic holds. Is there an analogous theorem in the number system of arithmetic? Explain.

8. Insert the missing plus signs and then add. Indicate where commutativity and associativity are used.

(a) $4\frac{1}{2} + 2\frac{3}{4}$ (b) $3\frac{5}{9} + 2\frac{2}{3}$ (c) $17\frac{7}{12} + 9\frac{2}{5}$ (d) $31\frac{8}{21} + 43\frac{5}{9}$

9. Insert the missing plus signs and then multiply. Indicate where various laws are used.

(a) $1\frac{1}{2} \cdot 3\frac{1}{4}$ (b) $2\frac{1}{3} \cdot 5\frac{1}{4}$ (c) $5\frac{2}{3} \cdot 3\frac{1}{5}$ (d) $11\frac{3}{7} \cdot 8\frac{2}{5}$

10. Do the multiplications of exercise 9 by first converting to fractional symbolism.

EXAMPLE. $1\frac{1}{2} \cdot 3\frac{1}{4} = \frac{3}{2} \cdot \frac{13}{4} = \frac{39}{8}$.

11. Prove: For any number of arithmetic

$$a\frac{b}{c}, \quad \text{where } `a\frac{b}{c}' \text{ is a symbol like } 2\frac{1}{3},$$

$$a\frac{b}{c} = \frac{a \cdot c + b}{c}.$$

12. Subtract

(a) $\frac{4}{5} - \frac{1}{6}$ (b) $\frac{9}{8} - \frac{5}{6}$ (c) $\frac{17}{15} - \frac{4}{10}$ (d) $\frac{11}{12} - \frac{6}{11}$

13. Prove: For any numbers of arithmetic a/c and b/c, where $a > b$,

$$\frac{a}{c} - \frac{b}{c} = \frac{a - b}{c}.$$

8. ORDER

The numbers of ordinary arithmetic can be ordered in much the same way that the whole numbers are ordered. It may be recalled that in Chapter 2 a definition of $>$ was made for whole numbers. That relation, being an order relation, ordered the set of whole numbers. The present task is to define, similarly, an order relation for arithmetic numbers. Two considerations should be given to the manner in which such a relation is defined. The relation should be compatible with, and an extension of, the one defined for whole numbers, if that is possible. It should also conform to the intuitive notions brought to mind by physical situations in which objects are cut into pieces.

It is easy to define an order relation which is an extension of that for whole numbers. For whole numbers, $x > y$ is defined to mean that $x - y$ is a natural number; in other words, $x - y$ exists and is not zero. For numbers of arithmetic, one would then simply define $a/b \ominus c/d$ to mean that $a/b - c/d$ exists and is not zero. For those numbers of arithmetic that are isomorphic to the whole numbers, this would reduce to the definition of $>$, and thus $\ominus$ would be an extension of $>$ (see Theorem XVI following). Before such a definition is made, however, physical interpretations should be considered. As an example of comparing portions of physical objects, consider taking $\frac{3}{5}$ of an object and $\frac{4}{5}$ of the object, as shown in Fig. 6–9. In cases like this, where the object has been divided into the same number of parts, it is easy to decide which amount is larger by counting the number of parts taken in each case. In this case $\frac{4}{5}$ is greater than $\frac{3}{5}$ because for the whole numbers 3 and 4, $4 > 3$. Conversely, since $\frac{4}{5}$ is a greater amount than $\frac{3}{5}$, also $4 > 3$. It is not quite so easy to decide which of $\frac{2}{3}$ and $\frac{5}{7}$ represents the larger amount. This case can, however, be reduced to the previous one. Instead of dividing an object into thirds and sevenths, one may divide it into twenty-firsts. Thus

$$\frac{2}{3} = \frac{2 \cdot 7}{3 \cdot 7} = \frac{14}{21} \quad \text{and} \quad \frac{5}{7} = \frac{5 \cdot 3}{7 \cdot 3} = \frac{15}{21}.$$

Now, since $15 > 14$, $\frac{15}{21}$ is greater than $\frac{14}{21}$, and conversely. Therefore $\frac{5}{7}$ is a larger amount than $\frac{2}{3}$. Generalizing from this kind of experience would lead one to define $\ominus$ for numbers of arithmetic by saying that $a/b \ominus c/d$ if and only if $a \cdot d > b \cdot c$.

FIGURE 6–9

The preceding discussions have produced motivation for two different ways of defining $\ominus$. As will be seen, the two ways of making a definition are equivalent. The first will be chosen and it will then be proved that the second is equivalent to it.

Definition 4. *For any numbers of arithmetic a/b and c/d, $a/b \ominus c/d$ if and only if $a/b - c/d$ exists and is not zero.*

The sentence $x/y \oslash z/w$ will of course be understood to mean that $z/w \ominus x/y$. The following theorem establishes that $\ominus$ could have been equivalently defined in accordance with physical considerations.

Theorem XV. For any numbers of arithmetic a/b and c/d, $a/b \ominus c/d$ if and only if $a \cdot d > b \cdot c$.

To test the truth of a sentence $x/y \ominus z/w$, one would quite naturally apply Definition 4, subtracting z/w from x/y. In view of Theorem XV, however, it is equally valid to test the truth of $x/y \ominus z/w$ by testing the truth of $x \cdot w > y \cdot z$. It is generally easier to do the latter.

The next theorem establishes that $\oslash$ is in fact an extension of $>$.

Theorem XVI. For any numbers of arithmetic nameable, '$a/1$' and '$b/1$,' $a/1 \oslash b/1$ if and only if $a > b$.

In view of Theorem XVI, the circle in $\oslash$ may be omitted without the risk of confusion.

EXERCISES

1. Draw diagrams similar to Fig. 6–9 to show which of the following represents the larger amount.

   (a) $\frac{5}{7}$ and $\frac{6}{7}$ (b) $\frac{2}{3}$ and $\frac{3}{4}$ (c) $\frac{9}{5}$ and $\frac{11}{5}$ (d) $\frac{5}{3}$ and $\frac{7}{5}$.

2. Apply Definition 4 to show which of the following is larger.

   (a) $\frac{5}{8}$ and $\frac{6}{8}$ (b) $\frac{5}{9}$ and $\frac{7}{11}$ (c) $\frac{9}{5}$ and $\frac{11}{7}$ (d) $\frac{12}{7}$ and $\frac{15}{11}$.

3. Apply Theorem XV to show which of the following is larger.

   (a) $\frac{3}{8}$ and $\frac{5}{8}$ (b) $\frac{21}{5}$ and $\frac{27}{7}$ (c) $\frac{5}{9}$ and $\frac{7}{11}$ (d) $\frac{31}{11}$ and $\frac{41}{13}$

4. Which is easier to apply generally, Definition 4 or Theorem XV? Why?

5. There is a similarity between Definition 1 and Theorem XV. Describe and discuss this.

6. Prove that $>$ for whole numbers is an order relation.

7. Prove that $\oslash$ for numbers of ordinary arithmetic is an order relation.

8. Prove Theorem XV.

9. Prove Theorem XVI.

REVIEW PRACTICE EXERCISES

Add

1. 316.25	2. 41.823	3. 659.403
18.12	614.915	916.812

Multiply

4. 31.82	5. 0.612	6. 18,000
7.15	81.7	2.02

Write expanded numerals for these numbers.

7. 6814.1035   8. 96402.0011   9. 16005.1101

Divide, to find the decimal numeral for each number. Continue dividing until a zero remainder is obtained or the digits begin to repeat.

10. $\frac{5}{6}$ 11. $\frac{7}{8}$ 12. $\frac{11}{9}$

The number line. The order of the numbers of arithmetic, as that set is ordered by the relation $\oslash$ can best be visualized by means of a line graph similar to that used for whole numbers, in which each number is associated with some point on the line.

Theorem XVI guarantees that the order of the numbers $a/1$ is like that for whole numbers. Therefore, a good way to start labeling a number line for the numbers of arithmetic is to use a whole-number line, as shown in Fig. 6–10. Other points can then be located or labeled in accordance with Definition 4 or Theorem XV. Since $0 < \frac{1}{2} < 1$, the point for $\frac{1}{2}$ will be between the points labeled '0' and '1.' Similarly, the point for $\frac{3}{2}$ will be between the points for 1 and 2, and $\frac{5}{2}$ between 2 and 3. Further intermediate points can be labeled as desired, as in Fig. 6–11.

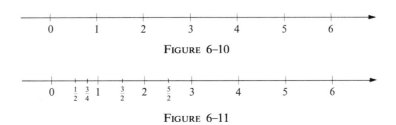

FIGURE 6–10

FIGURE 6–11

Density. Between any two arithmetic numbers there is at least one other number. In fact, the number halfway between two numbers can be found by averaging them. For example, the number halfway between $\frac{1}{2}$ and 1 is $\frac{1}{2}(\frac{1}{2} + 1)$, or $\frac{3}{4}$. The number halfway between a/b and c/d is

$$\frac{1}{2}\left(\frac{a}{b} + \frac{c}{d}\right).$$

Halfway between $\frac{3}{4}$ and 1 is the number $\frac{7}{8}$, and between $\frac{7}{8}$ and 1 is $\frac{15}{16}$. Between $\frac{15}{16}$ and 1 is $\frac{31}{32}$, and so on. The fact that between *any* two numbers there is another number actually implies that between any two numbers there is an endless set of others. This kind of order is known as *dense order*. Informally it has just been proved that:

> **The order of the numbers of arithmetic is dense, i.e., between any two different numbers there is a third.**

The set of whole numbers is not ordered densely. Between 2 and 3 there is no other whole number, for example. The set of whole numbers does have its own peculiar property with respect to order, however. If one takes any set of whole numbers, provided it is not empty, that set will contain a least element. This property is often described by saying that the set is *well-ordered*.

> **The set of whole numbers is well-ordered, i.e., any nonempty set of whole numbers contains a least element.**

It is easy to find nonempty sets of arithmetic numbers that do not contain least elements. The set $\{x \mid x > 1\}$ is an example. This set does not contain the number 1, but contains all numbers larger than 1. There is no smallest number that is larger than 1. If there were such a number, say t, then there would be no arithmetic number between 1 and t, which contradicts the fact that the arithmetic numbers have dense order.

EXERCISES

1. For each of the following pairs of numbers, tell which is larger, using Theorem XV.

   (a) $\frac{5}{12}, \frac{7}{18}$ (b) $\frac{10}{15}, \frac{13}{29}$ (c) $\frac{36}{49}, \frac{42}{56}$ (d) $\frac{195}{12}, \frac{217}{15}$

2. For each pair of numbers mentioned in exercise 1, find the number halfway between the two.

3. Plot the graph of each of the following numbers using a number line.

   (a) $\frac{6}{5}$ (b) $\frac{8}{9}$ (c) $\frac{17}{18}$ (d) $\frac{123}{15}$

4. (a) Find the arithmetic number halfway between 1 and 2. (b) Find the number halfway between 1 and the answer to (a). (c) Find the number halfway between 1 and the answer to (b). (d) Proceed in this manner to find five more numbers, and discuss the properties of the sequence of numbers thus found.

5. Prove: If t is the average of numbers x, y, where $x < y$, then $x < t$ and also $t < y$.

9. CALCULATIONS USING DECIMAL NUMERALS

The reader is of course aware that the fractional symbols just discussed are not the only kind used in elementary arithmetic. Base ten, or *decimal*, numerals and some of the principles of calculating with them have already been discussed in Chapter 1. It may be less clear that the numbers of arithmetic may be named by decimal numerals, and that a calculation may be performed using either decimal or fractional symbolism. The present purpose is to elaborate the notion that decimal numerals can be used for calculating in the number system of arithmetic, and to justify some of the familiar rules for manipulating them. Although only decimal numeration is considered here, it will be recognized that similar principles hold for Hindu-Arabic type numeration of any base.

Decimal numerals for the numbers of arithmetic. In Chapter 1, expanded numerals were used. Their purpose at that time was described as "explanatory," to aid in understanding the meaning of decimal numerals. Expanded numerals should now be regarded as *defining* decimal numerals in terms of the fractional numerals already developed. For example, '3542.142' by definition means the same as the following combination of fractional symbols:

$$\frac{3 \cdot 10^3}{1} + \frac{5 \cdot 10^2}{1} + \frac{4 \cdot 10}{1} + \frac{2}{1} + \frac{1}{10} + \frac{4}{10^2} + \frac{2}{10^3}.$$

Every fractional symbol a/b, with whole number numerator and nonzero whole number denominator, represents a number of arithmetic. Conversely, every number of arithmetic can be so represented. It is now important to investigate whether the same is true for decimal numerals. First, can every number of arithmetic be named with an expanded numeral as shown above? The answer, although not obvious, is affirmative. The following examples illustrate how expanded numerals, and then in turn decimal numerals, can be found for some numbers of arithmetic.

EXAMPLE 1.

$$\tfrac{3}{5} = \tfrac{3}{5} \cdot \tfrac{2}{2} = \tfrac{6}{10} = 0.6.$$

EXAMPLE 2.

$$\tfrac{7}{20} = \tfrac{7}{20} \cdot \tfrac{5}{5} = \tfrac{35}{100} = \tfrac{30}{100} + \tfrac{5}{100} = \tfrac{3}{10} + \tfrac{5}{100} = 0.35.$$

EXAMPLE 3.

$$\tfrac{9}{40} = \tfrac{9}{40} \cdot \tfrac{25}{25} = \tfrac{225}{1000} = \tfrac{200}{1000} + \tfrac{20}{1000} + \tfrac{5}{1000} = \tfrac{2}{10} + \tfrac{2}{100} + \tfrac{5}{1000} = 0.225.$$

EXAMPLE 4.

$$\tfrac{87}{25} = \tfrac{87}{25} \cdot \tfrac{4}{4} = \tfrac{348}{100} = \tfrac{300}{100} + \tfrac{40}{100} + \tfrac{8}{100} = \tfrac{3}{1} + \tfrac{4}{10} + \tfrac{8}{100} = 3.48.$$

It should be noted that in each example, the number in question was multiplied by the identity in order to find a symbol whose denominator was 10, 100, or 1000 (some power of ten). The number was then symbolized as a sum in such a way that an expanded numeral was obtained. The decimal numeral was then easy to determine, since it is defined in terms of expanded numerals.

In each of the previous examples, the denominator was a factor of some power of ten. Had this not been the case, the procedure would not have worked so well. Some difficulty is encountered in trying the method with $\tfrac{5}{6}$, for example. The denominator has the prime factor 3, exhibited when the number is named '$5/(2 \cdot 3)$.' When this number is multiplied by n/n, the denominator of the new symbol will have the factor 3, no matter what number is selected for n. It cannot therefore be a power of ten, because the only prime factors of any power of ten are 2 and 5. Since this is the case, it is necessary to use some modification of the method. A modified method is illustrated in the following examples.

EXAMPLE 1. Find a decimal numeral for $\tfrac{5}{6}$.

The first task is to find an expanded numeral. Since $\tfrac{5}{6} < 1$, there will be no non-zero digit symbols to the left of the decimal point, and therefore the expanded numeral will be

$$\frac{a}{10} + \frac{b}{100} + \frac{c}{1000} + \cdots,$$

where some of $a, b, c, \ldots$ may be zero. Thus $\tfrac{5}{6}$ will be multiplied by the identity, the symbol for the latter being chosen so that the new symbol will have a denominator of 10:

$$\frac{5}{6} \cdot \frac{\tfrac{10}{6}}{\tfrac{10}{6}} = \frac{\tfrac{50}{6}}{10} = \frac{8 + \tfrac{1}{3}}{10}.$$

Now

$$\frac{8 + \tfrac{1}{3}}{10} = \frac{8}{10} + \frac{\tfrac{1}{3}}{10},$$

and it is clear that the tenths digit is 8.

To make the next denominator 100, the symbol $\tfrac{10}{10}$ will be chosen for the identity:

$$\frac{\tfrac{1}{3}}{10} = \frac{\tfrac{1}{3}}{10} \cdot \frac{10}{10} = \frac{\tfrac{10}{3}}{100} = \frac{3 + \tfrac{1}{3}}{100} = \frac{3}{100} + \frac{\tfrac{1}{3}}{100}.$$

Therefore,

$$\frac{5}{6} = \frac{8}{10} + \frac{3}{100} + \frac{\frac{1}{3}}{100},$$

and the hundredths digit is 3.

In a similar way it can be shown that

$$\frac{\frac{1}{3}}{100} = \frac{3}{1000} + \frac{\frac{1}{3}}{1000}.$$

Therefore, the thousandths digit is 3. It soon becomes apparent that the digits are repeating and will continue to do so, and therefore, that the decimal numeral for $\frac{5}{6}$ is

$$0.83333\dots.$$

The dots here indicate an endless sequence of digits. When the endless sequence has a repeating pattern, as in this case, the dots are often replaced by a bar to indicate the repeating cycle, as follows:

$$0.8\overline{33}.$$

Symbols such as these are sometimes referred to as "endless" or "endlessly repeating," even though no *symbol* can actually be of unlimited extent.

EXAMPLE 2. Find a decimal numeral for $\frac{308}{3}$.

Since $\frac{308}{3} > 1$, the expanded numeral will have digit symbols to the left of the decimal point. They may be found first:

$$\frac{308}{3} = \frac{306}{3} + \frac{2}{3} = 1\cdot 10^2 + 0\cdot 10 + 2 + \frac{2}{3}.$$

$$\frac{2}{3} = \frac{2\cdot\frac{10}{3}}{\frac{10}{3}} = \frac{\frac{20}{3}}{10} = \frac{6 + \frac{2}{3}}{10} = \frac{6}{10} + \frac{\frac{2}{3}}{10},$$

$$\frac{\frac{2}{3}}{10}\cdot\frac{10}{10} = \frac{\frac{20}{3}}{10^2} = \frac{6 + \frac{2}{3}}{10^2} = \frac{6}{10^2} + \frac{\frac{2}{3}}{10^2},$$

$$\frac{\frac{2}{3}}{10^2}\cdot\frac{10}{10} = \frac{\frac{20}{3}}{10^3} = \frac{6 + \frac{2}{3}}{10^3} = \frac{6}{10^3} + \frac{\frac{2}{3}}{10^3}.$$

The digits are obviously repeating, and the decimal numeral for 308/3 is thus the endless symbol

$$\text{'}102.6666\dots.\text{'}$$

Although these examples do not constitute a proof, they illustrate the fact that whenever a terminating decimal numeral cannot be found for a number of arithmetic, a repeating one can. Thus if endlessly repeating symbols are allowed, every number of arithmetic can be named with a decimal numeral.

It is easy to see that a terminating decimal numeral represents a number of arithmetic, from the expanded numeral definition. For example '324.385' means the same as

$$\text{'}\frac{3\cdot 10^2}{1} + \frac{2\cdot 10}{1} + \frac{4}{1} + \frac{3}{10} + \frac{8}{10^2} + \frac{5}{10^3}.\text{'}$$

The latter symbol, containing fractional symbols, clearly indicates a sum of arithmetic numbers. Since the set of arithmetic numbers is closed under addition, that sum is also a number of arithmetic.

Although it is not quite so easy to see that an endlessly repeating decimal numeral also represents a number of arithmetic, the following examples should seem convincing.

EXAMPLE 1. Find a fractional numeral for 0.412 412 $\overline{412}$.

Call the number in question 'n.' Then $n = 0.412\,\overline{412}$. Multiplying by 1000, $1000n = 412.412\,412\,\overline{412}$. Subtracting n from $1000n$, $999n = 412$. Thus $n = 412/999$.

EXAMPLE 2. Show that '7.2334 34 $\overline{34}$' represents a number of arithmetic.

The first task is to isolate the initial set of digits from those which repeat in the cycle of two:

$$7.2334\,34\,\overline{34} = 7.23 + 0.00\,34\,34\,\overline{34}.$$

Let $n = 0.00\,34\,34\,\overline{34}$. Then $100n = 0.34\,34\,\overline{34}$, and $99n = 0.34$. Therefore, $n = 0.34/99$, or $34/9900$. Now $7.23 = 723/100$, and the number in question can then be represented by

$$\tfrac{723}{100} + \tfrac{34}{9900}.$$

This symbol clearly names a sum of arithmetic numbers, which by closure is an arithmetic number.

It has thus been illustrated that all numbers of arithmetic can be named by decimal numerals, terminating or repeating; and conversely that every decimal symbol which either ends or repeats represents a number of arithmetic.

The reader who has been conditioned to convert to decimal symbolism by long division may wonder why that process has not been used in this discussion. There is a very good logical reason, namely, that it is important to establish that decimal numerals exist before proceeding to use them in calculations.

EXERCISES

1. For each of the following numbers of arithmetic, find an expanded numeral, and in turn a decimal numeral.

   (a) $\frac{15}{8}$ (b) $\frac{13}{20}$ (c) $\frac{18}{15}$ (d) $\frac{63}{70}$ (e) $\frac{98}{80}$ (f) $\frac{651}{120}$

2. For each of these numbers of arithmetic, find an expanded numeral, and in turn a decimal numeral.

   (a) $\frac{1}{3}$ (b) $\frac{2}{3}$ (c) $\frac{22}{7}$ (d) $\frac{103}{33}$

3. Name with fractional numerals ten numbers of arithmetic whose decimal numerals do not terminate.

4. In repeating decimal numerals, the number of digits in the repeating cycle may vary. What can you discover, or guess, about the number of digits there can be in a repeating cycle?

5. The denominator of '$\frac{21}{6}$' has the factor 3, yet the decimal numeral for the number $\frac{21}{6}$ terminates. Why?

6. For each of the following numbers, find an expanded numeral, and in turn a fractional numeral.

   (a) 16.12   (b) 0.0304   (c) 3.14159   (d) 751.32

7. For each of the following numbers, find a fractional numeral.

(a) $0.55\overline{5}$ (b) $0.51\ 51\ \overline{51}$ (c) $3.12\ 12\ \overline{12}$ (d) $13.7\ 651\ \overline{651}$

8. For each of the following numbers of arithmetic, find an expanded numeral, and in turn a base six numeral.

(a) $\frac{3}{8}$ (b) $\frac{17}{12}$ (c) $\frac{3}{5}$ (d) $\frac{16}{15}$

9. For each of the following numbers, find an expanded numeral, and in turn a fractional numeral.

(a) 35.12_6 (b) 40.13_6

10. The decimal numeral for a number of arithmetic either terminates or repeats. Is the same thing true of the base five numeral? The base six numeral? The base n numeral?

11. Does the decimal numeral for $\frac{1}{3}$ end or repeat? Does the base three numeral for $\frac{1}{3}$ end or repeat?

12. For which numbers of arithmetic do base twelve numerals terminate? Does your answer suggest an advantage of duodecimal numeration over decimal numeration?

13. It is possible to construct some types of endless, nonrepeating symbols as follows:

$$0.01001000100001\ldots, \quad \text{or} \quad 3.556655566655556666\ldots.$$

Construct five more.

14. In the preceding development it was established that if n is a number of arithmetic, then it can be named by a terminating or repeating decimal numeral. Conversely, terminating or repeating numerals were shown to name numbers of arithmetic. It was not shown that endless, nonrepeating decimals do *not* name numbers of arithmetic. Why not?

15. In developing the properties of the numbers of arithmetic in this chapter, fractional numerals were used, and decimal numerals developed later. However, base ten numerals were used in symbols like $\frac{315}{12}$ from the start. Thus the development appears circular, and therefore not valid. Could numerals other than the Hindu-Arabic type have been used in the initial development? If so, why do you suppose that was not done?

16. In finding fractional numerals when repeating decimal numerals are given, a peculiar kind of multiplication is performed. For example,

$$10 \cdot (0.33\overline{3}).$$

Using an expanded numeral, the calculation can be symbolized

$$10 \cdot \left(\frac{3}{10} + \frac{3}{10^2} + \frac{3}{10^3} + \cdots \right).$$

What law do you suppose is then used?

REVIEW PRACTICE EXERCISES

Simplify

1. $3^6 \cdot 3^7$

2. $10^4 \cdot 10^{-2}$

3. $16^{-7} \cdot 16^2$

4. $3^{-5} \cdot 3^{-6}$

5. $10^{-7} \cdot 10^{-2}$

6. $5^{-6} \cdot 5^7$

7. $\dfrac{8^3}{8^2}$

8. $\dfrac{16^{-5}}{16^2}$

9. $\dfrac{10^4}{10^{-3}}$

10. $\dfrac{12^{-5}}{12^{-2}}$

11. $\dfrac{7^{-3}}{7^{-10}}$

12. $\dfrac{10^{-5}}{10^{-13}}$

13. $(3^2)^4$ 14. $(3^2 \cdot 4^2)^3$ 15. $(3^{-5})^2$
16. $(4^6)^{-5}$ 17. $(8^{-5})^{-4}$ 18. $(3^4 \cdot 6^{-2})^5$
19. $(6 \cdot 8^{-2})^4$ 20. $(7^{-5} \cdot 8^4)^{-3}$ 21. $(4 \cdot 10^{-3})^2$

Addition using decimal numerals. In Chapter 2, algorithms for multiplication and addition in the system of natural numbers, using decimal numerals, were discussed. It will be recalled that the procedures depend upon the commutative, associative, and distributive laws. Since these laws also hold in the number system of arithmetic, it may be expected that quite similar algorithms can be developed. This is indeed the case. They are so similar in fact that an illustrative example should suffice to describe the algorithm for addition using decimal numerals in the number system of arithmetic:

$$
\begin{array}{r}
7.231 \\
22.92 \\
\hline
30.151
\end{array}
$$

Using expanded numerals, the addition is symbolized

$$\left(7 + 2 \cdot \frac{1}{10} + 3 \cdot \frac{1}{10^2} + 1 \cdot \frac{1}{10^3}\right) + \left(2 \cdot 10 + 2 + 9 \cdot \frac{1}{10} + 2 \cdot \frac{1}{10^2}\right).$$

Using the commutative and associative laws of addition for numbers of arithmetic, thereby rearranging, one obtains

$$(2 \cdot 10) + (7 + 2) + \left(2 \cdot \frac{1}{10} + 9 \cdot \frac{1}{10}\right) + \left(3 \cdot \frac{1}{10^2} + 2 \cdot \frac{1}{10^2}\right) + 1 \cdot \frac{1}{10^3}.$$

The distributive law of multiplication over addition for numbers of arithmetic then yields

$$(2 \cdot 10) + (7 + 2) + (2 + 9) \cdot \frac{1}{10} + (3 + 2) \cdot \frac{1}{10^2} + 1 \cdot \frac{1}{10^3},$$

or

$$2 \cdot 10 + 9 + 11 \cdot \frac{1}{10} + 5 \cdot \frac{1}{10^2} + 1 \cdot \frac{1}{10^3}.$$

The third term has a factor 11, and since no digit can be larger than 9, some "carrying" or regrouping must be done. It is justified as follows:

$$11 \cdot \tfrac{1}{10} = (10 + 1) \cdot \tfrac{1}{10} = 10 \cdot \tfrac{1}{10} + 1 \cdot \tfrac{1}{10} = 1 + 1 \cdot \tfrac{1}{10}.$$

The 1 thus obtained is now associated with 9, to obtain 10, and the resulting 10 associated with $2 \cdot 10$:

$$2 \cdot 10 + (9 + 1) + 1 \cdot \frac{1}{10} + 5 \cdot \frac{1}{10^2} + 1 \cdot \frac{1}{10^3}$$

$$2 \cdot 10 + 10 = (2 + 1) \cdot 10 = 3 \cdot 10.$$

Thus the result is

$$3 \cdot 10 + 0 \cdot 1 + 1 \cdot \frac{1}{10} + 5 \cdot \frac{1}{10^2} + 1 \cdot \frac{1}{10^3}.$$

The procedure using expanded numerals justifies the more concise rule for adding when using decimal numerals. It should be noted that the usual algorithm is not the only possible one. By using the commutative, associative, and distributive laws, one can devise various schemes, or algorithms, for adding. In particular, it is worthy of note that it is not mandatory, as students are sometimes told, that the decimal points be aligned vertically when writing the numerals prior to adding. To be sure, it is more convenient to have decimal points aligned, but it is clearly not necessary. In fact, the various numerals could be written on different blackboards.

When decimal numerals are endless, the procedure for adding must be modified. It is sometimes possible to use endless numerals and also obtain an endless numeral for the result, as follows:

$$
\begin{array}{r}
0.333\ldots \\
0.666\ldots \\
\hline
0.999\ldots
\end{array}
$$

(This seems a very fancy way of saying that $\frac{1}{3} + \frac{2}{3} = 1$.) In other cases where numerals are endless, the problem of finding a repeating (or sometimes terminating) numeral for the result is quite complicated. Ordinarily, endless numerals are not used. Rather, whenever a number whose decimal numeral is endless is to be added, a terminating numeral is used. This provides a good approximation. The terminating numeral is selected simply by taking a part of the endless one. The more digits used, the better the approximation. For example, the sum of $18.3854\overline{3856}$ and $4.823\overline{223}$ would be approximated to the nearest hundredth as follows:

$$
\begin{array}{r}
18.385 \\
4.823 \\
\hline
23.208 \qquad \textbf{23.21}
\end{array}
$$

Multiplication using decimal numerals. The usual algorithm for multiplying numbers of arithmetic using decimal numerals parallels that for natural numbers, explained in Chapter 2. It will be recalled that the rationale depends upon the commutative, associative, and distributive laws. Since those laws also hold in the number system of arithmetic, a similar algorithm holds, as the following example illustrates:

$$
\begin{array}{r}
351.2 \\
1.65 \\
\hline
17560 \\
21072 \\
3512 \\
\hline
579480
\end{array}
$$

Hopefully, the reader will object that this problem is not yet finished, i.e., that the author, or printer, has forgotten the decimal point in the answer. The objection is a valid one. The error, however, illustrates an important point: in computing thus far, no reference to decimal points has been needed. Therefore, the work shown here is correct for multiplying 3512 and 165 (two natural numbers)! The answer thus obtained is too large by a factor of 10^3. If it is divided by 10^3, the answer to the stated problem will be obtained. Thus "counting over three places from the right end and placing a decimal point" will produce the correct result.

This illustration shows how the multiplication algorithm may be simply explained, but more concise symbolism might be more helpful. The same example might be explained as follows:

$$(351.2) \cdot (1.65) = \frac{3512}{10} \cdot \frac{165}{100} = \frac{3512 \cdot 165}{10^3}.$$

When repeating numerals occur, approximations are used in multiplication, as well as in addition.

EXERCISES

1. Perform these additions: (i) using the standard algorithm, (ii) using expanded numerals, showing each use of the laws of the number system of arithmetic.

(a) 37.45   (b) 48.76
    6.32   53.45

2. Perform these multiplications: (i) using the standard algorithm, (ii) using expanded numerals, showing each use of the laws of the number system of arithmetic.

(a) 24.7   (b) 3.82
    3.2   73.8

3. Perform these additions, obtaining an endless numeral for the result. Perform the same calculations using fractional numerals.

(a) $0.166\overline{6}$ (b) $0.833\overline{3}$ (c) $0.8333\overline{3}$
    $0.333\overline{3}$ $0.333\overline{3}$ 0.16666

4. Perform these additions, obtaining an endless numeral for the result.

(a) $2.671\overline{212}$ (b) $0.213213\overline{213}$
    $3.351\overline{351}$ $7.83838\overline{383}$

REVIEW PRACTICE EXERCISES

1. Find
    (a) 12% of 50   (b) 65% of 480
    (c) 120% of 75   (d) 0.1% of 40

2. (a) 10 is what percent of 20?   (b) 20 is what percent of 10?
    (c) 30 is what percent of 90?   (d) 90 is what percent of 30?

3. (a) 20 is 50% of what?   (b) 45 is 20% of what?
    (c) 60 is 120% of what?   (d) 120 is 130% of what?

Division using decimal numerals. Division, it will be recalled, is the operation opposite to multiplication. That is, to find $a \div b$, one looks for the number c such that $c \cdot b = a$. Since the nonzero numbers of arithmetic form a group under multiplication, the division may also be performed by multiplying a by the reciprocal of b. The latter method is most convenient when using fractional numerals, but decimal numerals for reciprocals are generally not easy to find. Thus a method based on the other idea of division is more convenient when using decimal numerals.

The following examples illustrate that division is easily accomplished if one does not mind having a fractional numeral for the result:

$$2.41\overline{)80.12}$$

This division may also be indicated by

$$\frac{80.12}{2.41} \quad \text{or} \quad \frac{80.12}{2.41} \cdot \frac{10^2}{10^2}, \quad \text{or} \quad \frac{8012}{241},$$

The division $24.1\overline{)8.012}$ may similarly be indicated by

$$\frac{8.012}{24.1} \cdot \frac{10^3}{10^3} \quad \text{or} \quad \frac{8012}{24100}.$$

In each case, a fractional numeral with whole number numerator and denominator was found for the result, by a simple multiplication by the identity. This procedure is well worth remembering, since it provides a simple means of converting any division of arithmetic numbers to a division of whole numbers. However, there remains the problem of finding a decimal numeral for the result.

It should be recalled that the division algorithm for whole numbers consists of repeated guessing of partial quotients, multiplying, and subtracting. The process is based on the associative law of addition and the distributive law of multiplication over addition. The partial quotients must of course be chosen so that subtractions are possible. Since the number system of ordinary arithmetic has the necessary properties, the division algorithm is also valid in this system. It can be used to find a decimal numeral for a quotient. One simply makes guesses for partial quotients in such a way that the digits of the answer are obtained. That is, one guesses numbers of thousands, hundreds, tens, etc. It would be possible to use the same process to find a base b numeral, for any base b. In that case one would guess numbers of b^3's, b^2's, b's, and so on.

To continue with the example above, the division algorithm for whole numbers produces the whole number part of the desired result here, as follows.

To find the tens digit:

$$
\begin{array}{r}
30 \\
241\overline{)8012} \\
7230 \\
\hline
782
\end{array}
$$

The tens digit is 3, because 40 is too large for a partial quotient. To find the units digit:

$$
\begin{array}{r}
30 + 3 \\
241\overline{)8012} \\
7230 \\
\hline
782 \\
723 \\
\hline
59
\end{array}
$$

The units digit is 3, because 4 is too large for a second partial quotient.

The whole number algorithm is now at an end because the remainder is smaller than the divisor.

To find further digits of the decimal numeral, one now continues to guess, multiply, and subtract. But now the guesses will be numbers of tenths, hundredths, and so on, as follows.

To find the tenths digit:

$$
\begin{array}{r}
2/10 \text{ or } 0.2 \\
\hline
241\overline{)59} \\
48.2 \\
\hline
10.8
\end{array}
$$

The tenths digit is 2, because 0.3 is too large for a partial quotient. To find the hundredths digit:

$$
\begin{array}{r}
4/100 \text{ or } 0.04 \\
\hline
241\overline{)10.8} \\
9.64 \\
\hline
1.16
\end{array}
$$

To find the thousandths digit:

$$
\begin{array}{r}
4/1000 \text{ or } 0.004 \\
\hline
241\overline{)1.16} \\
0.964 \\
\hline
0.196
\end{array}
$$

It may now be instructive to write the steps together:

$$
\begin{array}{r}
33.244 \\
\hline
241\overline{)8012} \\
7320 \\
\hline
782 \\
723 \\
\hline
59 \\
48.2 \\
\hline
10.8 \\
9.64 \\
\hline
1.16 \\
0.964 \\
\hline
0.196
\end{array}
$$

Since there is still a nonzero remainder, the process can be carried further, if desired. However, at this stage (or any stage) the product of the quotient and divisor, plus the last remainder, is the dividend. Thus the product of 241 and 33.244 differs from 8012 by only 0.196, and the quotient just obtained is a good approximation.

When the steps are written together, as they are above, the division process probably looks more familiar. It is not usual, however, to use decimal points except for the quotient, divisor, and dividend. Instead it is more usual that "zeros are annexed and brought down." In order to understand why the latter procedure is valid, the reader should perform the division

$$241\overline{)8012000}$$

and compare it with the above.

The placing of the decimal point in the preceding example would seem to pose no great problem. It occurs when the whole number algorithm comes to an end. Rules taught in school for placing decimal points often require the counting of decimal places in divisor and quotient, the placing of carets or the "moving over" of decimal points, the "annexing of zeros," the careful aligning of the decimal point of the quotient and the caret of the dividend, and so on. Not only does such procedure obscure the basic nature of the division algorithm, but it also fails its intended purpose, namely to produce accuracy. (The reader is no doubt well aware how easy it is to slip up somewhere and place a decimal point incorrectly.) Similar mechanical rules are taught for placing decimal points in multiplication, and with similar results.

Mechanical rules for placing decimal points in any kind of calculation must be seriously questioned, not only because they hinder understanding, but also because they give rise to many possibilities for error, and fail to produce the desired accuracy. If the only rule ever taught for placing decimal points were to use a roughly estimated result, it seems certain that errors would diminish. Furthermore, teaching time would be saved, and the time saved could be used to establish understanding of the algorithms, as well as for practice of them.

EXERCISES

1. Divide, finding a fractional numeral for the result.
    (a) $4.78\overline{)18.1}$ (b) $16.4\overline{)0.305}$ (c) $0.0374\overline{)9.052}$ (d) $857\overline{)0.0583}$

2. Divide, using the procedure of the example in the preceding text. Continue to approximate until the result is exact or until the hundredths digit is obtained.
    (a) $317\overline{)723}$ (b) $47\overline{)35}$ (c) $153\overline{)2450}$ (d) $251\overline{)674}$

3. Divide, by first converting to a problem involving only whole numbers, and then proceeding as in exercise 2.
    (a) $2.53\overline{)17.8}$ (b) $0.032\overline{)1053}$

4. Repeat the divisions of exercise 3, but without first converting to a problem involving whole numbers.

5. Repeat the divisions of exercise 2, but write them in the usual way. Discuss this method by comparing it with that used in exercise 2.

10. CALCULATIONS USING OTHER SYMBOLS

The two most common types of symbols used in ordinary arithmetic, the decimal symbols and the fractional symbols, have now been considered. There are other kinds of symbolism also in common use. Among these are symbols which contain the percent symbol %, and scientific notation.

The percent symbol. The symbol % can be interpreted in various ways. Probably the simplest and most useful is to regard it as part of a numeral. For example, '35%' can be defined to mean 35×0.01, or $35 \times \frac{1}{100}$. If, in general '$n\%$' is defined to mean $n \times \frac{1}{100}$, then the handling of symbolism involving the percent symbol presents no special problem. Numbers named using the percent symbol are numbers of ordinary arithmetic having properties already known, and no special rules for calculating are needed.

Conversion from percent symbolism to fractional or decimal notation is easy to accomplish by merely applying the definition.

EXAMPLE.

$$36.5\% = 36.5 \times 0.01 \text{ (by definition of \%)}$$
$$= 0.365.$$

Applying the definition (in reverse) also allows one to write percent notation for a arithmetic number.

EXAMPLES.

$$1.21 = 1.21 \times (100 \times 0.01) \quad \text{(multiplying by the identity)}$$
$$= (1.21 \times 100) \times 0.01$$
$$= 121 \times 0.01$$
$$= 121\% \quad \text{(applying definition of \%)}.$$

$$\tfrac{3}{8} = \tfrac{3}{8} \cdot (100 \cdot \tfrac{1}{100})$$
$$= (\tfrac{3}{8} \cdot 100) \cdot \tfrac{1}{100}$$
$$= \tfrac{75}{2} \cdot \tfrac{1}{100}$$
$$= \tfrac{75}{2}\%.$$

Scientific notation. Scientific notation is a special kind of decimal symbolism, or numeration. It is particularly useful when calculations involve very large or very small numbers, and is also useful in the study of common logarithms. Some examples of scientific notation are

$$3.1 \times 10^5, \quad 4.5 \times 10^{-3}, \quad 10^3.$$

Each symbol consists of a symbol for a power of ten, and if needed, a decimal numeral for a number between 1 and 10 and a multiplication sign.

To multiply using scientific notation the commutative and associative laws are employed, as in the following example:

$$(3.1 \times 10^5) \cdot (4.5 \times 10^{-3}) = (3.1 \times 4.5) \cdot (10^5 \times 10^{-3}) = 13.95 \times 10^2.$$

To find scientific notation for the result the multiplicative identity may be used:

$$(13.95 \times 10^2) \times \frac{10}{10} = \left(\frac{13.95}{10}\right) \times 10^3 = 1.395 \times 10^3.$$

Division of numbers of arithmetic, using scientific notation, is illustrated in the following example:

$$\frac{3.41 \times 10^5}{1.1 \times 10^{-3}} = \frac{3.41}{1.1} \times \frac{10^5}{10^{-3}} = 3.1 \times 10^8.$$

Scientific notation is also convenient for comparing numbers of arithmetic to see which of two numbers is larger. It is not especially convenient without modification, however, for addition or subtraction.

EXERCISES

1. For each of the following numbers, write a numeral using the percent symbol.
   (a) $\frac{1}{2}$ (b) $\frac{3}{4}$ (c) 1   (d) 2
   (e) 1.35   (f) 0.217   (g) 0.051   (h) 0.00012

2. For each of the following numbers, write a standard decimal numeral.
   (a) 17% (b) 150% (c) 12.5%
   (d) $\frac{1}{8}\%$ (e) $\frac{3}{4}\%$ (f) 0.015%

3. Write scientific notation for each of the following numbers.
   (a) 130,000,000   (b) 350 trillion   (c) 1,000,000
   (d) 0.0000031   (e) 0.000000000192   (f) 0.1

4. Multiply, using scientific notation, and write scientific notation for the result.
   (a) $10^3 \times 10^{-1}$ (b) $10^{-6} \times 10^{-4}$
   (c) $(1.2 \times 10^5) \cdot (1.3 \times 10^7)$ (d) $(3.2 \times 10^8) \cdot (4.1 \times 10^6)$
   (e) $(6.3 \times 10^7) \cdot (2.1 \times 10^{-5})$ (f) $(9.1 \times 10^{-17}) \cdot (8.2 \times 10^3)$
                    (g) $(6.2 \times 10^{-8}) \cdot (3.1 \times 10^{-15})$

5. Divide, using scientific notation, and write scientific notation for the result.
   (a) $\dfrac{4.26 \times 10^{12}}{2.13 \times 10^5}$ (b) $\dfrac{3.0 \times 10^{-5}}{1.2 \times 10^4}$ (c) $\dfrac{9.8 \times 10^6}{3.1 \times 10^{-7}}$ (d) $\dfrac{2.05 \times 10^{-4}}{8.1 \times 10^{-7}}$

11. TERMINOLOGY

In this book a distinction is made between *numbers* and *numerals*, or symbols for numbers. The numbers of arithmetic consist of two classes, namely the *whole numbers* (the numbers of arithmetic isomorphic to the whole numbers) and the *fractions*. Any number of arithmetic which is not a whole number is called a *fraction*.

All numbers of arithmetic, fractions or whole numbers, can be named by fractional symbols, or *fractional numerals*. They can also be named by symbols of the Hindu-Arabic type. The latter, when base ten, are called *decimal numerals*. There are other kinds of symbolism with which the numbers of arithmetic can be named.

The *numerator* and *denominator*, spoken of in connection with a fractional numeral, are clearly associated with the symbol, rather than the number named, for a single number can be named by many different fractional symbols. Yet one speaks of factors and multiples of denominators, of adding numerators, and the like. Thus, although numerators and denominators are associated with symbols, they are themselves numbers. The *numerator* of a fractional symbol is the number named by the top symbol. The *denominator* of a fractional numeral is the number named by the bottom symbol. The *simplest fractional numeral* for a number is the one whose numerator and denominator have no common prime factors.

Regardless of the symbolism used, additions, multiplications, and other operations are performed upon the numbers of arithmetic, and *not* upon symbols for them. One may add *using* decimal numerals, fractional numerals, expanded numerals, or other symbolism. The symbols are used as an aid, and generally one chooses the most convenient symbolism for the problem at hand.

It will be recognized that the terminology of this chapter is somewhat different from that traditionally used in school arithmetic. It is also different in some respects from that used by other contemporary writers. In order to hold to a distinction between numbers and symbols for them, altered terminology is absolutely essential, since traditionally, distinctions between numbers and numerals has not been made. Although the present terminology may at first seem a bit strange, it will be seen that it allows for keeping the distinction between numbers and symbols. It also corresponds to what one actually does; it is not ambiguous, and moreover it is in reality simpler than the traditional.

Among the words in the traditional vocabulary of arithmetic that do not appear here are the following:

| Common fraction, | Decimal fraction, | Improper fraction, |
| Reduce, | Lowest terms, | Mixed number. |

Below is a comparison of some of the present terminology with counterparts in traditional terminology.

Traditional	*Present*
Add these common fractions	Add (these numbers of arithmetic), using fractional numerals
Add these decimals	Add (these numbers of arithmetic), using decimal numerals
Change this fraction to a decimal	Find a decimal numeral for this number
Change this decimal to a common fraction	Find a fractional numeral for this number
Reduce this fraction to lowest terms	Find the simplest fractional numeral for this number (or simplify)
Change to an improper fraction	Find a fractional numeral for this number

12. APPLICATIONS

The number system of arithmetic has been constructed here in such a way as to find application to certain physical situations, namely those in which objects are, at least conceptually, divided or cut in pieces. One of the most common realms in which the system is applied is in commerce. In a monetary system, certain objects such as coins or pieces of paper symbolize particular values. They are conceptually cut up, with other similar objects used to represent the component values. Therefore, this number system is applicable, and is used to solve problems of discount, interest, commission, etc.

It is highly important to note that knowledge of mathematics alone does not enable one to solve applied problems. It is necessary also to have some knowledge of the area to which the mathematics is to be applied. To solve problems of interest and discount, for example, one must know how they are defined and applied. Knowledge of the number system of arithmetic alone, no matter how deep, will not suffice. This fact, once pointed out, is obvious, particularly when one considers applications of mathematics to science or engineering. It is obscure, however, when it comes to applications of mathematics to business problems, since by tradition these have been taught as if they were an integral part of arithmetic.

The number system of arithmetic also finds useful application to problems of measurement. In measuring distances, for example, certain distances are conceptually combined or cut in pieces. Therefore, this number system can be applied quite naturally. It is perhaps a little surprising that the same number system can be applied so well to the measurement of speed, acceleration, humidity, and viscosity, since it is difficult to see a very direct connection between these concepts and the notion of cutting objects apart.

It should seem even more surprising that the number system of arithmetic also finds useful applications to indirect measurement, as in surveying; to scale drawing; to problems of gear ratios or belt ratios; to problems of electricity, wind resistance, pendulums, games of chance, and operations strategy. But such is the nature of mathematics. It may be created on the basis of some physical idea. It then naturally finds application to the situation which inspired it, and similar ones, but it also finds application to other situations, ofttimes bearing little superficial resemblance to the situation which inspired the creation of the mathematical system.

CHAPTER 7

The System of Integers

The word *integer*, in many contexts, is a synonym for *whole number*. A recent
trend, based on a desire to use different names for numbers of different systems, is
to use the words *natural number* and *whole number* as they are used here in earlier
chapters, reserving the word *integer*, as is done here, to refer to the numbers 0, 1,
$-1, 2, -2, 3, -3, 4, -4, \ldots$.

The approach of this chapter somewhat parallels that of Chapter 6. There, using
the system of whole numbers, a new system was constructed. Here, the system of
whole numbers will be used to construct a new number system, i.e., the system of
integers. There, the numbers of arithmetic were conceptualized by equivalence
classes of ordered pairs of whole numbers. Here, equivalence classes of ordered pairs
of whole numbers will be used to conceptualize the integers.

There is, however, an essential difference in the points of view of these two chapters.
Operations for the numbers of arithmetic were defined to provide a description of
physical objects. The integers will be constructed without reference to physical
objects. This approach, moreover, accords well with the historical development of
these two types of numbers. Historically, the construction of the numbers of arithmetic was undoubtedly motivated by physical considerations. The construction of
negative numbers, on the other hand, was not so motivated. Rather, they were
invented in order that certain equations would then have solutions. There was considerable argument among early mathematicians about whether or not it was possible
for a number to be less than zero. The newly invented negative numbers were felt
by many to be at best useless curiosities, and they rather narrowly escaped being
dubbed "imaginary."

When originally constructed, negative numbers were not conceptualized by equivalence classes of ordered pairs of natural numbers, as is the case here. Neither, of course, were the numbers of arithmetic originally constructed as sets of ordered pairs. It would be possible to construct the system of integers by starting with the system of whole numbers and adding new elements to it in such a way that every number has an additive inverse. This would be more nearly in accord with early history, but the ordered pair approach is better suited to present purposes.

1. WHOLE NUMBERS AS DIFFERENCES

Every whole number is the difference of two whole numbers. For example,

$$0 = 9 - 9, \qquad 5 = 12 - 7,$$
$$1 = 5 - 4, \qquad 2 = 8 - 6,$$
$$3 = 30 - 27, \qquad 4 = 5 - 1.$$

Moreover, every whole number is a difference of two whole numbers in many ways. For example, the number 2 is

$$8 - 6, \quad 3 - 1, \quad 5 - 3, \quad 12 - 10, \quad 15 - 13, \quad \text{etc.}$$

Evidently with every whole number a set of ordered pairs of whole numbers can be identified. The preceding example indicates that with 2 is identified a set of ordered pairs

$$(8, 6), \quad (3, 1), \quad (5, 3), \quad (12, 10), \quad (15, 13), \ldots.$$

Any ordered pair of whole numbers (a, b) belongs to the set identified with 2 in case a is 2 greater than b. A better way to test, for present purposes, is to compare (a, b) with any ordered pair known to be in the set. It can be seen that for any two pairs in the set, (x, y) and (p, q), $x + q = y + p$. For example, $(8, 6)$ and $(3, 1)$ are both in the set, and it is true that $8 + 1 = 6 + 3$. Thus to test whether an ordered pair (a, b) is in the set, choose any known member, say $(5, 3)$ and test the truth of

$$a + 3 = b + 5.$$

The pair (a, b) is in the set if and only if that equation is true.

EXERCISES

1. Find ten ordered pairs of whole numbers in the set corresponding to the whole number 5.

2. Find ten ordered pairs of whole numbers in the set corresponding to the whole number 13.

3. Does $(4, 4)$ belong to any set (of the type defined above) corresponding to a whole number? A natural number?

4. Does $(3, 7)$ belong to any set (of the type defined above) corresponding to a whole number? Explain.

2. DEFINING THE SYSTEM

Selecting the set. The set of all ordered pairs of whole numbers is to be partitioned by an equivalence relation. That relation will be defined in accordance with the notion of whole numbers as differences, discussed above, where two ordered pairs of whole numbers (a, b) and (c, d) are identified in case $a + d = b + c$. A relation R is thus defined.

$$(a, b)R(c, d) \qquad \text{if and only if} \qquad a + d = b + c.$$

It is not difficult to prove that R is reflexive, symmetric, and transitive, and hence an equivalence relation. Details are left to the reader. Since R is an equivalence relation, it partitions the set of all ordered pairs of whole numbers. Each equivalence class will be called an *integer*, and will be a number in the new system being constructed. Some of the equivalence classes will correspond to whole numbers, as has been shown, and some will not. It is to be expected that the new system will therefore be an extension of the system of whole numbers in such a way that subtraction is universally possible. The set of integers will be called I, and may be precisely defined as follows.

Definition 1. *I is the set of all equivalence classes of ordered pairs of whole numbers* (a, b), *where any two pairs,* (p, q) *and* (r, s), *belong to the same class if and only if* $p + s = q + r$.

Square brackets will again be used to denote equivalence classes. The symbol $[2, 7]$ will be used to denote the equivalence class (integer) that contains the ordered pair $(2, 7)$. Thus '$[2, 7]$' is shorthand notation for $\{(a, b)|a + 7 = b + 2\}$.

Defining addition. Addition can of course be defined arbitrarily in a new system. It is desirable, however, that for those integers which correspond to whole numbers, addition be like that for whole numbers. Thus the new system of integers will, in effect, be an extension of the system of whole numbers. This idea provides a basis upon which to look for a means of defining addition.

An addition of whole numbers should then be considered. For example.

$$3 + 4 = 7.$$

Corresponding to 3 is a class of ordered pairs, one of which is $(11, 8)$. Corresponding to 4 is a class of ordered pairs, one of which is $(13, 9)$. If these are considered according to the interpretation of subtraction, the addition $3 + 4$ becomes

$$(11 - 8) + (13 - 9),$$

which can be equivalently stated

$$(11 + 13) - (8 + 9).$$

Thus one is motivated to define a *sum* $[11, 8] \oplus [13, 9]$ to be $[11 + 13, 8 + 9]$, or $[24, 17]$. The integer $[24, 17]$ clearly corresponds to 7, and thus it begins to appear that such a definition of addition for integers would have the desired property. That is, integers which correspond to whole numbers would act like whole numbers with respect to addition. This appearance, moreover, is not misleading. (See exercise 14 below.) A definition of addition of integers can now be made quite simply.

Definition 2. ***For any integers*** $[a, b]$ ***and*** $[c, d]$, $[a, b] \oplus [c, d] = [a + c, b + d]$.

The addition sign on the left has been circled to distinguish it from those on the right. The latter indicate additions in the system of whole numbers, already known, whereas the addition on the left is for integers, being defined here. The definition says in effect to add first members and add second members, respectively.

It is not yet clear that $\oplus$ is an operation, since it has not been shown that results are unique. The ordered pairs (a, b) and (c, d) used in adding may be chosen at random from the sets, according to the definition. If (a', b') had been chosen from the same set as (a, b) and (c', d') from the same set as (c, d), the name obtained for the result would have been '$[a' + c', b' + d']$,' and it must be shown that the result is unique. That is, $[a + c, b + d] = [a' + c', b' + d']$.

It should first be shown that the set of integers is closed under $\oplus$.

Theorem I. The set of integers is closed under $\oplus$.

This theorem may be proved in a manner analogous to that of Theorem I for numbers of arithmetic, and the proof is left as an exercise.

Theorem II. In the set of integers, $\oplus$ is an operation, that is, if $[a, b] = [a', b']$ and $[c, d] = [c', d']$, then $[a + c, b + d] = [a' + c', b' + d']$.

This theorem may be proved in a manner analogous to that of Theorem II for numbers of arithmetic, and the proof is left as an exercise.

Addition of integers is both commutative and associative, as the following theorems state.

Theorem III. For any integers $[a, b]$ and $[c, d]$,

$$[a, b] \oplus [c, d] = [c, d] \oplus [a, b].$$

Theorem IV. For any integers $[a, b]$, $[c, d]$, and $[e, f]$,

$$\{[a, b] \oplus [c, d]\} \oplus [e, f] = [a, b] \oplus \{[c, d] \oplus [e, f]\}.$$

Proofs of these theorems are straightforward and are asked for in the following exercises.

EXERCISES

1. Find five members of the set $[8, 3]$.
2. Find five members of the set $[x + 3, x]$.
3. Find five members of the set $[4, 4]$.
4. Find five members of the set $[x, x + 6]$.
5. Find the sum $[8, 2] \oplus [7, 3]$. Exhibit five members of the resulting set (or sets).
6. Find the sum $[3, 10] \oplus [7, 2]$. Exhibit five members of the resulting set (or sets).

7. Find the sum [12, 7] ⊕ [10, 10]. Exhibit five members of the resulting set (or sets).

8. Find the sum [11, 4] ⊕ [5, 3]. Choose an ordered pair of [11, 4] other than (11, 4) and an ordered pair of [5, 3] other than (5, 3); use them to find the sum, and show that the results are the same.

9. Find the sum [5, 8] ⊕ [2, 9]. As in exercise 8, choose another ordered pair of [5, 8] and another ordered pair of [2, 9]; use them to find the sum, and show that the results are the same.

10. Prove that the set of integers is closed under ⊕ (Theorem I).

11. Prove that ⊕ for integers is an operation (Theorem II).

12. Prove that addition of integers is commutative (Theorem III).

13. Prove that addition of integers is associative (Theorem IV).

14. Prove that the whole numbers under addition are isomorphic to a certain subset of the integers, under integer addition. [*Hint:* Consider integers which can be named '[x + n, x],' where n is a specific natural number and 'x' can represent any whole number].

15. Is there an identity for ⊕ in the system of integers? If so, name it, and prove that it is an identity.

In the above exercises it has been established that ⊕ for integers is an operation, that the set of integers is closed under this operation, and that the operation is commutative and associative. Moreover, the definition is such that it extends the addition for whole numbers to the set of integers. That is, for the integers corresponding to whole numbers (exercise 14), integer addition acts exactly like whole number addition. In more precise terms, the set of whole numbers n under addition is isomorphic to the set of those integers [x + n, x] under integer addition ⊕.

Theorem V. The set of integers [x + n, x] is isomorphic to the set of whole numbers n, under addition.

In view of Theorem V it will now be sensible to drop the circle around '⊕' when convenient to do so.

There is an identity for the operation + for integers, as proved in exercise 15. This fact is now stated as a theorem:

Theorem VI. For any integer [a, b],

$$[a, b] \oplus [n, n] = [a, b].$$

Furthermore, every integer has an additive inverse.

Theorem VII. For every integer [a, b], there is an additive inverse, [b, a].

Proof. For any integer [a, b], [a, b] ⊕ [b, a] = [a + b, b + a], which is the additive identity.

Since the integers under addition have the properties thus far established, it is clear that they form an Abelian *group*. By applying some group theorems, one may easily draw several conclusions. For example, the additive identity is unique, and each integer has exactly one additive inverse.

EXERCISES

1. Restate, for integers, Group Theorem. I. (The group operation symbol 'o' is to be replaced by '+' for integers.)

2. Restate, for integers, Group Theorem IV.

3. Restate, for integers, Group Theorem VII. (The inverse symbol in 'x^{-1}' is to be replaced by the additive inverse symbol for integers, as in '^{-}x.')

4. Restate, for integers, Group Theorem VIII.

5. Restate, for integers, Group Theorem IX.

6. Prove that the relation R defined in the preceding text is an equivalence relation.

Defining multiplication. In order to find a means of defining multiplication for integers which will make it an extension of the natural numbers, consider the following multiplication in natural numbers:

$$3 \cdot 4 = 12.$$

The integer corresponding to 3 is a set of ordered pairs, one of which is $(5, 2)$. The integer corresponding to 4 contains $(7, 3)$. If these pairs are considered according to the interpretation of subtraction, the multiplication $3 \cdot 4$ becomes

$$(5 - 2) \cdot (7 - 3),$$

which can be equivalently stated

$$5 \cdot 7 + 2 \cdot 3 - 5 \cdot 3 - 2 \cdot 7,$$

or

$$(35 + 6) - (15 + 14).$$

Thus one is motivated to define a *product* $[5, 2] \odot [7, 3]$ to be $[5 \cdot 7 + 2 \cdot 3, 5 \cdot 3 + 2 \cdot 7]$, or $[41, 29]$. The integer $[41, 29]$ clearly corresponds to 12. Thus it may be hoped that such a definition would have the desired property. That is, integers which correspond to whole numbers would act like whole numbers with respect to multiplication. Again it will be found that a hope is realized. Accordingly, multiplication for integers will be defined.

Definition 3. **For any integers $[a, b]$ and $[c, d]$,**

$$[a, b] \odot [c, d] = [a \cdot c + b \cdot d, \ a \cdot d + b \cdot c].$$

The multiplication sign on the left has been circled to distinguish it from whole number multiplication. The former is being defined here. In effect, this definition says to multiply first members and second members, respectively, and then add. The result is the first member of an ordered pair of the product. Then multiply first and second members and second and first members, respectively, and add. The result is the second member of an ordered pair of the product. This procedure should be reminiscent of multiplying two binomials.

EXERCISES

1. Find the product [5, 1] $\odot$ [6, 4]. Exhibit five members of the resulting set (or sets).

2. Find the product [5, 2] $\odot$ [3, 5]. Exhibit five members of the resulting set (or sets).

3. Find the product [4, 8] $\odot$ [2, 4]. Exhibit five members of the resulting set (or sets).

4. Find the product [3, 9] $\odot$ [5, 5]. Exhibit five members of the resulting set (or sets).

5. Find the product [3, 6] $\odot$ [7, 2]. Choose an ordered pair of [3, 6] other than (3, 6) and an ordered pair of [7, 2] other than (7, 2); use them to find the product, and show that the results are the same.

6. Prove that the set of integers is closed under multiplication.

*7. Prove that multiplication of integers is an operation.

8. Prove that multiplication of integers is commutative.

9. Determine whether multiplication of integers is associative. If so, prove it.

10. Is there a multiplicative identity for integers? If so, name it and prove that it is an identity.

11. If your answer to exercise 10 was *yes*, which, if any, integers have multiplicative inverses?

12. Prove that for any integer [a, b], [a, b] $\odot$ [n, n] = [n, n].

13. Prove that the whole numbers under multiplication are isomorphic to a certain set of integers under integer multiplication.

14. Prove that in the system of integers, $\odot$ is distributive over $\oplus$, i.e., for any integers [a, b], [c, d], and [e, f],

$$[a, b] \odot \{[c, d] \oplus [e, f]\} = \{[a, b] \odot [c, d]\} \oplus \{[a, b] \odot [e, f]\}.$$

Successful efforts in accomplishing the exercises above will have established that multiplication of integers is an operation, with the properties stated in the following theorems.

Theorem VIII. The set of integers is closed under $\odot$.

Theorem IX. (Commutativity) For any integers [a, b] and [c, d], [a, b] $\odot$ [c, d] = [c, d] $\odot$ [a, b].

Theorem X. (Associativity) For any integers [a, b], [c, d], and [e, f],

$$\{[a, b] \odot [c, d]\} \odot [e, f] = [a, b] \odot \{[c, d] \odot [e, f]\}.$$

Theorem XI. (A multiplicative identity) For any integer [a, b], [a, b] $\odot$ [x + 1, x] = [a, b].

Theorem XII. For any integer (a, b), (a, b) $\odot$ (n, n) = (n, n).

Theorem XIII. (A distributive law) For any integers [a, b], [c, d], and [e, f],

$$[a, b] \odot \{[c, d] \oplus [e, f]\} = \{[a, b] \odot [c, d]\} \oplus \{[a, b] \odot [e, f]\}.$$

Theorem XIV. The set of integers [x + n, x] is isomorphic to the set of whole numbers n, under multiplication.

Positive and negative integers. It has been proved that certain of the integers are isomorphic to the whole numbers under both addition and multiplication. It is therefore sensible to drop the circles around the operation symbols. Under the isomorphism, the integer $[n, n]$ corresponds to the whole number 0, and is the additive identity. The remaining integers in the isomorphic set $[x, y]$ all have the property that $x > y$ in each ordered pair (x, y). These integers correspond to the natural numbers. For example [6, 5] corresponds to 1, [5, 3] corresponds to 2, [9, 6] corresponds to 3, and so on. These integers will be called *positive.*

Definition 4.   An integer $[x, y]$ is positive if and only if $x > y$.

In view of the isomorphism, it is sensible to simplify notation for integers by using whole number notation. The integer [6, 6] may be named '0,' the integer [6, 5] may be named '1,' the integer [5, 3] may be named '2,' and so on. In general, for any positive integer $[x, y]$, one merely subtracts y from x to obtain the whole number $x - y$. A name for that whole number can also be used for the corresponding positive integer. In other words, zero and the positive integers can be named

$$0, 1, 2, 3, 4, 5, 6, 7, 8, \ldots .$$

The positive integers $[x, y]$ have the property that $x > y$. For the zero integer, $x = y$. The remaining integers then have the property that $x < y$. These integers will be called *negative.*

Definition 5.   An integer $[x, y]$ is negative if and only if $x < y$.

For any whole numbers x and y, one and only one of the following hold (see Chapter 2)

$$x < y \quad \text{or} \quad x = y \quad \text{or} \quad x > y.$$

Thus every integer must be positive or negative or zero. No integer can be both positive and negative, for example, nor can an integer be both zero and negative. To prove that no integer can be both positive and negative, for example, one must show that no integer can contain an ordered pair (a, b) for which $a < b$ and also contain an ordered pair (c, d) for which $c > d$. Details are left to the reader.

The following are some of the negative integers:

$$[4, 5], \quad [6, 8], \quad [1, 4], \quad [5, 9], \quad \text{and} \quad [6, 11].$$

By Theorem VII each of these integers has an additive inverse. The respective additive inverses are

$$[5, 4], \quad [8, 6], \quad [4, 1], \quad [9, 5], \quad \text{and} \quad [11, 6].$$

It is easily noted that the latter integers are all positive. In fact the additive inverse of any negative integer is positive. For if $[x, y]$ is negative, x must be less than y. The additive inverse of $[x, y]$ is $[y, x]$, and of course $x > y$; hence $[y, x]$ is positive. Conversely, the additive inverse of any positive integer is a negative integer, by similar reasoning.

Symbolism. Since the negative integers are all additive inverses of the positive integers, they may be named in a simple way. The negative integer [4, 5] is the additive inverse of [5, 4]. The latter, it has been agreed, may be named '1.' Its additive inverse can then be named quite naturally '⁻1' or '−1.' Thus a simple name for [4, 5] is '⁻1.' Similarly, the simpler name '⁻2' could be used for [6, 8] and '⁻3' for [1, 4], and so on. In general, to write simplified notation for a negative integer [x, y], one subtracts x from y to find a natural number. A name for that natural number is then written, preceded by an additive inverse sign. The symbols ⁻5 and −5 may be read "negative five," or "the additive inverse of five." The symbol ⁻x, if 'x' represents an integer, represents the additive inverse of x and may not be negative.*

EXERCISES

1. Write simplified notation for the following integers.

   (a) [18, 5]   (b) [4, 21]   (c) [5, 35]
   (d) [18, 3]   (d) [17, 17]   (e) [43, 85]

2. Find five ordered pairs in the integer ⁻6.

3. Find five ordered pairs in the integer 14.

4. Find five ordered pairs in the integer 0.

5. Find the following sums, and write simplified notation for the result.

   (a) [18, 3] + [14, 2]   (b) [4, 12] + [5, 8]
   (c) [13, 8] + [6, 20]   (d) [13, 15] + [12, 7]

6. Find the following sums and write simplified notation for the result.

   (a) 5 + 13   (b) ⁻12 + 6   (c) ⁻14 + ⁻3   (d) 14 + ⁻4

7. Find the following products and write simplified notation for the result.

   (a) [6, 4] · [8, 4]   (b) [8, 6] · [10, 6]
   (c) [6, 3] · [6, 4]   (d) [4, 7] · [5, 9]

8. Find the following products and write simplified notation for the result.

   (a) 5 · 9   (b) ⁻5 · 3   (c) ⁻6 · 0   (d) ⁻5 · ⁻6

9. Prove that (a) no positive integer is also negative, (b) no negative integer is zero.

3. THE SYSTEM OF INTEGERS IS A RING

It may be recalled that any system which is an Abelian group under one operation, and which is closed with respect to a second, associative, operation, and for which the second operation is distributive over the first, is known as a *ring*. It has been established that the integers have all of these properties; hence the system is a ring. Since multiplication of integers is commutative, the integers form a commutative ring. Since there is a multiplicative identity, the system is also said to be a ring with unity. The system fails to be a field in only one respect. Not every integer has a multiplicative inverse. In fact, the only integers having multiplicative inverses are 1 and ⁻1.

Since the system of integers is a ring, much is already known about it. All of the theorems about rings (Chapter 5) hold.

---

* It is therefore advisable to read '⁻x' as "the additive inverse of x," or simply "the inverse of x," rather than "negative x."

EXERCISES

1. (a) Rewrite Group Theorem VIII as it applies to the additive group of integers. Use '+' for the operation symbol, and '^-x' to denote the inverse of x.
   (b) What does this theorem tell us about adding two negative integers?

2. (a) Rewrite Group Theorem IX as it applies to the additive group of integers.
   (b) What does this theorem tell us about the additive inverse of a negative integer?

3. Does Ring Theorem I make any of the theorems of this chapter superfluous? If so, which?

4. What does Ring Theorem V tell us about multiplying a positive integer by a negative integer? Illustrate with an example.

5. What does Ring Theorem VI tell us about multiplying two negative integers? Illustrate with an example.

6. Prove that to do the subtraction of integers $x - y$, one may do the addition $x + {}^-y$. [*Hint:* This proof is like that on page 60, Chapter 3.]

The group and ring theorems mentioned in the preceding exercises, when applied to the ring of integers, result easily in the following important theorems.

Theorem XV. For any positive integers x and y, $^-x + {}^-y = {}^-(x + y)$. [The sum of any two negative integers is negative.]

One might describe how to add two negative integers by saying to take their additive inverses, add them, and then find the additive inverse of the result.

Theorem XVI. For any positive integers x, y, $^-x \cdot y = {}^-(x \cdot y)$. [The product of a negative integer and a positive integer is negative.]

One might describe how to multiply a positive and a negative integer by saying to first find the additive inverse of the negative one, multiply it by the positive one, and then find the additive inverse of the result.

Theorem XVII. For any positive integers x, y, $^-x \cdot {}^-y = x \cdot y$. [The product of two negative integers is the same as the product of two positive integers. Hence it is positive.]

Theorem XVII shows how to multiply two negative integers. One simply finds the product of their additive inverses.

No divisors of zero. In the system of integers, a product cannot be zero unless at least one factor is zero. In other words,

$$a \cdot b = 0 \rightarrow a = 0 \quad \text{or} \quad b = 0.$$

Not all rings enjoy this property. For example, in arithmetic mod 6, $3 \cdot 4 = 0$, but $3 \neq 0$ and $4 \neq 0$. Thus it is said that 3 and 4 are *divisors of zero*. In the ring of integers there are no divisors of zero, because any zero product must have at least one zero factor.

The system of integers is an integral domain. Any commutative ring in which there are no divisors of zero is called an *integral domain*. Thus the system of integers is an integral domain. The fact that a system has no zero divisors is important. It is this fact upon which a familiar principle for solving certain equations is based. The principle is illustrated in the following example.

Solve $(x - 2) \cdot (x - 3) = 0$ in integers:

$$(x - 2) \cdot (x - 3) = 0,$$
$$x - 2 = 0 \quad \text{or} \quad x - 3 = 0,$$
$$x = 2 \quad \text{or} \quad x = 3.$$

Both 2 and 3 satisfy the original equation, so the solution set is $\{2, 3\}$.

EXERCISES

1. Solve the following equations in integers:
   (a) $(x - 5) \cdot (x - 3) = 0$
   (b) $(x - {}^-8) \cdot (x - 7) = 0$
   (c) $(x - 2) \cdot (x - 5) \cdot (x - 8) = 0$
   (d) $(x + 4) \cdot (x - 5) \cdot (x + 7) = 0$
2. Prove that if a and b are integers, $a \cdot b = 0$ if and only if $a = 0$ or $b = 0$.
3. Prove that every field is an integral domain.

REVIEW PRACTICE EXERCISES

Multiply

1. $\dfrac{{}^-3}{4} \cdot \dfrac{5}{7}$

2. $\dfrac{{}^-3}{4} \cdot \dfrac{{}^-5}{{}^-7}$

3. $\dfrac{5}{{}^-9} \cdot \dfrac{2}{{}^-3}$

4. $\dfrac{{}^-5}{9} \cdot \dfrac{2}{{}^-3}$

5. $\dfrac{{}^-5}{9} \cdot \dfrac{{}^-2}{3}$

6. $\dfrac{4}{5} \cdot \dfrac{{}^-1}{{}^-1}$

7. $\dfrac{{}^-3}{5} \cdot \dfrac{{}^-1}{{}^-1}$

8. $\dfrac{4}{{}^-7} \cdot \dfrac{{}^-1}{{}^-1}$

9. $\dfrac{{}^-7}{{}^-5} \cdot \dfrac{{}^-1}{{}^-1}$

10. $\dfrac{{}^-3}{2} \cdot \dfrac{5}{{}^-7}$

11. $\dfrac{3}{2} \cdot \dfrac{5}{7}$

12. $\dfrac{{}^-3}{2} \cdot \dfrac{5}{{}^-7} \cdot \dfrac{{}^-1}{{}^-1}$

Simplify

EXAMPLES:

$$\frac{{}^-12}{{}^-18} = \frac{{}^-1 \cdot 6 \cdot 2}{{}^-1 \cdot 6 \cdot 3} = \frac{{}^-6}{{}^-6} \cdot \frac{2}{3} = \frac{2}{3}$$

$$\frac{{}^-9}{15} = \frac{{}^-1 \cdot 3 \cdot 3}{3 \cdot 5} = \frac{{}^-3}{3} \cdot \frac{3}{5} = {}^-1 \cdot \frac{3}{5} = -\frac{3}{5}$$

13. $\dfrac{{}^-15}{{}^-25}$

14. $\dfrac{{}^-36}{{}^-34}$

15. $\dfrac{{}^-75}{{}^-15}$

16. $\dfrac{^{-}27}{18}$ 17. $\dfrac{^{-}45}{120}$ 18. $\dfrac{^{-}35}{75}$

19. $\dfrac{45}{^{-}75}$ 20. $\dfrac{16}{^{-}48}$ 21. $\dfrac{49}{^{-}63}$

4. OTHER EXTENSIONS OF THE NATURAL NUMBERS

Theorems XVI and XVII have established that the product of a negative integer and a positive integer is negative; also that the product of two negative integers is positive. An important question which naturally arises is whether the natural numbers could have been extended in some other way, such that one or both of these properties do not hold. That is, could a system have been devised in which there is an additive identity and in which every element has an additive inverse; where part of the system has properties identical to the natural numbers and the other part consists of their inverses and the identity; in which the commutative, associative, and distributive properties hold for the entire system; and yet in which the product of two negatives is not always positive or the product of a positive and a negative is not always negative?

To answer this question, one looks for some system S, in which the commutative, associative, and distributive laws hold, and where there is an additive identity, and for each element an inverse (in other words, S would be a *commutative ring*), in which products are not like those in integers. Theorems V and VI for rings show that in any system S which is a commutative ring, for any $a, b \in S$

(i) $$^{-}a \cdot b = {}^{-}(a \cdot b),$$

and

(ii) $$^{-}a \cdot {}^{-}b = a \cdot b.$$

These theorems show that any system S, as described, where part of it is like the natural numbers, and where their additive inverses are called *negative*, must have products of negatives and products of negatives and positives like those of the integers. In other words, it has now been shown that:

If a system has the properties mentioned (commutative, distributive, etc.), *then* products must be as they are in the integers.

The contrapositive of the above statement guarantees that in any system where products are not like those of the integers, at least some of the properties (commutative, distributive, etc.) must fail to hold.

The question posed has now been answered. It is not possible to extend the system of natural numbers to a system like the integers without having products like the integers, unless some of the familiar properties are sacrificed.

5. ORDER OF THE INTEGERS

An order relation $>$ was defined for whole numbers and an extension of it was also defined for numbers of ordinary arithmetic. Since the system of integers is an extension of the system of whole numbers, it will be advisable to define an order relation for integers that is compatible with, or an extension of, that for whole numbers. Such a definition is easy to make, as follows.

Definition 6.   For any integers x, y, x ⊘ y if and only if x − y is positive.

It is not difficult to see that this definition is an extension of that of > for whole numbers. A sentence $x > y$ referring to whole numbers is true if and only if $x − y$ exists and is not zero. The corresponding sentence referring to nonnegative integers, $x ⊘ y$, is true if and only if $x − y$ is positive. In other words, $x − y$ exists and is not zero (and of course is not negative). It is therefore sensible to drop the circle around the inequality symbol for integers. It remains to show that this relation for integers is actually an order relation. Details are left to the reader. The order of the nonnegative integers is exactly like that for the whole numbers, and can be pictured as in Fig. 7–1.

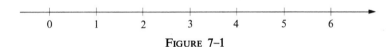

FIGURE 7–1

It will be understood also that the sentences $x > y$ and $y < x$ are equivalent. A sentence $x < y < z$ will be understood to be an abbreviation for the conjunction $x < y$ and $y < z$. To say that y is between x and z will mean that $x < y < z$ or $z < y < x$. The sentence $x \leq y$ will be understood to be an abbreviation for the disjunction

$$x < y \qquad \text{or} \qquad x = y.$$

By the definition it follows that a sentence $x > 0$ means that $x − 0$ is positive, or simply that x is positive. Thus the sentence $x > 0$ may be read "x is positive" or "x is greater than 0."

From Definition 6 it now follows that $^-3 < 5$, because $5 − {}^-3 > 0$. Similarly, if follows that any negative number is less than any positive number. The negative integers would therefore be pictured to the left of the positive integers on the number line. From Definition 6 it also follows that $^-1 > {}^-2, {}^-2 > {}^-3, {}^-3 > {}^-4$, and so on. Thus the familiar order of the integers is established. It is of course usually pictured as in Fig. 7–2.

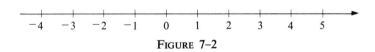

FIGURE 7–2

EXERCISES

1. Show that the following are true, using Definition 6.
    (a) $^-7 < {}^-2$ (b) $^-5 < 0$ (c) $^-12 < 16$

2. Prove that for any negative integer x, $x < 0$. Discuss the placement of 0 on the line.

3. Prove that if an integer y is between integers x and z, then x, y, and z are all different.

4. A definition of > could have been made using the ordered pair concept. Make such a definition which is equivalent to Definition 6.

Some further properties of the relation $<$ for integers will now be established. It will be wise, however, to note that everything to be said in this section applies not only to the ring of integers, but to any ordered ring. There are several other number systems that are ordered rings, and therefore this section applies to them as well as the integers.

Order in a ring may be defined abstractly using the integers as a guide. The important thing apparently is the existence of a certain subset of the set of integers, known as the *positive* elements. This set is closed under both addition and multiplication. Furthermore, every integer is either positive, its additive inverse is positive, or else it is zero.

Definition 7. *A ring R is said to be ordered if and only if there is a set R_p which is a subset of R, having the following properties:*

(i) R_p is closed under both operations of the ring.

(ii) For every $x \in R$, exactly one of the following is true:

    (a) $x \in R_p$,   (b) $^-x \in R_p$,   (c) $x = 0$.

It should be noted that there are rings which are not ordered; arithmetic mod 4 is an example. It would not be possible to choose a set of positive elements having the properties required by the definition. (The reader may wish to try, in order to convince himself.) None of the modular arithmetics can in fact be ordered.

As for integers, the sentence $x > y$ in any ordered ring will mean that $x - y$ is positive, i.e., $x - y \in R_p$. Some of the basic properties of the relation $>$ will now be established. Although they are stated for integers, it should be remembered that they hold in any ordered ring.

Theorem XVIII. For any integers a, b, and c,

$$a > b \rightarrow a + c > b + c.$$

Proof. By hypothesis $a > b$, which means that $a - b > 0$. Now $a - b = (a - b) + (c - c)$, for any integer c, since $c - c = 0$. Thus $a - b = (a + c) - (b + c)$, by the commutative and associative laws of addition. Since $a - b > 0$, also $(a + c) - (b + c) > 0$. The latter sentence, by definition of $>$ means the same as $a + c > b + c$. Therefore, for any integers a, b, c, if $a > b$, then $a + c > b + c$, which was to be shown.

Theorem XVIII says, in effect, that one may add the same number to each member of an inequality. If the original sentence is true, the resulting sentence will also be true. This fact furnishes a principle used to solve inequalities, similar to Principle K, used in finding solutions of equations.

Theorem XIX. For any integers a, b, and any positive integer c.

$$a > b \rightarrow a \cdot c > b \cdot c.$$

Proof. By hypothesis $a > b$, which means that $a - b > 0$. Also, by hypothesis $c > 0$. Since the set of positive integers is closed under multiplication, $(a - b) \cdot c > 0$, and by the distributive law it follows that $a \cdot c - b \cdot c > 0$. Thus $a \cdot c > b \cdot c$. Therefore, if $a > b$ and $c > 0$, then $a \cdot c > b \cdot c$.

Theorem XIX also has application to solving inequalities. In that connection it is important to note that the converses of both of these theorems are also true. Their converses are the next two theorems.

Theorem XX. For any integers a, b, and c,

$$a + c > b + c \rightarrow a > b.$$

Theorem XXI. For any integers a, b, and any positive integer c,

$$a \cdot c > b \cdot c \rightarrow a > b.$$

Proofs of these theorems, as well as the following ones, are left as exercises.

Theorem XXII. For any integers a, b, and for any negative integer c,

$$a > b \text{ if and only if } a \cdot c < b \cdot c.$$

Theorem XXIII. For any positive integers a, b, c, and d,

$$a > b \text{ and } c > d \rightarrow a \cdot c > b \cdot d.$$

Solving inequalities. To solve an inequality is to find its solution set. In view of the preceding theorems, a procedure very much like that often used for solving simple equations may be used. It consists of proving a conditional and its converse.

EXAMPLE 1. Solve $^{-}14 + x > 2$.

$14 + (^{-}14 + x) > 14 + 2$ (adding 14 to both members, Theorem XVIII)

$(14 + ^{-}14) + x > 16$

$x > 6.$

The solution set of $^{-}14 + x > 2$ has now been shown to be a subset of $\{x | x > 6\}$. The converse is now to be established. Since $\{x | x > 6\}$ is an infinite set, the converse cannot be established by substitution as might be done for an equation.

$x > 6$

$^{-}14 + x > ^{-}14 + 6$ (using Theorem XVIII)

$^{-}14 + x > 2.$

The solution set of $x > 6$ has been shown to be a subset of $\{x | ^{-}14 + x > 2\}$.

The solution set of the original inequality is thus $\{x | x > 6\}$.

In the preceding example, the second part (the proof of the converse) is not actually necessary. Theorems XVIII and XX show that for any integers a, b, and c, $a > b$ *if and only if* $a + c > b + c$. In other words, $a > b$ and $a + c > b + c$ are equivalent and hence have the same solution set. Since $x > 6$ was derived from $^{-}14 + x > 2$ by adding 14, the two sentences are equivalent and therefore have the same solution set.

EXAMPLE 2. Solve $3x > 6$.

$$3 \cdot x > 3 \cdot 2 \quad \text{(factoring 6)}$$
$$x > 2 \qquad \text{(using Theorem XXI)}.$$

Proving the converse is unnecessary, in view of Theorem XIX. The solution set of the inequality is therefore $\{x|x > 2\}$.

EXAMPLE 3. Solve $^-4x + 6 < {}^-2$.

$$(^-4x + 6) + {}^-6 < {}^-2 + {}^-6 \quad \text{(adding } ^-6)$$
$$^-4x + (6 + {}^-6) < {}^-8$$
$$^-4x < {}^-8$$
$$^-4x < {}^-4 \cdot 2 \quad \text{(factoring)}$$
$$x > 2 \quad \text{(using Theorem XXII. Note reversal of inequality sign)}.$$

The solution set is $\{x|x > 2\}$.

EXAMPLE 4. Solve $2x - 1 > 4$.

$$(2x - 1) + 1 > 4 + 1$$
$$2x > 5.$$

Since 5 does not have the factor 2, it is not possible to get 'x' alone, as in the preceding examples. The sentence $2x > 5$ is, however, simple enough that its solution set may be easily determined. That set may be described in two ways,

$$\{x|2x > 5\} \qquad \text{or} \qquad \{3, 4, 5, 6, \ldots\}.$$

EXERCISES

1. Solve each inequality and plot its graph on a line.

(a) $3x - 2 > 4$ (b) $4x + 5 < 6x - 3$
(c) $^-5x < 25$ (d) $6 - 4x < 8x + 2$

2. Prove Theorem XIX.

3. Prove Theorem XXI.

4. Prove Theorem XXII.

5. (a) Prove Theorem XXIII. (b) Show that this theorem would not be true if some or all of a, b, c, d were allowed to be negative.

6. Prove that any ordered commutative ring is an integral domain.

7. Prove that there is no integer between 0 and 1.

6. ABSOLUTE VALUE

The absolute value of a positive integer is that integer itself. The absolute value of a negative integer is its additive inverse. The absolute value of 0 is 0. Absolute value, symbolized $|x|$, is similarly defined in any ordered ring. Thus the following definition, although stated for integers, holds for any ordered ring.

***Definition 7.**   For any integer x,*

(i) $|x| = x$ *when $x \geq 0$*

and

(ii) $|x| = {}^{-}x$ *when $x < 0$.*

According to this definition $|5| = 5$, $|0| = 0$, and $|214| = 214$, since 5, 0, and 214 are all nonnegative. The absolute value of a nonnegative integer is that integer itself. Also according to the definition $|{}^{-}4| = 4$, $|{}^{-}7| = 7$, and $|{}^{-}35| = 35$, since ${}^{-}4$, ${}^{-}7$, and ${}^{-}35$ are all negative. The absolute value of a negative integer is its additive inverse, and is therefore positive.

The absolute value symbol obeys certain rules, stated in the following theorems, and following from the definition. These theorems also hold in any ordered ring.

Theorem XXIV. For any integers x, y,

$$|x \cdot y| = |x| \cdot |y|.$$

This theorem says that the absolute value of a product is the product of the absolute values. For example,

$$|{}^{-}3 \cdot 2| = |{}^{-}3| \cdot |2| = 3 \cdot 2 = 6.$$

Proof. This proof will be accomplished by considering several cases:†

    (i) One or both of x, y is zero.

    (ii) Neither x nor y is zero.

        (a)   Both x, y positive.

        (b)   Both x, y negative.

        (c)   One of x, y positive, the other negative.

If one of x, y is zero, then $x \cdot y = 0$, and by Definition 7, $|x \cdot y| = 0$. If $x = 0$, then also $|x| = 0$ and hence $|x| \cdot |y| = 0$. Similarly, if $y = 0$, $|x| \cdot |y| = 0$. Thus the theorem is proved for case (i).

If both x and y are positive, then $|x| = x$ and $|y| = y$, by Definition 7. Thus $|x| \cdot |y| = x \cdot y$. Since the set of positive integers is closed under multiplication, $x \cdot y > 0$, and therefore by Definition 7, $|x \cdot y| = x \cdot y$. The theorem is then established for case (ii a).

If both x and y are negative, then ${}^{-}x$ and ${}^{-}y$ are positive, and the product ${}^{-}x \cdot {}^{-}y$ is positive. But for any integers x, y, ${}^{-}x \cdot {}^{-}y = x \cdot y$, so $x \cdot y$ is positive. Then by Definition 7, $|x \cdot y| = x \cdot y$. Since x and y are negative, $|x| = {}^{-}x$ and $|y| = {}^{-}y$, by Definition 7. Therefore, $|x| \cdot |y| = {}^{-}x \cdot {}^{-}y$, and it follows that $|x| \cdot |y| = x \cdot y$. Finally, $|x \cdot y| = |x| \cdot |y|$, when x and y are negative integers and the theorem is established for case (ii b).

———————

    * An older definition of absolute value, often found in elementary textbooks, defines absolute value to be "numerical value without regard to sign." This definition is vague; in fact, logically it is nonsense.

    † In a proof such as this, where several cases are considered separately, one must make sure that the list of cases is exhaustive. It is easy to note that cases (i) and (ii) include all possibilities, and that subcases (a), (b), and (c) cover all possibilities of case (ii).

The proof of case (ii c) and proofs of the following theorems are left as exercises.

Theorem XXV. For any integer x, $|x| \geq 0$. [The absolute value of any integer is nonnegative.]

Theorem XXVI. For any integer x, $|{}^-x| = |x|$. [The absolute value of any integer is the same as the absolute value of its additive inverse.]

Theorem XXVII. For any integer x, $|x^2| = |x|^2$. [The absolute value of a square is the square of the absolute value.]

Theorem XXVIII. (The so-called *triangle* inequality) For any integers x, y,

$$|x + y| \leq |x| + |y|.$$

[The absolute value of a sum is less than or equal to the sum of the absolute values.]

EXERCISES

1. Prove Theorem XXIV for case (ii c).
2. Prove Theorem XXV.
3. Prove Theorem XXVI.
4. Prove Theorem XXVII.
5. Prove Theorem XXVIII.
6. By trial, find the solution set of each sentence and plot its graph on a line.

    (a) $|x| = 5$ (b) $|x| < 6$ (c) $|x| > 3$

    (d) $|x| + 4 = 10$ (e) $|x| + 5 \leq 12$ (f) ${}^-3 \cdot |x| + 3 > {}^-3$

7. With examples, illustrate each of Theorems XXIV through XXVII.
8. (a) Illustrate Theorem XXVIII with an example to show that it is possible for the equality to hold.

    (b) Illustrate Theorem XXVIII with an example to show that the sum of the absolute values may be greater than the absolute value of the sum.

7. FACTORING INTEGERS

The natural numbers were categorized as being either prime, composite, or the number 1, the primes being those natural numbers for which there is no factorization which does not include the number 1. The *fundamental theorem of arithmetic*, it will be recalled, states that any composite natural number has a unique prime factorization, if order of factors is disregarded.

Since the positive integers have properties identical with those of the natural numbers, the former may be factored like the latter. The fundamental theorem of arithmetic holds for the positive integers. Negative integers can also be factored. For example, ${}^-12 = 3 \cdot {}^-4$. Other factorizations of ${}^-12$ are ${}^-3 \cdot 4$, $2 \cdot {}^-6$, ${}^-2 \cdot 6$, $2 \cdot 2 \cdot {}^-3$, ${}^-2 \cdot 2 \cdot 3$, ${}^-1 \cdot 12$, ${}^-1 \cdot 2 \cdot 2 \cdot 3$, ${}^-1 \cdot {}^-1 \cdot {}^-1 \cdot 2 \cdot 2 \cdot 3$. There are many more factorizations of the integer ${}^-12$. In integers, the number 12 has factorizations besides those containing only positive integers. For example, ${}^-2 \cdot 2 \cdot {}^-3$.

Under the definition of primes for natural numbers, no integer would be prime, because every integer has a factorization which does not include the number 1. For example, $7 = {}^-1 \cdot {}^-7$. Therefore, in order to define prime integers in such a way that the definition is an extension of that for natural numbers, one must make some alteration. The usual definition of prime integers is, or amounts to, the following.

(i) A positive integer is prime if and only if its corresponding natural number is prime.

(ii) A negative integer is prime if and only if its additive inverse is a prime integer.

(iii) The integers 1, $^-1$, and 0 are neither prime nor composite.

(iv) All other integers are composite.

The fundamental theorem of arithmetic for integers is slightly different than for natural numbers. It is not true that every composite integer has a unique prime factorization. The integer 12, for example, has prime factorizations $2 \cdot 2 \cdot 3, {}^-2 \cdot {}^-2 \cdot 3$, and $^-2 \cdot 2 \cdot {}^-3$. For other composites the situation is similar. If, however, factorizations of nonzero integers are restricted to those containing only positive primes, and the factor $^-1$ is allowed to occur just once in a factorization, then composite integers have unique factorizations. For example, the standard factorization of $^-12$ is $^-1 \cdot 2 \cdot 2 \cdot 3$. Thus the fundamental theorem of arithmetic for integers might be stated as follows.

Every composite integer has a unique standard factorization, i.e., a factorization containing only positive primes and a possible factor $^-1$.

In natural numbers, an *even* number was defined to be a number having the factor 2. Happily, *even integers* may be defined in an identical way. Thus the even integers are those positive integers which correspond to even natural numbers, as well as the integers 0, $^-2$, $^-4$, $^-6$, $^-8$, ... Any integer which is not even is called *odd*, as was the case for natural numbers.

EXERCISES

1. Find the standard factorization of each of the following integers.

    (a) 16   (b) $^-16$ (c) $^-35$ (d) $^-36$ (e) $^-25$

2. Is the set of even integers closed under addition? Prove your answer.

3. Is the set of even integers closed under multiplication? Prove your answer.

4. Is the set of odd integers closed under addition? Multiplication? Prove your answers.

5. (a) Do the even integers form a group under addition? (b) Do the odd integers form a group under addition? (c) Do the odd integers form a group under multiplication? (d) Do the even integers form a group under multiplication?

6. (a) Do the even integers form a commutative ring? If so, has it a unity? (b) Do the odd integers form a commutative ring? If so, has it a unity?

7. Discuss the division algorithm for integers.

8. Use the division algorithm to find quotient and remainder, where the remainder is nonnegative and less than the absolute value of the divisor.

    (a) $^-6\overline{)49}$ (b) $17\overline{)^-284}$ (c) $^-14\overline{)^-732}$ (d) $^-219\overline{)4528}$

8. APPLICATIONS

The construction of the system of integers was not based on physical considerations. Rather, it was inspired by a desire to extend the system of natural numbers so as to gain new properties without losing any of the old ones. This has been done successfully, with no reference to the possibility of finding areas in which the new system may be applied. New mathematics is often created in just such a fashion, being inspired, not by physical considerations, but by a desire to achieve completeness, internal consistency, and beauty. When mathematics is created in this way, it would seem that the mathematician bears a closer resemblance to the composer, the poet, and the painter, than he does to the engineer, the physicist, or the accountant.

Nevertheless, as the reader is already aware, the system of integers does find many useful applications. A simple example is that of keeping scores in card games where negative scores are possible. Similar applications are found in accounting, the measurement of temperature, etc.

CHAPTER **8**

The Systems of
Rational Numbers
and Real Numbers

The two preceding chapters were devoted to formalizing extensions of number systems. It will be recalled that the whole numbers were, in effect, extended when the number system of arithmetic was devised. The important gain, from the structural viewpoint, was the fact that in the new system, all divisions were possible, except division by zero. In fact the nonzero numbers of arithmetic constitute a group under multiplication. When the whole numbers were extended to the system of integers, in Chapter 7, there was a similar important gain. The system of integers is a group under addition. Thus all subtractions became possible.

Neither the number system of arithmetic nor the system of integers is as complete as might be desired. One system lacks additive inverses, the other multiplicative inverses. The present task is to attempt to create another number system, preserving the familiar properties of integers and numbers of arithmetic, in which division is universally possible, or at least nearly so. In other words, it is desired to extend the number systems to a field. It is not clear, *a priori*, that it is possible to construct such a number system, but it turns out to be possible. The numbers of the new system will be called *rational numbers*, the word *rational* stemming from the word *ratio*.

There are various ways of approaching the construction of the new number system. Briefly, three of them may be described as follows.

(1) Start with the numbers of arithmetic. Adjoin to the set an additive inverse for each number not already having one. Then define multiplication and addition for the newly defined numbers and determine which properties hold.

(2) Start with the numbers of arithmetic. Consider numbers of arithmetic as differences, and obtain equivalence classes of ordered pairs. Make definitions of multiplication and addition in the same way as was done for integers. Then determine which properties hold.

(3) Start with the integers. In a manner similar to that used in Chapter 6, for numbers of arithmetic, define the new numbers to be equivalence classes of ordered pairs of integers. Then determine what properties hold.

The method to be used here is that described in (3). Under this approach it is fairly certain that the new system will be an extension of the numbers of arithmetic. It turns out also to be an extension of the integers.

In view of the similarity of approach here and in the previous two chapters, most of the proofs will be left as exercises. The reader who has begun to feel the thrill of original thinking in mathematics might well wish to go a long step further: make his own definitions, determine properties, and prove his own theorems, using this chapter only for after-the-fact reference and comparison.

REVIEW PRACTICE EXERCISES

1. List the squares of the first 25 natural numbers.

2. Find the natural number square root of each of the following.

   (a) 25   (b) 121   (c) 225   (d) 169

3. Find the square root of each of the following.

   (a) $\frac{4}{9}$ (b) $\frac{49}{100}$ (c) $\frac{121}{225}$ (d) $\frac{400}{441}$

4. Simplify

   (a) $\sqrt{36}$ (b) $\sqrt{\dfrac{100}{16}}$ (c) $\sqrt{\dfrac{162}{450}}$ (d) $\sqrt{\dfrac{121}{196}}$

1. DEFINING THE SYSTEM

Selecting the set. Each rational number will be defined to be an equivalence class of ordered pairs of integers. In order that the new system be an extension of the numbers of arithmetic, it will be advisable to make the definitions in the same way as there, where equivalence classes of ordered pairs of numbers are the numbers in the new system. That the defining relation given by Definition 1 is actually an equivalence relation is not difficult to prove, and the proof is left to the reader. The set of rational numbers will be called 'R.'

Definition 1. R is the set of all equivalence classes of ordered pairs of integers, (a, b), where b ≠ 0, and where any two pairs, (p, q) and (r, s), belong to the same class if and only if p · s = r · q.

As before, square brackets will be used. Thus '[2, ⁻5]' represents an equivalence class (rational number) containing such ordered pairs of integers as (4, ⁻10) and (⁻2, 5).

Operations and their properties.

Definition 2. (Addition). For any rational numbers [a, b] and [c, d],

$$[a, b] \oplus [c, d] = [ad + bc, bd].$$

Definition 3. (Multiplication). For any rational numbers [a, b] and [c, d],

$$[a, b] \odot [c, d] = [ac, bd].$$

As before, the operation symbols on the left of the above definitions have been circled to distinguish them from those on the right. The latter are operations in the system of *integers.* The former are for rational numbers, being defined here. Later, when the important isomorphisms have been established, the circles may be appropriately dropped.

The following theorems parallel those for integers and the numbers of arithmetic.

Theorem I. The set of rational numbers is closed under $\oplus$ and also under $\odot$.

Theorem II. In the set of rational numbers, $\oplus$ is an operation; also $\odot$ is an operation.

Theorem III. (Commutative laws) For any rational numbers [a, b] and [c, d]

$$[a, b] \odot [c, d] = [c, d] \odot [a, b],$$

and

$$[a, b] \oplus [c, d] = [c, d] \oplus [a, b].$$

Theorem IV. (Associative laws) For any rational numbers [a, b], [c, d], and [e, f],

$$\{[a, b] \odot [c, d]\} \odot [e, f] = [a, b] \odot \{[c, d] \odot [e, f]\},$$

and

$$\{[a, b] \oplus [c, d]\} \oplus [e, f] = [a, b] \oplus \{[c, d] \oplus [e, f]\}.$$

Theorem V. (Distributive law) For any rational numbers [a, b], [c, d], and [e, f],

$$[a, b] \odot \{[c, d] \oplus [e, f]\} = \{[a \cdot b] \odot [c, d]\} \oplus \{[a, b] \odot [e, f]\}.$$

EXERCISES

1. Find five members of each of the following sets (rational numbers), using Definition 1.
   (a) [3, ⁻5]   (b) [⁻4, ⁻7]   (c) [4, 4]   (d) [0, ⁻6]
2. Show that the following are true, using Definition 1.
   (a) [3, ⁻2] = [⁻3, 2]   (b) [8, 5] = [⁻8, ⁻5]   (c) [⁻12, ⁻5] = [12, 5]

3. Find the product [⁻3, ⁻5] ⊙ [⁻4, 3]. Exhibit five members of the resulting set.

4. Find the sum [⁻3, 8] ⊕ [5, 4]. Exhibit five members of the resulting set.

5. Prove Theorem I.

6. Prove Theorem II.

7. Prove Theorem III.

8. Prove Theorem IV.

9. Prove Theorem V.

10. See if you can find a multiplicative identity in the set of rational numbers.

11. If a multiplicative identity exists, which rational numbers have multiplicative inverses?

12. See if you can find an additive identity in the set of rational numbers.

13. If an additive identity exists, which rational numbers have additive inverses?

14. Prove that if $[a, b] \odot [c, d] = [0, 1]$, then $[a, b] = [0, 1]$ or $[c, d] = [0, 1]$, i.e., that the system of rational numbers is an integral domain.

15. Prove that for any rational numbers $[a, b]$, $[c, b]$, $[a, b] \oplus [c, b] = [a + c, b]$. Interpret the result in terms of ordinary fractional symbolism.

16. Prove that the relation implicitly given in Definition 1 is an equivalence relation.

This system is a field. In the preceding exercises the reader will have shown several important facts about the new system. There are two *operations* under which the set is closed. Under addition the system is an Abelian group. That is, the operation is commutative, associative, there is an identity, $[0, 1]$, and for each element there is an additive inverse. The additive inverse of $[a, b]$ is $[⁻a, b]$ or $[a, ⁻b]$. These facts are stated in the following theorems.

Theorem VI. The rational number $[0, 1]$ is an additive identity, i.e., for any rational number

$$[a, b], [a, b] \oplus [0, 1] = [a, b].$$

Theorem VII. For any rational number $[a, b]$, there is an additive inverse $[⁻a, b]$.

Under multiplication the system fails to be a group because the additive identity has no multiplicative inverse. However, if the additive identity is omitted from the set, the resulting system is an Abelian group under multiplication. That operation is commutative and associative, and there is a multiplicative identity $[1, 1]$ or $[n, n]$. For each rational number different from $[0, 1]$ there is a multiplicative inverse, or reciprocal. Thus all divisions are possible except division by $[0, 1]$. The reciprocal of $[a, b]$ is $[b, a]$.

Theorem VIII. The rational number $[1, 1]$ is a multiplicative identity, i.e., for any rational number

$$[a, b], [a, b] \odot [1, 1] = [a, b].$$

Theorem IX. For any rational number $[a, b]$, except $[0, 1]$, there is a multiplicative inverse $[b, a]$.

The above properties, together with the distributive law of multiplication over addition, fulfill the conditions of the definition of a *field*. Thus the system of rational numbers is a field and certain of its properties, not stated in the definition, are known by the theorems previously established about fields.

EXERCISES

1. (a) The rational number [5, 3] corresponds to what number of ordinary arithmetic?
    (b) Find five ordered pairs in [5, 3], some of which contain at least one negative integer.
    (c) Is there an ordered pair (a, b) in [5, 3] for which a is negative and b positive? For which a is positive and b negative? Why?
    (d) What can you say about the ordered pairs in any rational number that corresponds to a number of ordinary arithmetic?
    (e) Can you identify the set of rational numbers that correspond to the set of numbers of arithmetic?

2. (a) For a rational number $[a, b]$ corresponding to a nonzero number of ordinary arithmetic, what can you say about the product $a \cdot b$?
    (b) For the additive inverse of any rational number $[a, b]$ corresponding to a nonzero number of arithmetic, what can you say about the product $a \cdot b$?
    (c) What is the product $a \cdot b$ for any (a, b) in the additive identity?

3. (a) The rational number [7, 1] corresponds to what integer?
    (b) The rational number [⁻5, 1] corresponds to what integer?
    (c) Can you identify the set of rational numbers that corresponds to the set of integers? Which of these correspond to the positive integers?

4. Prove: For any rational number $[a, b]$, $[a, b] = [⁻a, ⁻b]$.

5. Prove: For any rational number $[⁻a, b]$, $[⁻a, b] = [a, ⁻b]$.

2. ORDER OF THE RATIONAL NUMBERS

In accordance with experience such as that provided in the preceding exercises, one is motivated to define a rational number $[a, b]$ to be positive when a and b are both positive integers or both negative integers; or, what amounts to the same thing, when the product $a \cdot b$ is positive.

Definition 4.   A rational number $[a, b]$ is said to be positive if and only if $a \cdot b$ is a positive integer.   A rational number $[a, b]$ is said to be negative if and only if $a \cdot b$ is a negative integer.

Thus [3, ⁻2] and [⁻5, 4] are negative because $3 \cdot ⁻2$ and $⁻5 \cdot 4$ are negative integers; [⁻5, ⁻8] and [4, 13] are positive because $⁻5 \cdot ⁻8$ and $4 \cdot 13$ are positive integers. It remains to be shown that the positive rational numbers are hereby well defined. It has not yet been established that if $[a, b]$ is positive (i.e., $a \cdot b > 0$) then for *every* ordered pair (x, y) of $[a, b]$, the product $x \cdot y$ is a positive integer. If this were not true, then Definition 4 would not be sensible, because some rational numbers would accordingly be both positive and not positive. The proof required is not difficult and is left to the reader.

If it can be established that the rational numbers under Definition 4 satisfy the conditions of an *ordered ring* (Chapter 7), then the theorems concerning order and absolute value, established there, will automatically hold for the system of rational numbers. It must be shown that the set of positive rational numbers is closed under addition and multiplication, and that every rational number is positive, or else its additive inverse is positive, or else it is zero.

Theorem X. The set of positive rational numbers is closed under addition, and also under multiplication.

Theorem XI. The additive inverse of any positive rational number is negative. The additive inverse of any negative rational number is positive. Zero is neither positive nor negative.

These theorems, whose proofs are left as exercises, establish that the desired conditions hold and thus an order relation $>$ can be defined as for integers, and all of the theorems about order proved for integers, or any ordered ring, will also hold in the system of rational numbers.

Definition 5. For any rational numbers $[a, b]$ ***and*** $[c, d]$***,*** $[a, b] \oslash [c, d]$ ***if and only if*** $[a, b] \ominus [c, d]$ ***is positive.***

EXERCISES

1. Write an expression equivalent to $[a, b] \ominus [c, d]$ as follows: $[a, b] \oplus [\ \ ,\ \ ]$.

2. Find the following:
    (a) $[2, 3] \ominus [5, 6]$ (b) $[4, 7] \ominus [8, 9]$
    (c) $[^-4, 6] \ominus [11, 12]$ (d) $[^-6, 11] \ominus [4, ^-3]$

3. Using Definition 5, tell which of the following are true.
    (a) $[9, 8] > [3, 4]$ (b) $[^-5, 1] > [2, 8]$
    (c) $[6, ^-5] > [^-1, 3]$ (d) $[^-7, ^-8] > [4, 5]$

4. Restate, for rational numbers, the properties of the relation $>$ established for integers (or any ordered ring).

5. In Chapter 6 it was established that for any numbers of arithmetic $[a, b]$ and $[c, d]$, $[a, b] > [c, d]$ if and only if $a \cdot d > b \cdot c$. Does a similar property hold for rational numbers? If so, state and prove it.

6. Prove that the positive rational numbers are well defined, i.e., if for one ordered pair (a, b) of a given rational number $a \cdot b > 0$, then for any other ordered pair (c, d) in the same equivalence class, also $c \cdot d > 0$.

7. Prove Theorem X.

8. Prove Theorem XI.

9. Restate the definition of absolute value for rational numbers.

10. Restate, for rational numbers, the properties of absolute value, established for the integers (or any ordered ring).

Symbolism. The rational numbers $[n, 1]$ correspond to the integers n. This is a one-to-one correspondence, under which both operations are preserved. In other words, a certain subset of the set of rational numbers is isomorphic to the system of integers. This fact, stated in Theorem XII, is easily proved and is left as an exercise.

It guarantees that the system of rational numbers is an extension of the system of integers.

Theorem XII. The set of rational numbers nameable [n, 1], where n is any integer, is isomorphic to the system of integers.

The nonnegative rational numbers comprise a system which is isomorphic to the number system of ordinary arithmetic. The nonnegative rational numbers are nameable [a, b], where neither a nor b is negative, and the correspondence is one-to-one between these rational numbers and the numbers of arithmetic a/b. This isomorphism, stated in Theorem XIII, is also easy to prove, and guarantees that the system of rational numbers is also an extension of the number system of ordinary arithmetic. Proof of Theorem XIII is left to the reader.

Theorem XIII. The set of rational numbers nameable [a, b], where neither a nor b is a negative integer, is isomorphic to the number system of ordinary arithmetic.

In view of the isomorphisms established by Theorems XII and XIII, it is sensible, as well as convenient, to drop the circles in the operation symbols $\oplus$, $\odot$, and $\ominus$. It will also be sensible and convenient to use fractional symbols for rational numbers, in much the same way as for numbers of arithmetic. The number [4, 5] can thus be named '$\frac{4}{5}$' or '$\frac{8}{10}$,' for example. In a similar fashion, any rational number [a, b] can be named 'a/b.' The number [$^-4$, 5] can be named '$^-4/5$' or '$4/^-5$.'

The additive inverse of any rational number [a, b] can be named [^-a, b] or [a, ^-b]. In fractional symbolism, the additive inverse of a/b could be named '$^-a/b$' or '$a/^-b$.' The symbol $-a/b$ could also be used. Thus these three fractional symbols are equivalent, and all name the additive inverse of a/b:

$$-\frac{a}{b}, \qquad \frac{^-a}{b}, \qquad \frac{a}{^-b}.$$

Since [a, b] = [^-a, ^-b] for any rational number [a, b], it follows that the symbol

$$-\frac{^-a}{^-b}$$

also names the additive inverse of a/b. In other words,

$$-\frac{^-a}{^-b} \qquad \text{and} \qquad -\frac{a}{b}$$

are equivalent.

This topic has implications in elementary algebra. In many books there is a discussion of "three signs of a fraction," with directions to the effect that "any two of them may be changed without changing the *value* of the fraction." In view of the present development, the semantics in those discussions is poor at best. From a pedagogical viewpoint, such semantic formulations are untenable, since they force a student to learn, by rote, a rule which he cannot hope to really understand.

The preceding development also provides a way of naming negative rational numbers. Each negative rational number is the additive inverse of a positive rational number. Hence additive inverse notation may be used to name negative numbers.

The number [4, 5] is positive, for example, while its additive inverse [⁻4, 5] is negative. Thus the negative number [⁻4, 5] may be named

$$\frac{^-4}{5} \quad \text{or} \quad \frac{4}{^-5} \quad \text{or} \quad -\frac{4}{5}.$$

It could also be named

$$-\frac{^-4}{^-5}$$

if it should ever be convenient to do so.

Certain of the rational numbers are isomorphic to the integers, and it is therefore sensible to use integer notation for them. The additive identity [0, 1] corresponds to the integer 0; hence it may be named '0.' Similarly the multiplicative identity [1, 1] may be named '1.' Also according to this scheme, [8, 4] may be named '2,' as well as '$\frac{8}{4}$,' and [9, ⁻3] may be named '⁻3,' as well as '$-\frac{9}{3}$.'

It would be difficult to advocate the approach of this chapter with respect to additive inverse symbolism for beginning algebra students, especially since a simpler, yet fairly rigorous, approach is possible. In brief, it consists of:

(a) Establishing that $^-1 \cdot x = ^-x$, for all x.

(b) Noting that $^-1/^-1 = 1$, the multiplicative identity.

(c) Multiplying by 1, in various ways as illustrated below:

$$\frac{a}{b} = \frac{^-1}{^-1} \cdot \frac{a}{b} = \frac{^-1 \cdot a}{^-1 \cdot b} = \frac{^-a}{^-b},$$

$$\frac{a}{b} = \frac{-1}{-1} \cdot \frac{a}{b} = \frac{-1}{1} \cdot \frac{1}{^-1} \cdot \frac{a}{b} = -1 \cdot \frac{a}{^-1 \cdot b} = -\frac{a}{^-b}.$$

EXERCISES

1. Write fractional notation for each of the following rational numbers.

    (a) [4, 7]   (b) [⁻8, 3]   (c) [4, ⁻11]   (d) [⁻7, ⁻13]

2. Write integer notation for each of the following rational numbers.

    (a) [8, 4]   (b) [⁻12, 2]   (c) [18, ⁻3]   (d) [⁻81, ⁻9]

3. Write four different fractional symbols for each of the following rational numbers.

    (a) [⁻7, 5]   (b) [4, ⁻13]   (c) [⁻12, ⁻25]   (d) [3, 4]

4. Write four different fractional symbols for the additive inverse of each of the following rational numbers.

    (a) [⁻2, 3]   (b) [5, ⁻9]   (c) [⁻2, ⁻5]   (d) [7, 3]

REVIEW PRACTICE EXERCISES

In a right triangle (Fig. 8–1) the lengths of the sides are related as follows: $a^2 + b^2 = c^2$.

1. If two sides of a right triangle have lengths as given, what is the length of the third side?

    (a) $a = 3, b = 4$ (b) $b = 8, c = 10$

    (c) $a = 16, c = 20$ (d) $a = 5, b = 12$

2. If two sides of a right triangle have lengths as given, what is the length of the third side?

EXAMPLE:

$$a = 4, b = 7$$
$$a^2 + b^2 = c^2$$
$$c^2 = 4^2 + 7^2 = 16 + 49 = 65$$
$$c = \sqrt{65}$$

(a) $a = 5, b = 7$ (b) $b = 11, c = 12$

(c) $a = 1, b = 1$ (d) $a = 15, b = 7$ FIGURE 8–1

Multiplicative inverses. The multiplicative inverse of a nonzero rational number $[a, b]$ is the number $[b, a]$, as stated in Theorem IX. The reciprocal of 2/3 is thus 3/2, and the reciprocal of ⁻4/5 is 5/⁻4. In accordance with symbolism used earlier, the reciprocal of 2/3 could also be named

$$\frac{1}{2/3}.$$

Before deciding to adopt this symbolism here, it should be determined whether it would be compatible with the use of the symbol to indicate division. This requires but a moment's reflection. The division $1 \div (a/b)$ is equivalent to the multiplication $1 \cdot (b/a)$ that is, multiplication by the reciprocal of a/b. Since 1 is the multiplicative identity, the result is b/a.

It is interesting, at least from the pedagogical point of view, to show this in another way, using the multiplicative identity:

$$\frac{1}{a/b} = \frac{1}{a/b} \cdot \frac{b/a}{b/a} = \frac{b/a}{1} = \frac{b}{a}.$$

EXERCISES

1. Write five different symbols for the multiplicative inverse of each of these rational numbers.

    (a) $[2, {}^-3]$ (b) $[4, 5]$ (c) $[{}^-10, 4]$ (d) $[{}^-6, {}^-5]$

2. Restate rational number Theorems VI through IX, using fractional symbolism.

3. Restate the order theorems about integers, as they apply to rational numbers. Use fractional symbolism.

4. Prove that the rational numbers are densely ordered, i.e., between any two rational numbers there is at least one other.

5. Prove that the multiplicative inverse of a positive integer is positive.

6. Prove that the multiplicative inverse of a negative integer is negative.

The order of the integers was pictured on a line. Since the relation $>$ is an extension of that relation in integers, the order of the rational numbers can be pictured on a line, superimposed upon the integers, as in Fig. 8–2. There are of course many rational points not identified in this picture. As with the numbers of arithmetic, the order is dense. Between any two rational numbers there is an unlimited number of

FIGURE 8–2

others. The number halfway between two rational numbers may be found by averaging them. The order of the positive rational numbers is, moreover, exactly like that for the numbers of arithmetic. One can, in fact, use the terminology "nonnegative rational numbers" as a synonym for what were earlier called the "numbers of arithmetic."

Solving equations and inequalities. The system of rational numbers is a field, and thus every number has an additive inverse, and all nonzero numbers have multiplicative inverses. Therefore the use of Principle K allows one to solve any simple equation in one variable. One simply uses that principle a sufficient number of times, adding inverses of certain elements or multiplying by reciprocals of certain elements, until a variable stands alone on one side.

EXAMPLE.

Solve:

$$3x + {}^-7 = -\tfrac{5}{3}x + \tfrac{1}{5}.$$

$$\tfrac{5}{3}x + 3x + {}^-7 = \tfrac{5}{3}x + (-\tfrac{5}{3}x) + \tfrac{1}{5} \qquad (\text{adding } \tfrac{5}{3}x)$$

$$\tfrac{14}{3}x + {}^-7 = \tfrac{1}{5}$$

$$\tfrac{14}{3}x + {}^-7 + 7 = \tfrac{1}{5} + 7 \qquad (\text{adding } 7)$$

$$\tfrac{14}{3}x = \tfrac{36}{5}$$

$$\tfrac{3}{14}(\tfrac{14}{3}x) = \tfrac{3}{14} \cdot \tfrac{36}{5} \qquad (\text{multiplying by } \tfrac{3}{14})$$

$$1 \cdot x = \tfrac{3}{14} \cdot \tfrac{36}{5}$$

$$x = \tfrac{54}{35}.$$

The number $\tfrac{54}{35}$ checks; hence it is a solution of the original equation.

Since the system of integers is an ordered ring, all of the theorems about ordered rings (Chapter 7) hold. Thus inequalities may be solved in the same way as for integers.

EXAMPLE.

Solve:

$$2x - 1 > 4.$$

$$2x - 1 + 1 > 4 + 1 \qquad (\text{adding } 1)$$

$$2x > 5$$

$$\tfrac{1}{2}(2x) > \tfrac{1}{2} \cdot 5 \qquad (\text{multiplying by } \tfrac{1}{2})$$

$$x > \tfrac{5}{2}$$

The solution set is $\{x \mid x > \tfrac{5}{2}\}$.

EXERCISES

1. Solve the following equations.

(a) $\frac{3}{4}x - 5 = x + 2$

(b) $-\frac{6}{5}x + \frac{12}{5} = -\frac{19}{3}$

(c) $\frac{-2}{3}x + \frac{4}{5}x - \frac{5}{9} = \frac{6}{10}x + \frac{4}{3}$

(d) $-0.6x + \frac{4}{5} = \frac{4}{5}x - 35\%$

2. Solve each of the following inequalities. Plot a graph of each on a line if so directed.

(a) $\frac{4}{5}x - \frac{2}{3} < 2x + \frac{1}{2}$

(b) $-\frac{4}{3}x + \frac{17}{5}x > \frac{9}{5}x + \frac{2}{3}$

(c) $-0.6x + \frac{4}{5} < 3.61x - 5.1$

(d) $6.2x - 9.1 > -\frac{12}{5}x + 1.2$

(e) $4x - \frac{1}{2} > {}^-5$

(f) $\frac{3}{2}y + 6 < \frac{1}{2}y - \frac{1}{3}$

(g) $^-6x \le 3.6$

(h) $-\frac{8}{5} - \frac{3}{10}y < \frac{3}{5}y + \frac{7}{10}$

3. Restate the definition of absolute value for rational numbers.

3. REAL NUMBERS

The extension of number systems carried out so far has resulted in a system in which all additions, subtractions, multiplications, and divisions are possible, except for division by zero. An attempt to sensibly define division by zero would necessarily lead to frustration, and thus it might appear that the system of rational numbers is as much a finished product as it can be. Indeed if ordered pairs of rational numbers were considered, and operations defined on equivalence classes of them in the manner used to create the rational numbers from the integers, the result would be a number system with no new properties at all. It would be isomorphic to the system of rational numbers. Thus with respect to ordinary addition, multiplication, and their inverses, the system of rational numbers is a finished product. It is a *field*.

It may be recalled that arithmetic mod 5 is also a field. That small system is just as much a finished product, with respect to the possibility of performing the two basic operations, as is the system of rational numbers. Yet one would not expect that it is as rich in properties as a system can be. As will presently be seen, neither is the system of rational numbers. A further enrichment of properties, through the creation of a new number system, will now be discussed. The new system will be called the system of *real* numbers, a name which is misleading today. Its christening was inspired by the French mathematician and philosopher Descartes (1637), who sought to distinguish these numbers from the so-called *imaginary* numbers, which were relatively new and in dispute at the time.

Square roots. It is easy to see that in the systems of natural numbers and integers, certain numbers have no square roots. In the number system of arithmetic or the system of rational numbers, this is not so clear. Since the rational numbers are used so extensively for measurement, it would be hoped that there is some rational number whose square is 2, otherwise the hypotenuse of a right triangle as shown in Fig. 8–3(a) has no number for its length. Similarly if there is no square root of 3 in the rational numbers, one of the legs of the right triangle shown in Fig. 8–3(b) has no number for its length. Actually, rational numbers do not exist for either of these lengths, as will be shown presently. The reader interested in mathematical history might wish to look up the *Pythagorean* school of ancient Greek mathematics in this connection.

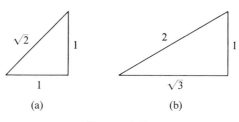

FIGURE 8–3

Their discovery of the fact that $\sqrt{2}$ is not rational proved to be more than mildly upsetting to them.

In order to prove the principal theorem of this section, a preliminary theorem, or *lemma*,* will be needed, stating in effect that every natural number which is a perfect square has a prime factorization in which each factor occurs an even number of times.

Lemma I. Any natural number n is a perfect square if and only if each factor in its prime factorization occurs an even number of times.

Proof. First suppose that n is a perfect square. This means that it has a factorization $r \cdot r$ for some natural number r. Now complete the factorization of n by writing the complete factorization of r twice. Each factor must clearly appear an even number of times.

To prove the converse, suppose that in the prime factorization of n each factor occurs an even number of times. The factors can then be divided equally, $(p_1 p_2 p_3 \ldots) \cdot (p_1 p_2 p_3 \ldots)$. The number n is therefore a perfect square.

It is now not difficult to prove that there is no square root of 2 in the number system of arithmetic.

Theorem XV. There is no number of arithmetic a/b for which

$$\left(\frac{a}{b}\right)^2 = 2.$$

Proof. (i) It will first be established that in the number system of arithmetic $(a/b)^2 = 2$ is equivalent to $a^2 = 2b^2$, where $b^2 \neq 0$.

(a) Assume $(a/b)^2 = 2$. Then $(a/b) \cdot (a/b) = 2$ by definition of exponents. Also by definition of multiplication of arithmetic numbers and definition of exponents, it follows that $a^2/b^2 = 2$. Since a/b is a number of arithmetic, $b \neq 0$, and also $b^2 \neq 0$. Thus it follows that $a^2 = 2b^2$, upon multiplying by b^2.

(b) Assume $a^2 = 2b^2$ and $b^2 \neq 0$. Multiplication by $1/b^2$ results in $a^2/b^2 = 2$. The expression a^2/b^2 is equivalent to $(a/b)^2$, and it follows that $(a/b)^2 = 2$.

Since the two equations imply each other, they are equivalent, and thus have the same solution set. It will be convenient to use $a^2 = 2b^2$.

---

* A "lemma" is merely a theorem regarded as preliminary.

(ii) It will now be shown that there are no natural numbers a and b for which $a^2 = 2b^2$.

By Lemma I, a^2, being a perfect square, has a prime factorization in which every factor occurs an even number of times. This is of course also true for b^2. Thus the problem is reduced to finding certain prime numbers satisfying the equation

$$(a_1^2 a_2^2 a_3^2 \ldots) = 2 \cdot (b_1^2 b_2^2 b_3^2 \ldots),$$

where the expressions in parentheses represent the prime factorizations of a^2 and b^2, respectively.

Note that all factors are prime, including 2. Thus for the above equation to be satisfied, the two sides must represent the prime factorization of the same number. But this cannot be, for prime factorizations are unique, and those shown in the equation are clearly different, for the factor 2 occurs once, three times, five times, or some *odd* number of times on the right; and an even number of times on the left, if at all.

Thus no natural numbers a and b exist for which $a^2 = 2b^2$, and it follows that no number of arithmetic is a square root of 2.

A brief look at the preceding proof shows that the use of the number 2 is not crucial. An exactly similar proof could be used to show that there is no square root of 3 in the number system of arithmetic. In fact, the number 2 could be replaced by *any* prime number without altering the validity of the proof. Thus no prime number has a square root. By a slight alteration of the preceding proof it may be shown that the only natural numbers which do have square roots in the number system of arithmetic are those which are perfect squares (as natural numbers). Similar proofs may also be given to show that the only natural numbers which have cube roots in the number system of arithmetic are the perfect cubes. The following theorems are related to Theorem I. Proofs are left as exercises.

Theorem XVI. Any natural number n has a square root in the number system of arithmetic if and only if it has a square root in the system of natural numbers.

Theorem XVII. (Generalization of Theorem XVI) Any natural number n has a kth root in the number system of arithmetic if and only if it has a kth root in the system of natural numbers (where k represents any natural number greater than 1).

These theorems establish that there are many natural numbers without kth roots, but do not indicate which numbers of arithmetic a/b do not have rational square roots, or kth roots. The next two theorems answer this question.

Theorem XVIII. A nonzero number of arithmetic a/b has a square root in the number system of arithmetic if and only if, its simplest fractional numeral a'/b' (where a' and b' have no common factor other than 1) has perfect squares for both numerator and denominator.

This theorem says that, for example, $\frac{3}{2}$ has no square root, because the numerator and denominator are not perfect squares, and no simpler fractional numeral for the number exists. On the other hand, $\frac{4}{9}$ has a square root $\frac{2}{3}$. Also $\frac{50}{32}$ has a square root, because $\frac{50}{32} = \frac{25}{16}$, and the latter symbol has perfect squares for numerator and denominator.

Outline of Proof: A number a/b has a square root m/n if and only if $(m/n)^2 = a/b$, or equivalently $m^2 b = n^2 a$. Choose the simplest fractional numeral for a/b and consider prime factorizations:

$$(m_1^2 m_2^2 \ldots)(b_1 b_2 \ldots) = (n_1^2 n_2^2 \ldots)(a_1 a_2 \ldots).$$

Since a and b have no common prime factors, each of the factors of a (which are $a_1, a_2, \ldots$) must appear in the factorization of m^2. If a is not a perfect square, then at least one of its factors occurs an odd number of times. But this is impossible, and therefore m and n do not exist such that $(m/n)^2 = a/b$.

Conversely, if a and b are perfect squares, then $a = r \cdot r$ for some natural number r, and $b = q \cdot q$ for some natural number q. Thus

$$\frac{a}{b} = \frac{(r \cdot r)}{(q \cdot q)} = \frac{r_2}{q^2} = \left(\frac{r}{q}\right)^2,$$

and a/b has the square root r/q.

Theorem XIX. (Generalization of Theorem XVIII) A nonzero number of arithmetic a/b has a kth root in the system of arithmetic if and only if its simplest fractional numeral 'a/b' has perfect kth powers for both numerator and denominator (where k represents any natural number greater than 1).

According to this theorem $\frac{3}{5}$ has no rational cube root, but $\frac{27}{8}$ and $\frac{250}{16}$ do.

EXERCISES

1. Write the prime factorization of each of the following numbers. Show that they are perfect squares.

    (a) 25   (b) 100   (c) 3600   (d) 2025

2. Show that $(a/b)^2 = 3$ is equivalent to $a^2 = 3b^2$, where a and b are natural numbers.

3. Prove that no negative rational number has a square root.

4. Prove that if a rational number a has a square root r, then ^-r is also a square root of a.

5. Find the cube root, if it exists, in the number system of arithmetic, of each of the following.

    (a) $\dfrac{216}{125}$ (b) $\dfrac{56}{189}$ (c) $\dfrac{144}{450}$ (d) $\dfrac{448}{189}$

6. Prove Theorem XVI.

7. Prove Theorem XVII.

8. Write a complete proof of Theorem XVIII.

9. Prove Theorem XIX.

Odd and even roots. The theorems of the preceding section establish criteria by which it may be decided whether roots of numbers of arithmetic exist. For *rational* numbers the question is only partly answered. Since the positive rational numbers are isomorphic to the nonzero numbers of arithmetic, the preceding theorems apply to positive rational numbers. To generalize those results, it is convenient to consider separately odd and even roots.

It is fairly obvious that the rational number zero has one and only one kth root for every natural number k greater than 1. It remains, then, to investigate the existence of kth roots for the positive and the negative rational numbers.

Every positive rational number which has a square root has two square roots, one negative and one positive. Negative numbers do not have square roots. No positive number, however, has more than two square roots. More generally, every positive number has either zero or two kth roots, where k is an even number. The next two theorems establish these results.

Theorem XX. Every positive rational number has either two square roots, or has no square roots. No negative number has a square root.

Outline of Proof. Assume that for a rational number a, there is a square root r. Now if there is a square root x, then $x^2 = a = r^2$. Then $x^2 - r^2 = 0$, and $(x + r)(x - r) = 0$. Thus $x = r$ or $x = {}^-r$. Therefore a cannot have more than two square roots. It is easy to show (exercise 4 above) that if r is a square root of a, then also ^-r is a square root of a. Negative numbers have no square roots because the square of any rational number is nonnegative.

Theorem XXI. (Generalization of Theorem XX) Every positive rational number for an even number k has either two kth roots, or has no kth roots. No negative number has an even kth root.

A proof of this theorem parallels that of Theorem XX.

Negative rational numbers may have odd roots. If such roots exist, they must be negative. Positive numbers of course may also have odd roots, but if they exist, they must be positive. Every rational number has at most one odd root. The next theorem states the general fact more precisely.

Theorem XXII. Every rational number has either one kth root or no kth roots for an odd integer k greater than 1. If the kth root of a positive number exists, it is positive. If the kth root of a negative number exists, it is negative. The kth root of 0 exists, and is 0.

Outline of Proof. If a negative number q has an odd kth root r, then $r^k = q$, or equivalently $^-r^k = {}^-q$. The latter equation is also equivalent to $({}^-r)^k = {}^-q$. Thus if q has an odd kth root r, then ^-q has the kth root ^-r. Conversely, if the positive number ^-q has an odd kth root, then q also has an odd kth root. Thus a negative number q has an odd kth root if and only if ^-q has a kth root, and it follows that some rational numbers have a kth root and others have none.

An odd kth root of a positive number must be positive, because odd powers of negative numbers are all negative. An odd kth root of a negative number must be negative, because all powers of positive numbers are positive. Then if a negative number should have two different kth roots, r_1 and r_2, they would both be negative, but have different absolute values. But if $|r_1| < |r_2|$, then it is impossible that $r_1^k = r_2^k$.

EXERCISES

1. Find the following, if they exist, in rational numbers.
   (a) The square root(s) of $\frac{289}{625}$ (b) The square root(s) of $\frac{14}{11}$
   (c) The square root(s) of $-\frac{25}{36}$ (d) The cube root(s) of $-\frac{27}{64}$
   (e) The fourth root(s) of $\frac{16}{81}$ (f) The fourth root(s) of $-\frac{162}{32}$
   (g) The fourth root(s) of $-\frac{48}{35}$

2. Write a complete proof of Theorem XX.

3. Write a proof of Theorem XXI.

4. Write a complete proof of Theorem XXII.

Constructing the real numbers. The system of rational numbers has now been shown to lack completeness with respect to taking square roots and roots of higher order. In fact, if only the positive rational numbers are considered, leaving aside problems of powers of negative numbers, completeness is still lacking.

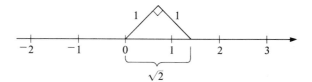

FIGURE 8–4 $\sqrt{2}$

When the number line is considered in this light, it is apparent that there are many points for which there is no rational number. Figure 8–4, for example, shows a right triangle (whose hypotenuse has length $\sqrt{2}$) and a number line. The right end of the hypotenuse falls on some point of the line, yet there is no rational number for that point. The system of *real numbers* is constructed so that there is a real number for each point of the line, and so that it is an extension of the system of rational numbers (so that there is a subsystem isomorphic to the system of rational numbers). It is of course problematic whether or not this can be accomplished in such a way that the new system has all the properties of an ordered field, but it turns out to be possible.

A rigorous and complete development of the system of real numbers is beyond the scope of this book. For present purposes it will suffice to regard the real numbers as consisting of the rational numbers and in addition, a number for each point of a number line for which there is not already a rational number. In other words, to the set of rational numbers is adjoined a set of numbers in such a way that there is a one-to-one correspondence between the points of a line and the entire set of numbers. The set of numbers that results is called the set of *real numbers*, and the new numbers that are adjoined to the set of rational numbers are called *irrational numbers*.

The operations of the system of rational numbers are also extended to the new number system, and the new system turns out to be a field—in fact, an ordered field. Thus none of the properties of number systems studied earlier is lost. In fact, the system of real numbers is an extension of every number system studied so far, except the finite ones. Thus the procedures for calculating, solving equations, inequalities and the like, learned before, also hold for the system of real numbers.

Approximation of irrational numbers. Decimal numerals. Decimal numerals, it will be recalled, can be used to name rational numbers. Some of them terminate, while others do not terminate, but repeat. For example,

$$\tfrac{3}{2} = 1.5 \quad \text{and} \quad \tfrac{2}{3} = 0.666\ldots.$$

It is easy to construct decimal symbols which neither terminate nor repeat. An example is

$$3.0100100010000100001\ldots,$$

where between each successive pair of '1's there is one more '0.' Such symbols cannot name rational numbers. Thus if they name anything, they must name irrational numbers.

It is in fact possible to consider nonterminating decimal symbols to represent all real numbers, whether rational or irrational. Even a number like $\tfrac{3}{2}$ can be represented by a nonterminating symbol, as in the following examples:

$$\tfrac{3}{2} = 1.4999\ldots, \qquad \tfrac{2}{3} = 0.66666\ldots,$$
$$1 = 0.9999\ldots, \qquad \tfrac{3}{4} = 0.749999\ldots,$$
$$\pi = 3.14159\ldots, \qquad \sqrt{2} = 1.414\ldots.$$

In actual practice, of course, such endless symbols are not used. Rather the sequence of digit symbols is terminated somewhere. In that case the symbol represents a rational number which *approximates* the number named by the endless symbol. The more digits retained, the better the approximation, of course. The following sequence shows successively better approximations to $\tfrac{1}{3}$:

$$0.3, \quad 0.33, \quad 0.333, \quad 0.3333, \quad 0.33333, \quad 0.333333.$$

Here a rational number is approximated by rational numbers. Irrational numbers are approximated in a similar fashion. The following sequence shows successively better approximations to the irrational number π:

$$3, \quad 3.1, \quad 3.14, \quad 3.141, \quad 3.1415, \quad 3.14159.$$

EXERCISES

1. Add the following, and represent the result with an unending decimal symbol.
   (a) $0.111\overline{1}$ and $0.666\overline{6}$ (b) $0.333\overline{33}$ and $0.666\overline{66}$
   (c) $0.1212\overline{12}$ and $3.4124\overline{12}$ (d) $6.2323\overline{23}$ and $0.0132\overline{132}$

2. In each part of exercise 1, find fractional numerals for the numbers named. Check the addition by adding again, using the fractional numerals.

The rational numbers can all be named according to a concise scheme, which uses pairs of integers. When they are named by decimal symbols, the scheme is not so concise because some of the symbols are nonterminating. It has just been stated that the real numbers may be named by a not-so-concise scheme of unending decimal symbols. A natural question now is whether or not there is some more concise scheme for naming the real numbers. The answer is negative. It has been proved (elsewhere) to be impossible. Therefore, real numbers are named as follows.

(1) Rational real numbers are named like the rational numbers.
(2) Irrational real numbers are either:
    (a) approximated, and symbols for rational numbers used, or
    (b) certain special irrational numbers which command attention are given names as convenient.

Examples are $\sqrt{2}$, $\sqrt[3]{5}$, π, $\log_{10} 2$, $\sin 7.3$. Actually only a very few irrational numbers are ever favored by being given such names. It is important to note also that there are many irrational numbers which are not roots of rational numbers. The number π is an example. It cannot be named $\sqrt[n]{a}$ for any index n or any rational number a. If it could, it would not be necessary to use a letter such as π for it.

Radical signs. In the system of real numbers, a great many square roots, cube roots, and other roots exist, whereas in rational numbers, relatively few such roots exist. Therefore, radical signs are more useful and important with the system of real numbers.

A symbol $\sqrt[n]{x}$, referring to real numbers, represents a real number for any nonnegative radicand x, and for any *index n* (the index a natural number greater than 1). If the radicand is negative, the symbol is meaningful if and only if the index is odd.

For any even index and any positive radicand two roots exist. The positive root is called the *principal value*, and is denoted by $\sqrt[n]{x}$. The negative root is of course the additive inverse of the principal value. It is denoted by $-\sqrt[n]{x}$. Thus for an even index, a radical sign which is not preceded by a minus sign never represents a negative number.

For odd indices, roots are unique, and therefore principal value is not so important. An odd root of a negative number is negative, and thus a radical symbol with odd index, and not preceded by a minus sign, may represent a negative number.

It is important to remark here that for any real number x, $\sqrt{x^2} = |x|$, since this fact is so often overlooked in elementary algebra books. On occasion it is even stated, incorrectly, that $\sqrt{x^2} = x$. That this is incorrect can be seen by taking x to be -3. Then $\sqrt{x^2} = {}^-x$, and not x.

It is also bad practice to use an ambiguous sign without thorough explanation. The following example illustrates a usual use of the ambiguous sign, compared with a more correct use of principal value.

EXAMPLE 1.
Solve:

$$x^2 + 4x + 4 = 25.$$
$$\sqrt{x^2 + 4x + 4} = \pm\sqrt{25},$$
$$\sqrt{(x + 2)^2} = \pm 5,$$
$$x + 2 = \pm 5,$$
$$x = \pm 5 - 2.$$

EXAMPLE 2.
    Solve:

$$x^2 + 4x + 4 = 25.$$
$$(x + 2)^2 = 25,$$
$$\sqrt{(x + 2)^2} = \sqrt{25} \text{ (taking } principal \text{ square root)},$$
$$|x + 2| = 5,$$
$$x + 2 = 5 \text{ or } ^-(x + 2) = 5 \text{ (using definition of absolute value)},$$
$$x = 3 \quad \text{ or } \quad x = ^-7.$$

Checking has been omitted in the preceding examples. Example 2 lends itself to clear explanation, while Example 1 seems to involve a shortcut. Shortcuts, of course, should seldom if ever be taught before an understanding of a complete process is established. Accordingly the ambiguous sign would be used cautiously, if at all, in elementary algebra by a careful teacher.

EXERCISES

1. Simplify the following.
   (a) $\sqrt{49}$ (b) $-\sqrt{25}$ (c) $\sqrt[3]{125}$ (d) $-\sqrt[3]{27}$
   (e) $\sqrt[3]{-125}$ (f) $-\sqrt[3]{-8}$ (g) $\sqrt[4]{16}$ (h) $-\sqrt[4]{81}$

2. Solve, using radicals as in Example 2 above.
   (a) $x^2 - 6x + 9 = 16$ (b) $4x^2 + 4x + 1 = 36$
   (c) $4x^2 - 12x + 9 = 49$ (d) $9x^2 + 6x + 1 = \frac{16}{25}$

3. Solve by taking principal cube roots.
   (a) $8x^3 = 27$ (b) $^-27x^3 = 125$ (c) $x^3 - 3x^2 + 3x - 1 = ^-8$

Bibliography

ANDREE, RICHARD, *Selections from Modern Abstract Algebra*. New York, Henry Holt Co., Inc., 1958.

BRANT, VINCENT and M. L. KEEDY, *Elementary Logic for Secondary Schools*. New York, Holt, Rinehart & Winston, Inc., 1962.

COURANT, RICHARD and H. W. ROBBINS, *What Is Mathematics?* New York, Oxford University Press, 1941.

DANTZIG, TOBIAS, *Number, the Language of Science*. New York, The Macmillan Co., 1930.

EVES, HOWARD and CARROLL V. NEWSOM, *An Introduction to the Foundations and Fundamental Concepts of Mathematics*. New York, Rinehart and Co., 1958.

EXNER, ROBERT M. and MYRON F. ROSSKOPF, *Logic in Elementary Mathematics*. New York, McGraw-Hill Book Co., 1959.

HADAMARD, JACQUES, *Psychology of Invention in the Mathematical Field*. Princeton, N.J., Princeton University Press, 1949.

JONES, B. W. *The Theory of Numbers*. New York, Rinehart and Co., 1955.

LANDAU, EDMOND G. H., *Foundations of Analysis*. New York, Chelsea Publishing Co., 1951.

LE VEQUE, W. J. *Elementary Theory of Numbers*. Reading, Mass., Addison-Wesley Publishing Co., Inc., 1962.

LIEBER, HUGH and LILLIAN LIEBER, *The Education of T. C. Mits*. New York, W. W. Norton and Co., Inc., 1944.

McCOY, NEAL H. *Introduction to Modern Algebra*. Boston, Allyn and Bacon, 1960.

National Council of Teachers of Mathematics, *Insights Into Modern Mathematics, Twenty-third Yearbook*. Washington, D.C., The National Council of Teachers of Mathematics, 1957.

National Council of Teachers of Mathematics, *The Growth of Mathematical Ideas Grades K–12, Twenty-fourth Yearbook*. Washington, D.C., The National Council of Teachers of Mathematics, 1959.

National Council of Teachers of Mathematics, *Instruction in Arithmetic, Twenty-fifth Yearbook*. Washington, D.C., The National Council of Teachers of Mathematics, 1960.

NEUGEBAUER, OTTO, *The Exact Sciences in Antiquity*. Princeton, N.J., Princeton University Press, 1952.

POLYA, GEORGE, *Mathematics and Plausible Reasoning, Vol. I, Induction and Analogy in Mathematics*. Princeton, N.J., Princeton University Press, 1954.

POLYA, GEORGE, *How to Solve It*. Princeton, N.J., Princeton University Press, 1946.

REID, CONSTANCE, *From Zero to Infinity*. New York, Thomas Y. Crowell Co., 1955.

SMITH, D. E., *History of Mathematics*. Boston, Ginn and Co., 1923.

THURSTON, H. A., *The Number System*. New York, Interscience Publishers, Inc., 1956.

VAN DER WAERDEN, B. L., *Science Awakening*. Noordhoff, 1954.

WEYL, HERMANN, *Symmetry*. Princeton, N.J., Princeton University Press, 1952.

Answers to Selected Exercises

Answers to Selected Exercises

CHAPTER 1

Review Practice Set 1, p. 3

1. 4	3. 0	5. 25	7. −4	9. −6	11. −13
13. −8	15. −22	17. 8	19. −6	21. −14	23. −22
25. 10	27. 42	29. 4	31. 4	33. −61	

Review Practice Set 2, p. 4

1. 8^6	3. 4^6	5. 6^2	7. 9^{-2}	9. 6^4
11. 6^{-14}	13. $(-5)^6$	15. y^{-6}	17. 5^4	19. 6^{-7}
21. 5^{-11}	23. 5^0, or 1	25. 9^2	27. 14^2	29. y^{-11}

Set 1, p. 6

1. (a) $2 \times 10^4 + 5 \times 10^3 + 3 \times 10^2 + 1 \times 10 + 4 + 1 \times 10^{-1} + 7 \times 10^{-2}$
$+ 8 \times 10^{-3}$
(c) $0 \times 10^{-1} + 0 \times 10^{-2} + 1 \times 10^{-3} + 0 \times 10^{-4} + 3 \times 10^{-5} + 4 \times 10^{-6}$
2. (a) **XXXVI** (c) **MCMLXIII**
3. (a) ?∩∩||| (d) ???????∩∩∩∩∩∩∩∩∩|||||||||
4. (a) ten thousand (c) one ten-thousandth

Review Practice Set 3, p. 6

1. 3^8	3. 5^{16}	5. 6^{-12}	7. 9^{-6}
9. 3^{-20}	11. 3^{-8}	13. x^{-15}	15. x^{30}

Set 2, p. 7

1. (a) 440 (c) 312 (e) 41 (g) 68

Review Practice Set 4, p. 7

1. $\frac{5}{4}$	3. $\frac{5}{4}$	5. $\frac{3}{2}$	7. $\frac{3}{2}$	9. $\frac{41}{35}$

11. $\frac{107}{143}$

Set 3, p. 9

1. (a) 101	2. (b) 10644	3. (a) 13125
4. (b) 224	5. (a) 105	6. (b) 11
7. (a) 2202	8. (b) 154143	9. (a) 1770

Set 4, p. 12

3. (a) 1056_7 (c) 1111_4
4. (a) 1056_7 (c) 110000000_2 (e) 20423_6 (g) 11221_3

Set 5, p. 13

1. 23102310 . . . 3. 0.110002 . . . 5. 0.6 7. 0.53061

Set 6, p. 15

2. (b) 1010011 3. (b) 122 4. (b) 110111 5. (b) 598_ϵ
6. (a) 10001 (c) 111111 7. (a) 0.6 (c) 0.424972497 . . .

Review Practice Set 5, p. 16

1. 8	3. -10	5. 20	7. -20	9. -6
11. 3^{-1}	13. 5^8	15. 8^{12}	17. 5^{-6}	19. -12
21. 25	23. -2	25. 24	27. -72	

CHAPTER 2

Review Practice Set 1, p. 18

1. 204   3. 1132   5. 1453_7 7. 212   9. 684   11. 312 $R10$

Review Practice Set 2, p. 21

1. 78   3. 1033   5. 1009   7. 9   9. -8. Not a natural number.
11. 413   13. 84   15. 910   17. 1624   19. 14   21. 27
24. $\frac{1}{2}$. Not a natural number.

Set 1, p. 22

1. Yes, the quotient (if it exists) is unique. No, the quotient of two natural numbers is not always a natural number.
4. Yes, no.

Review Practice Set 3, p. 23

1. -6	3. $\frac{15}{4}$	5. -2	7. 5	9. -5
11. 5	13. 0	15. 0	17. 8	19. -30
21. $-(x \cdot y)$	23. $x \cdot y$	25. $-8x$	27. $-(x \cdot y \cdot z)$	29. $-3x$
31. 0	33. $3x^2$			

Set 2, p. 26

1. (a) 41   (c) 64   (g) 6500
2. (a) $a + (b + c)$
   $(a + b) + c$ (Associative law of addition)
   $c + (a + b)$ (Commutative law of addition)

Review Practice Set 4, p. 26

1. $2x^2 + 3x$ 3. $2x^2 + 8x$ 5. $xy + xz$
7. $30yx - 10y^2$ 9. $4 + 8y^3$ 11. $2x(x^2 + 1)$
13. $5(x^2 + 1)$ 15. $y(5x^2 - 1)$ 17. $3(x + y)$

Set 3, p. 28

6. (a) commutative law of addition
   (e) left-distributive law of multiplication over addition
   (i) associative law of addition, commutative law of addition

Review Practice Set 5, p. 31

1. 0   3. $2x$ 5. $4x^2$ 7. 0   9. $2y$ 11. 0

Set 4, p. 33

1. $(3000 + 200 + 70 + 6) + (100 + 40 + 8) + (8000 + 700 + 90 + 5)$
   $= 11,000 + 1,000 + 200 + 19 = 12,000 + 200 + 10 + 9 = 12,219$

Set 5, p. 38

2. (a)

$$\frac{200 + 100 + 50 + 5 \qquad 355_7 \ R \ 3_7}{12_7 \overline{)4626_7}}$$

$$\begin{array}{r} 2400 \\ \hline 2226 \\ 1200 \\ \hline 1026 \\ 630 \\ \hline 66 \\ 63 \\ \hline 3 \end{array}$$

Review Practice Set 6, p. 39

1. $x = 13$ 3. $x = -2/17$ 5. no solution
7. $x = 9.7/5.4$ 9. $x = -19.3/2.5$

Set 6, p. 41

1. (a) $5 - 3 = 2$, a natural number, so $5 > 3$.

Review Practice Set 7, p. 42

1. $-4x^2 + 7x - 4$ 3. $x^2 - 5x - 2$
5. $17x^7 + 13x^6 + 6x^4 + 5x^3 - 5x^2 + 11x - 2$
7. $2x^3 - 3x^2 - 10$ 9. $-14x^4 + x^3 - x^2 + 4x + 14$

Review Practice Set 8, p. 44

1. $3x^2 + 6x$ 3. $5x^4 + 20x^3$ 5. $4x^2 + 12x + 4$
7. $9x^4 + 15x^3 + 3x^2$ 9. $3x^7 + 12x^2$ 11. $x^{-6} + x^{-2}$
13. $5x - 10$ 15. $x^4 - x^3$ 17. $4x^{-7} - 4x^{-2}y^{-1}$

Review Practice Set 9, p. 45

1. $30x^3 - 28x^2 + 21x - 9$
3. $-21x^6 - 15x^5 + 28x^4 + x^3 + 3x^2 - 8x + 12$
5. $91x^6 + 78x^5 + 81x^4 + 71x^3 + 55x^2 + 21x + 3$
7. $-18x^9 + 3x^8 + 42x^5 - 37x^4 + 5x^3$

Set 7, p. 46

3. (a) $2 \cdot 2 \cdot 3 \cdot 3 \cdot 5$ (e) $3 \cdot 37 \cdot 41$
4. (a) $2 \cdot 2 \cdot 3 \cdot 3 \cdot 5 \cdot 7$ (e) $2 \cdot 3 \cdot 5 \cdot 7$
5. (a) $3 \cdot 5$ (e) 3

Review Practice Set 10, p. 50

1. $x^2 - 4x + 6$ 3. $x + 2 \ R \ 2x - 1$ 5. $6x + 8$ 7. $x^2 - x + 1$

CHAPTER 3

Set 1, p. 56

3. (a) 2   (c) 2   (g) 1

Review Practice Set 1, p. 57

1. $\frac{2}{15}$ 3. $\frac{4}{35}$ 5. $\frac{1}{125}$ 7. $\frac{1}{93}$ 9. 1   11. $\frac{8}{77}$

13. $\frac{13}{15}$ 15. $\frac{33}{35}$ 17. $\frac{6}{25}$ 19. $\frac{53}{14}$ 21. $\frac{125}{66}$ 23. $\frac{9}{11}$

Set 3, p. 59

2. (a) 1   (e) 0   3. (a) 1   (d) 4

4. (a) 4   (e) 2   (h) 4   5. (a) 2   (c) 2   (g) 1

Set 4, p. 60

1. (a) 4   (c) 0   (e) 0

Set 5, p. 61

1. (a) 2   (d) 4   2. (a) 1   (d) 2   (h) 3

3. (a) 4   (d) 4   (h) 2

Set 7, p. 63

1. (a) 0   (c) 3   (h) 5   (k) 2   2. (a) 2   (c) 5

3. (a) 5   (c) 2   (g) 3   (i) 5   4. (a) 2   (c) 5

5. (a) 5   (c) 4   (e) 3   (g) 0   (j) 1

6. (a) 0   (c) 4   (e) 2   (g) 3

7. (a) 0   (c) 0   (f) 3   (h) 4

8. (a) 0   (c) 4   (f) 0   (h) 2

9. (a) 2   (c) 1   (e) 1   (g) 3   (i) 3

10. (a) 2   (c) 4   (e) 1   (g) 2

11. (a) 2   (c) 1   (e) 2   (g) 2

12. (a) 4   (c) 1   (e) 2   (g) 1   (j) 2   (l) 2   (n) 2

13. (a) 4   (c) 1   (e) 2   (g) 3   (j) 3   (l) 3

Set 9, p. 69

9. (a) 3   (c) 3   10. (a) *H*   (c) *R*

11. (a) no solution   (c) 0, 2, 4

CHAPTER 4

Set 1, p. 73

2. '7' is not a number.   6. The number 25 can be named with a '2' and a '5.'

Review Practice Set 1, p. 74

2. (a)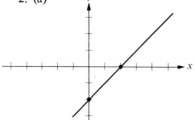

(c)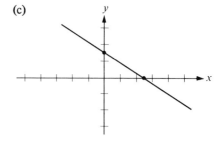

Set 2, p. 77

1. (a) 'x,' 'y'   (c) 'he'

Set 3, p. 79

1. (a) 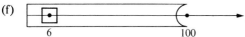   (d)

(f)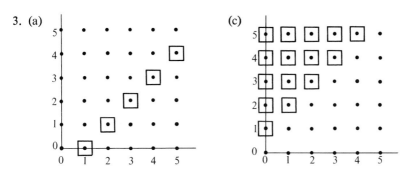

2. (a)

3. (a) 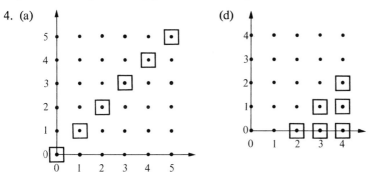   (c)

Graphs are incomplete. Only part of an infinite pattern is shown.

4. (a)   (d)

Set 4, p. 82

1. (a) Type I   (f) Type III   (m) Type II   (p) Type III
2. (a) T, 5 = 4 + 1   (d) F, 20 − 1 ≠ 4 + 15, F   (g) T, 10 − 3 > 17 + 4, F
3. (a)

Set 5, p. 87

1. (a) {1, 10}   (e) ∪   (l) {0, 7}   (q) {0, 2, 5, 7, 10}
2. (a) ∅, {p}, {q}, {p, q}

8. (a)   (d)   (m)   (o)

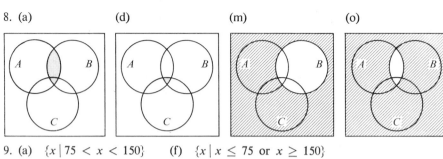

9. (a) $\{x \mid 75 < x < 150\}$ (f) $\{x \mid x \leq 75 \text{ or } x \geq 150\}$

10. (a)   (f)

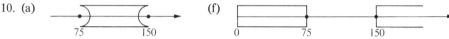

Set 8, p. 92

  1. (a) 6, 2, 5, 3, 1, 7, 4   (c) 7, 6, 5, 4, 3, 2, 1

Set 9, p. 95

  1. (a) July has 30 days and Christmas is December 25th.   F.
     (e) The first prime number is 4 and 8 is not a multiple of 2.   F.
  4. (a) The smallest prime is not 2.   (e) $3 + 7 = 10$
     (h) Mathematics is not exact.

Set 10, p. 97

  1. If it rains, then this hat will be ruined.
  6. If a figure is a triangle, then it is not a square.
  10. If a natural number is not odd, then it is even.

Set 12, p. 99

  1. If $5 = 5$, then $2 + 2 = 4$.   4. If 6 is a prime number, then $1 = 2$.
  8. If John Adams was Socrates, then Jefferson was the first president of the United States.
  10. If a mathematical system has an associative operation, then it is a group.

Set 13, p. 101

  1. If $5 \neq 5$, then $2 + 2 \neq 4$.
  5. If monkeys are not birds, then triangles are not squares.
  11. If it does not have two commutative operations, then a mathematical system is not a field.

Set 14, p. 103

  1. (a) July does not have 30 days or Christmas is not December 25th.
     (d) Parallel lines intersect or pastry is not fattening.
  2. (a) July does not have 30 days and Christmas is not December 25th.
     (d) Parallel lines intersect and pastry is not fattening.
  3. (1) $2 + 2 = 4$ and $5 \neq 5$.

CHAPTER 5

Review Practice Set 1, p. 111

  1. $x = \frac{3}{4}$ 3. $x = \frac{5}{3}$ 5. $x = 5.6/1.7$ 7. $y = -\frac{4}{65}$

Review Practice Set 2, p. 113

1. 3   3. $^-12$ 5. $x \cdot y$ 7. -3 9. $-3x^2$ 11. $30y^3$ 13. $(xy)^{-1}$
15. $(x^2 \cdot y^2)^{-1}$ 16. 1   17. 1   19. $(6x^2)^{-1}$ 21. $(15y^2)^{-1}$

Review Practice Set 3, p. 118

1. $3y$ 5. cannot simplify   7. 0   9. 0   11. 1
13. 1   15. 1   19. $x^2/(2y^2)$

CHAPTER 6

Review Practice Set 1, p. 125

1. $\frac{15}{56}$ 3. $\frac{10}{27}$ 5. $\frac{48}{35}$ 7. $\frac{4}{5}$ 9. $\frac{3}{8}$ 11. $\frac{14}{9}$ 13. $\frac{3}{2}$
15. $\frac{16}{25}$ 17. $\frac{1}{4}$ 19. $\frac{3}{2}$ 21. x/y

Review Practice Set 2, p. 128

1. $\frac{6}{5}$ 3. $\frac{8}{9}$ 5. $\frac{41}{24}$ 7. $\frac{3}{17}$ 9. $\frac{2}{15}$ 11. $\frac{26}{75}$
13. $(3y + 2x)/xy$ 15. $(x^3 + 5x^2 - 4x + 4)/(x^2 + 2x - 8)$

Set 1, p. 130

4. (a) $\frac{2}{4}$ and $\frac{4}{8}$, $\frac{8}{4}$ and $\frac{4}{2}$

Set 2, p. 132

1. (a) '[7, 11]' represents $\{(a, b) \mid 7 \cdot b = 11 \cdot a\}$.
4. (a) True, since $5 \cdot 8 = 4 \cdot 10$ implies (5, 4) and (10, 8) belong to the same equivalence class.
   (c) False, (5, 12) and (10, 25) represent two different ordered pairs of numbers.
   (g) True, since (10, 12) is an ordered pair such that $10 \cdot 6 = 12 \cdot 5$.
   (k) False, 'ϵ' indicates (3, 4) is a member of a set, (6, 8), but '(6, 8)' does not represent a set; it represents one element of a set.

Review Practice Set 3, p. 139

1. $\frac{9}{20}$ 3. $\frac{68}{9}$ 5. $\frac{1}{9}$ 7. $\frac{9}{2}xy$ 9. $(2x^2 - 8)/(x - 5)$

Review Practice Set 4, p. 141

1. $10\frac{3}{8}$ 3. $27\frac{13}{14}$ 5. $\frac{25}{3}$

Set 8, p. 143

1. (a) $\frac{30}{54}$ (c) $\frac{20}{85}$ (f) $\frac{81}{306}$
2. (a) $\frac{33}{55}$ (c) $\frac{76}{84}$ (f) $\frac{186}{282}$ 3. (a) $\frac{10}{21}$ (c) $\frac{1}{3}$ (f) $\frac{3}{13}$
4. (a) 5   (c) $\frac{9}{40}$ 6. (a) $\frac{5}{21}$ (c) $\frac{143}{60}$ (f) $\frac{3}{2}$

Set 9, p. 146

1. (a) $\frac{41}{35}$ (c) $\frac{102}{72}$ (f) $\frac{59}{30}$ 2. (a) $\frac{10}{15}$ (c) $\frac{320}{1050}$ (e) $\frac{96}{105}$
3. (a) $\frac{2}{9}$ (c) $\frac{13}{210}$ 5. (a) $\frac{1}{4} + \frac{2}{4}$ 6. (a) $\frac{3}{5} \cdot \frac{4}{3}$ etc.

Set 10, p. 149

2. (a) $\frac{6}{8}$, since $\frac{6}{8} - \frac{5}{8} = \frac{1}{8}$ 3. (a) $\frac{5}{8}$, since $5 \cdot 8 > 8 \cdot 3$

Review Practice Set 5, p. 149

1. 334.37   3. 1576.215   5. 50.0004

7. $(6 \times 10^3) + (8 \times 10^2) + (1 \times 10) + 4 + (1 \times 10^{-1}) + (3 \times 10^{-3})$
   $+ (5 \times 10^{-4})$
9. $(1 \times 10^4) + (6 \times 10^3) + 5 + (1 \times 10^{-1}) + (1 \times 10^{-2}) + (1 \times 10^{-4})$
11. 0.875

Set 11, p. 151

1. (a) $\frac{5}{12} > \frac{7}{18}$ since $5 \cdot 18 > 12 \cdot 7$ (c) $\frac{42}{56}$
2. (a) $\frac{29}{12}$ (c) $\frac{291}{392}$ 4. (a) $\frac{3}{2}$ (c) $\frac{9}{8}$

Set 12, p. 154

1. (a) 1.875   (c) 1.2   6. (a) $\frac{1612}{100}$ (c) $\frac{31459}{100000}$
7. (a) $\frac{5}{9}$ (c) $\frac{103}{33}$ 8. (a) 0.213_6 (c) $0.33\overline{3}_6$

Review Practice Set 6, p. 155

1. 3^{13} 3. 16^{-5} 5. 10^{-9} 7. 8^1 or 8   9. 10^7 11. 7^7
13. 3^8 15. 3^{-10} 17. 8^{20} 19. $6^4 \cdot 8^{-8}$ 21. $4^2 \cdot 10^{-6}$

Set 13, p. 158

3. (a) $0.499\overline{9}$ or $\frac{1}{2}$

Review Practice Set 7, p. 158

1. (a) 6   2. (a) 50%   3. (a) 40

Set 14, p. 161

1. (a) $\frac{1810}{478}$
2. (a)

$$\begin{array}{r} 2 \\ 317\overline{)723} \\ 634 \\ \hline 89 \end{array} \qquad \begin{array}{r} 0.2 \\ 317\overline{)89} \\ 63.4 \\ \hline 25.6 \end{array} \qquad \begin{array}{r} 0.08 \\ 317\overline{)25.6} \\ 25.36 \\ \hline 0.24 \end{array} \qquad 2.28$$

3. (a)

$$\begin{array}{r} 7 \\ 253\overline{)1780} \\ 1771 \\ \hline 9 \end{array} \qquad \begin{array}{r} 0.03 \\ 253\overline{)9} \\ 7.59 \\ \hline 1.41 \end{array} \qquad 7.03$$

4. (a)

$$\begin{array}{r} 7 \\ 2.53\overline{)17.8} \\ 17.71 \\ \hline 0.09 \end{array} \qquad \begin{array}{r} 0.03 \\ 2.53\overline{)0.09} \\ 0.0759 \\ \hline 0.0141 \end{array} \qquad 7.03$$

Set 15, p. 163

1. (a) 50%   (c) 100%   (e) 135%
2. (a) 0.17   (c) 0.125   (e) 0.0075
3. (a) 1.3×10^8 (c) 10^6 (e) 1.92×10^{-10}
4. (a) 10^2 (c) $(1.2 \times 1.3) \times (10^5 \times 10^7) = 1.56 \times 10^{12}$ (e) 1.323×10^3
5. (a) 2×10^{-7}

CHAPTER 7

Set 2, p. 169

1. (7, 2), (20, 15), etc.   5. [15, 5]; (11, 1), (12, 2), etc.

Set 4, p. 172

1. [34, 26]; (34, 26), (9, 1), etc.
5. [33, 48]; [1, 4] ⊙ [6, 1] = [10, 25] ⊙ [33, 8] = [10, 25], since 33 + 25 = 58 = 48 + 10.

Set 5, p. 174

1. (a) 13   (c) ⁻30 or − 30   (e) 0
3. [15, 1], [16, 2], etc.
5. (a) [32, 5], 27   (c) [19, 28], ⁻9 or −9
6. (a) 18   (c) ⁻17 or − 17
7. (a) [64, 56], 8   8. (a) 45

Set 7, p. 176

1. (a) {3, 5}

Review Practice Set 1, p. 176

1. ⁻15/28   3. 7/27   5. 10/27   7. 3/⁻5   9. 7/5   11. 15/14
13. 3/5   15. 5/1 or 5   17. 3/⁻8 or ⁻3/8
19. ⁻3/5 or 3/⁻5   21. ⁻7/9 or 7/⁻9

Set 8, p. 178

1. (a) ⁻2 − ⁻7 = 5

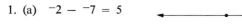

Set 9, p. 181

1. (a) {x | x > 2}

Set 10, p. 183

6. (a) {⁻5, 5}

(e) {x | −7 ≤ x ≤ 7}

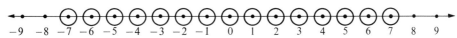

Set 11, p. 184

1. (b) −1 · 2 · 2 · 2 · 2   8. (a) 49 = ⁻6 · ⁻8 + 1

CHAPTER 8

Review Practice Set 1, p. 187

2. (a) 5   (c) 15   3. (a) $\frac{2}{3}$ (c) $\frac{11}{15}$ 4. (a) 6   (c) $\frac{9}{15}$

Set 1, p. 188

1. (a) (6, ⁻10), (−9, 15), etc.   (c) (2, 2), (−5, −5), etc.
2. (a) 3 · 2 = ⁻2 · ⁻3 = 6

Set 2, p. 190

1. (a) $\frac{5}{3}$ 3. (a) 7

Set 3, p. 191

1. $[a, b] + [-c, d]$ or $[a, b] + [c, -d]$
3. (a)   [9, 8], since $[9, 8] - [3, 4] = [3, 8]$ and $3 \cdot 8 = 24$, which is positive.
   (c) $[-1, 3]$, since $[-1, 3] - [6, -5] = [13, 15]$ and $13 \cdot 15 > 0$
4. (a)   For any rational numbers a, b and c, $a > b \to a + c > b + c$.
10. (a)   For any rational numbers $x, y, |x \cdot y| = |x| \cdot |y|$.

Review Practice Set 2, p. 193

1. (a)   5   (c)   12   2. (a) $\sqrt{74}$ (c) $\sqrt{2}$

Set 4, p. 193

1. (a)   4/7   (b) $(-8)/3$, or $8/(-3)$ or $[(-8)/(-3)]$
2. (a)   2   (c) -6 3. (a) $(-7)/5$, $7/(-5)$, $-[(-7)/(-5)]$, $-(7/5)$
4. (a) $2/3$, $(-2)/(-3)$, $-[(-2)/3]$, $-[2/(-3)]$

Set 5, p. 194

1. (a) $(-3)/2$, $3/(-2)$, $-(3/2)$, $-[(-3)/(-2)]$, $1/(-\frac{2}{3})$

Set 6, p. 196

1. (a) -28 (c) $-\frac{85}{21}$ 2. (a) $x \mid x > -\frac{35}{36}$

Set 7, p. 199

1. (a) 5^2 (c) $2^4 \cdot 3^2 \cdot 5^2$ 5. (a) $\frac{6}{5}$ (c)   does not exist

Set 8, p. 201

1. (a) $17, 25, -\frac{17}{25}$ (c)   do not exist   (e) $\frac{2}{3}, -\frac{2}{3}$

Set 9, p. 202

1. (a) $0.77\overline{77}$ (c) $3.533624\overline{533624}$
2. (a) $\frac{1}{9} + \frac{2}{3} = \frac{7}{9} = 0.77\overline{77}$ (c) $\frac{12}{99} + 3 + \frac{412}{999} = 3 + \frac{5864}{10989}$

Set 10, p. 204

1. (a)   7   (c)   5   (f)   2   2. (a) $\{7, -1\}$ (c) $\{2, 5\}$ 3. (a) $\frac{3}{2}$

Index

Index